GLASS PAPERWEIGHTS

Alfred R. Anderson
18 Hadwen Lane
Worcester, Mass. 01602

GLASS PAPERWEIGHTS
OF THE BERGSTROM ART CENTER

The Complete Collection of Glass Paperweights
and Related Items Reproduced in Full Color

EVELYN CAMPBELL CLOAK

Introduction by HELEN McKEARIN

BONANZA BOOKS · NEW YORK

This edition published by Bonanza Books
a division of Crown Publishers, Inc.
by arrangement with Prentice-Hall, Inc.
a b c d e f g h

CONTENTS

ACKNOWLEDGMENTS

My debt is great to all who have written on the subject of glass paperweights. In particular, I am grateful to Evangeline H. Bergstrom, whose pioneer effort in 1940, *Old Glass Paperweights,* concerns itself directly with this collection; to Paul Hollister, Jr., *The Encyclopedia of Glass Paperweights* (1969); Roger Imbert and Yolande Amic, *Les Presse-Papiers Français* (1948); Paul Jokelson, *Antique French Paperweights* (1955), *One Hundred of the Most Important Paperweights* (1966), and *Sulphides* (1968); Patricia K. McCawley, *Antique Glass Paperweights from France* (1968); Frank J. Manheim, *A Garland of Weights* (1968); Jean Sutherland Melvin, *American Glass Paperweights and Their Makers* (1967); J. P. Boore and Robert A. Elder, Jr., who have made available the results of their extensive research; and to all whose articles have appeared in the *Bulletin of the Paperweight Collectors' Association* and in various periodicals. Special thanks are due Helen McKearin for her helpful advice and support. Final decisions, of course, have been mine, and I assume responsibility for misattributions, errors, and lack of data.

Three more expressions of appreciation must be made: the first to Ralph S. Johns for giving the initial impetus to this publication, when he suggested in 1965 that lists of the Bergstrom weights be printed, and for his subsequent generous donations which have helped defray the costs of color reproductions; the second to the photographers, the Munroe Studios, Inc., of Neenah, Wisconsin, whose artistry and diligence have fulfilled the demands and hopes of collector friends that all illustrations in this book be in color; and the third to my husband, F. Theodore Cloak, for his encouragement and patience.

INTRODUCTION

by Helen McKearin

Beauty is but an abstract concept until a work of nature or, more particularly, of man evokes that word from the beholder. Yet that which is beautiful to one people, to one era, or to one generation may not have beauty in the eyes of another. Tastes and standards do change, filling some advocates of the new with scorn for those of the past, but, fortunately, widening the horizons for others of more elastic and catholic vision. Among the glass objects which, even upon first acquaintance, almost invariably evoke the adjective "beautiful" are glass paperweights, especially those of the classic period, as Paul Hollister, Jr., so perceptively calls the years in which near perfection in their creation was attained by artists in glass—circa 1842–1861 in Europe; circa 1851–1871 in the United States. But, sometimes the casual glance of the Philistine may render the verdict "pretty." And, perhaps, in general, glass paperweights *were* little more than pretty, useful novelties to Victorians, and their counterparts on the Continent and in America, who purchased paperweights in local stationery and similar shops or received them as gifts. Nevertheless, although purchasers and makers seem to have left no tangible evidence of beholding any glass paperweights as embodied beauty, to *some* of them *some* weights must have been just that. Surely the glassblowers must have regarded their handiwork as works of art, and were not alone in so doing. Yet, except for a few discerning collectors, the classic glass paperweights had to wait a century for full appreciation.

However these nineteenth-century innovations may have been regarded by their human contemporaries, glass paperweights, at their finest, are regarded by twentieth-century collectors as a form of art created from glass by an artist-craftsman, and

1

as a group merit classification under Art. But what kind? Since the Middle Ages the concept of art, or the arts, has been changing, broadening with man's horizons and techniques to include more classes of art. In their era, many Victorians doubtless would have placed glass paperweights, along with sculpture and carving, in the mechanical arts—"more requiring the labour of the Hand and Body than of the mind"—a baroque classification apparently adopted when the works of man's hands as well as of his mind were elevated to the arts. Some, less appreciative, probably would have classed them as industrial art, a nineteenth-century category arising from the creeping displacement of man's hands by mechanical devices. Probably the avant-garde would have taken the view that, since glass paperweights were ornamental as well as useful products, or by-products, of industry, they belonged under decorative arts, the new category to which the decoration-conscious and -loving mid-Victorian era had given birth. Probably, too, the avant-garde would have agreed with the professor of logic at the University of Aberdeen, who wrote in 1855, ". . . in its fancies of decorative art, nature has very little place." Still others may have felt, as did the writer of the *Supplemental Report* on "Sculpture, Models and Plastic Art" at London's 1851 Crystal Palace, that "the intimate connection of the Fine Arts and many branches of manufacture [including porcelain and glass]" often made decision as to "rank or class" difficult in placing those objects "in which industry and taste have been jointly employed." Glassmakers would have said "Art of Glass."

Excepting industrial art, which, to me, de-individualizes and smacks of the assembly line, glass paperweights qualify for each category mentioned. They are mechanical art, for they are fashioned by hands using a few simple tools. They are plastic art, for their substance must be manipulated, modeled, or molded as must metals and clays, likewise "true fruits of the Art of fire." They are decorative art, for their designs, whether a floral-bouquet "motif" or nicely arranged air bubbles, proclaim them to be. They are art of glass, for they crown a summit of technical achievement attained through the ultimate in rapport between the artist-craftsman and a dictatorial medium. As a craftsman, the glassblower submitted to the limits set by the nature of glass, and so learned to control and bend the metal to his will, which was expressed by the artist in his creative designs. My own feeling is that, just as paintings, whether judged to be masterpieces or mediocre, are classified under the "Fine Arts," so too, whether "the extraordinary" or "the usual" (to borrow Mrs. Cloak's words), glass paperweights may be considered fine art, if only a minor one. In any event, their fabrication is neither a lost nor a dead art. Today, a hundred years after the classic period, it may be said that a few of our mid-twentieth-century artist-craftsmen in glass, Charles Kaziun of Brockton, Massachusetts, and Paul Ysart of Scotland among them, have been creating a neoclassic period, and others, for instance George Thompson of Steuben at Corning, New York, are evolving designs more distinctly of their own era.

Although the sort of art represented by glass paperweights may be perennially moot, I know of no student or collector of glass who questions their fabrication being an art, not merely a craft—and to some of us more than an art. Even the glass itself seems a product of the art of alchemy. That dull base materials—sand with potash and lead or soda and lime—can be transmuted through the heat of fire into a brilliant transparent, or luminous translucent, or shiny opaque material, colored or colorless, that must be magic. Add the glassblower's mastery of this medium, than which no other demands more nicety of judgment and educated dexterity; his forming of rods for canes such as those in the French Saint Louis millefiori weight, No. 11, Plate 24, of leaves and petals for flowers such as that in the American Mt. Washington weight, No. 516, Plate 42, and fruits like those in the French Clichy weight, No. 300, Plate 18, all to be used later in motifs upon a cushion or ground of glass and all to be encased by glass, and there is the magician. Moreover, he does not make regiments in identical uniform. Rather, and inevitably, each paperweight born of the union of glass in its workable state and the glassblower's imagination and skill is an individual. Even among the commercially produced glass paperweights of Baccarat, Saint Louis, and Clichy in France, of Bacchus in England, and of the New England Glass Company and the Boston & Sandwich Glass Company in New England, no two are absolutely identical—as study of the remarkable illustrations in this book vividly demonstrates. Thus, though the weights fall into various design groups, the individual designs seem marching toward infinity. Herein lies another dimension in the fascination of glass paperweights.

Collections of these paperweights to see, to compare, and, if possible, to handle, and also of literature providing the proper historical and technical background—settings for the weights so often likened to jewels—these are essential to aesthetic satisfaction from and knowledge of glass paperweights. One who contributed immeasurably to both these sources of pleasure and appreciative knowledge was Evangeline Bergstrom, a pioneer worker in this glass field in the United States. It was during the 1930's that Mrs. Bergstrom started collecting glass paperweights and kindred items such as the French Clichy doorknobs No. 316A, Plate 17, and English ink bottle attributed to Whitefriars No. 88, Plate 35, related by the millefiori feature; the French ruler attributed to Saint Louis No. 162, Plate 35, and the English gemel flask No. 363, Plate 37, cousins by a technique of combining colors; the French (Baccarat) tumbler No. 298, Plate 9, with sulphide, an ingenious and tricky union of molded ceramic figure and glass. During about a quarter century, as Mrs. Bergstrom's collection increased in numbers, it grew in comprehensive representation of techniques, designs, origins—in fact, all facets of paperweights. Equal importance in quality and coverage has been attained perhaps in only two other American collections—the Sinclair Collection now owned by the New-York Historical Society and the Houghton Collection in the Corning Museum of Glass— two of the twenty-one museums in various parts of the United States in which glass paperweights may be seen. But, only a comparatively small portion of each is on display for the public to see. On the other hand, for a decade now Mrs. Bergstrom's entire outstanding collection has been, and will continue to be, on view in the John Nelson Bergstrom Art Center and Museum at Neenah, Wisconsin, to which she bequeathed it. And to it have been added, by purchase and generous gift, about 100 contemporary examples. Since 1959 when the museum was opened to the public, it has become a mecca to student and collector of glass paperweights.

There, not only are the glass paperweights physically present to be seen and studied, but likewise available is a growing repository of vital reference material. As yet, neither literature nor original research material can be voluminous, but there would be far less had not Evangeline Bergstrom's *Old Glass Paperweights*—now itself a collector's item—ignited a fuse to wider interest in and collecting of glass paperweights, which, in turn, sparked further research. In 1940, while realizing the incompleteness of her own and others' researches, Mrs. Bergstrom still had the courage, that pioneers in any field must have, to share information by publishing it. Mrs. Bergstrom's handsome book was "small" only because information was limited then. During the 1930's only about half a dozen articles on glass paperweights appeared in American, and perhaps two in English, magazines, and in 1939, one "small" book on American weights. Since then, many articles have appeared, mainly in American publications and mainly in the 1950's and 1960's. The same decades saw the publication of a few books devoted to glass paperweights. In this field, as indeed in all fields, as its literature evolves, the body of information grows in depth and breadth, sometimes confirming and sometimes disproving previous "facts" and opinions, always establishing new ones.

The latest book, the twelfth, about glass paperweights, to benefit from the researches into the subject during the past thirty years and to make its own tremendous contribution is *Glass Paperweights of the Bergstrom Art Center*. Mrs. Cloak disclaims being a scholar and researcher, but she has employed the attitude and approach of each and given us an important book. By division of the paper-weight family into geographical and maker-origin groups, familiarization with the characteristics of paperweights from a particular glassworks is facilitated, thus pro-viding a firm foundation for a comparative study of weights of the various makers. And if, to compare the motifs of one glassworks with those of others, for instance, millefiori concentrics of Baccarat, Bacchus, and the New England Glass Company, the student has to turn from one plate to another, that is excellent training in observation and visual memory. But one annoying act he will not have to perform: He will not have to turn even one page to bring the paperweight and its description together—the captions are opposite the plates, a perfect feature. Also, though it may seem a small point for comment, the measurements in both inches and centi-meters are to be applauded. Although some museums have discarded inches for the more international centimeters, few American glass students and collectors, if any, have deserted inches. Of course, the glory of the book is its color illustrations—63 plates showing each of the 700 pieces in the collection at the John Nelson Berg-strom Art Center and Museum. In no other book has such a wealth of glass appeared in the color so essential to full appreciation of colored objects and to study of them. True they cannot substitute fully for visual and tactile contact with the actual glass and color, but they can come close to it.

For the many of us who cannot make the pilgrimage to Neenah, this book is a godsend: It brings to each of us, and in their colors, all the paperweights and other articles now in the Bergstrom Collection.

HELEN MCKEARIN

NANTUCKET, MASSACHUSETTS

FOREWORD

The opportunity of working with and studying a collection of seven hundred glass paperweights—and that collection for the most part Evangeline Bergstrom's—has been my good fortune. That I should be presumptuous enough to attempt writing a catalogue of the collection is quite another matter. Museum training teaches that catalogues of collections should be written, but if my attention had not been called to a statement made by Thomas P. F. Hoving, director of The Metropolitan Museum of Art, I doubt that I would ever have had the courage to pursue the project. Mr. Hoving said, "It's a great deal more important to get out the catalogues of the Museum's collections than to have them faultless. Catalogues that are faultless *never* get out and do not exist anyway."

The collection of glass paperweights and related items at The John Nelson Bergstrom Art Center and Museum in Neenah, Wisconsin, consists of the acquisitions brought together by Evangeline Hoysradt Bergstrom (1872–1958), and approximately one hundred additional items, predominantly gifts, acquired since the founding of the museum. It is hoped that this catalogue or book will serve as a reference document or "encyclopedia" on the subject of glass paperweights, as well as a guide to the collection and an extension of Mrs. Bergstrom's monumental research contributions on the subject. Though she cannot personally set her seal of approval on the author's efforts, Mrs. Bergstrom might be said to have collaborated in the work, since all her notes appear as part of the textual material, and since the book is in effect carrying out her expressed wishes of sharing the collection with the public. In fact, though thousands of visitors come to the museum every year to see and study the collection, this book should make it accessible to a much greater public.

As I have said, the records left by Mrs. Bergstrom, although incomplete, are the nucleus of the book. They consist of two card files, one noting descriptions of individual weights, the other noting date of purchase, the seller, and the amount paid. The cards are numbered from one through 535 (though some numbers are missing); the dates of purchase run from March, 1935, through May, 1944. It is generally believed that her interest in paperweights and her actual collecting of them started years before 1935, but no purchase was recorded before March of that year.

About fifty items listed in the file of purchases were not included in Mrs. Bergstrom's bequest to the museum. There is no record of the disposition of these, although a few letters preserved in her correspondence file reveal that she did dispose of some, either by sale or gift. For example, neither of the two PY (Paul Ysart) weights pictured in her 1940 edition of *Old Glass Paperweights* (Illustrations 32 and 33), but removed from subsequent editions of the book, are in the museum collection. A letter dated 1941 from Theodore Horton of Sandwich, Massachusetts, indicates that she gave one of these PY weights to him. There is also correspondence with Charles Guernsey of Buffalo, New York, regarding a sale of three overlay weights, and one of these is known to be the Baccarat (Illustration 17) in her book. The Millville ship (Illustration 76, 1940 edition; Illustration 74, 1948 and 1963 editions) is not in the collection; weight 492 in Plate 47 of this book is similar, but is not the one pictured in Mrs. Bergstrom's book. (Incidentally, the Millville tulip, Plate XX of Mrs. Bergstrom's book, was not hers but was borrowed from Arthur L. Kramer of Dallas, Texas, in order to photograph it in color.) These transactions, it is true, do not account for fifty missing weights, but they are evidence of some sales and some gifts. Just as her accumulation of weights went beyond the 1944 recorded date, so perhaps did it include many acquired before the beginning record in 1935; the number of "unrecorded" weights would indicate that this might be the case.

A few statistics compiled from Mrs. Bergstrom's records may be of interest. The items purchased between 1935 and 1944 fall into the following price groups: under $50—165 weights; between $51 and $100—111 weights; between $101 and $200—127 weights; between $201 and $500—86 weights; over $500—21 weights. The year 1941 was the peak for purchases—120 weights being bought that year. The highest price ever paid was $2,200, and this amount was paid twice: in 1941 for the Saint Louis paperweight vase (413, Plate 22), and in 1943 for the possibly Sandwich (Nicholas Lutz?) weight (534, Plate 41). In descending purchase price were the Clichy (505, Plate 14) at $1,450 in 1942; three of unknown origin (531, 532, and 533 in Plate 58) at approximately $1,000 each in 1943, from the same source as the Sandwich weight above; the Baccarat (474, Plate 8) at $960 in 1942; and the Clichy (506, Plate 13) at $725, also in 1942.

With the exception of two purchases in Canada, all the weights were bought in the United States. C. W. Lyon, Inc., New York City, supplied the greatest number, with A. Starr Best, Chicago, and Arthur Ackermann & Sons, Chicago, running second and third. Mrs. Bergstrom worked with many other dealers and individuals, and it is evident that wherever her travels with Mr. Bergstrom took her—Florida, Atlantic City, New York State, New England—she made purchases if she found weights that she loved.

The second of Mrs. Bergstrom's card files is more important; it includes descriptions of the individual pieces and lists them numerically. The descriptions of some pieces are detailed, but in most cases the information is sparse. Known attributions are more common in the French weights than in the other groups. I have taken care to include in this catalogue all notes that Mrs. Bergstrom made over the years, and have precisely recorded her attributions whether they agree with mine or not. This is not to say that mine are correct, but I have suggested changes only after careful study and the collation of my judgment with the authoritative research done by others since the time Mrs. Bergstrom made her records.

The objects listed in this catalogue fall into three groups: 1) those included in the Bergstrom bequest, identified or unidentified, but specifically mentioned in her records; 2) items in the Bergstrom bequest that were not recorded in Mrs. Bergstrom's files; and 3) all additions to the paperweight collection acquired after the founding of the museum.

Most readers of this book will, without doubt, have already heard of Mrs. Bergstrom's importance in the history of paperweight collecting, though they may know little else about her. She was born on May 23, 1872, in Ithaca, New York, the only child of Dr. (Dentist) and Mrs. George W. Hoysradt, née Adelaide Gregg, and was christened Evangeline. She attended the Anna Brown School for Girls in Ithaca, and met John Nelson Bergstrom (born in Neenah, Wisconsin, 1874) while he was a student at Cornell University. In 1901, they were married and came to live in DePere, Wisconsin, a town not far from his birthplace. In 1904, with his father D. W. Bergstrom, Mr. Bergstrom founded the Bergstrom Paper Company, and thereafter the young couple moved to Neenah, where even today that company remains one of the leading firms. Conjectures have been made about there being a connection between paper-making and an interest in paperweight collecting. The notion is intriguing, almost like an educated guess, but substantiating evidence is lacking.

Few personal notes relevant to Mrs. Bergstrom's collecting activities between 1904 and 1935 remain, except where her personal history parallels economic history. Her correspondence with "Cousin Joel" in 1932 and 1933 reveals that Neenah did not escape the general economic slump of those years, for she wrote, "John is on the road much of the time trying to get orders to keep the mill running. It is running only two and three days a week during these dreadful days of depression." Thus, even if her collecting activities had begun by then, it hardly seems likely that she bought many of her paperweights during those years.

Small of stature but a vital personality, Evangeline Bergstrom was religious, strong-willed and outspoken, and shrewd. She knew how to drive a hard bargain, but she gained and kept the respect of all who dealt with her. Mrs. Bergstrom took great pride in her colonial ancestry, and in her memberships in the Mayflower Society of Massachusetts, the Colonial Dames of Wisconsin, the Daughters of the American Revolution, the Antiquarian Society of Wisconsin, and the Historical Society of Wisconsin. In 1945, she ordered from the Historical Publication Society in Philadelphia a hand-painted grouping of her four ancestral coats of arms: Hoysradt, Priest, Pratt, and Gregg. Both Mr. and Mrs. Bergstrom also took pride in their church, the First Presbyterian Church of Neenah, and were active in its affairs.

The Bergstroms were childless, and so it is understandable that Mrs. Bergstrom was free to lavish a good deal of time and effort on her collecting activities. She also had another of the requisites necessary for such a hobby—a sympathetic spouse who provided financial backing. As the collection grew, so did her desire to know more about each specimen; and with her rising fever of acquisition she was led to begin serious research and study of the subject. There is something truly remarkable in the fact that this woman, in Middle West America, not only brought together such an amazing collection, but delved so deeply into the history and techniques of making paperweights and the factory sources of the specimens in her collection. It is even more astonishing that as early as 1940 she had the temerity to publish the results of her scholarly work in the handsome book *Old Glass Paperweights*.

Much credit is due Mr. Bergstrom for underwriting the very costly publication of that book, which included eighty-eight halftones and twenty magnificent color reproductions of paperweights, the finest that had been printed up to that time. Although it was Mr. Bergstrom's generosity that made possible the first edition of her book, it was Evangeline Bergstrom's creativity and tenacity that brought it to its completion. The book was privately printed by The Lakeside Press, Chicago. (Fortunately, it is still available in subsequent printings by Crown Publishers, Inc., New York, including one printing in 1947 by Crown for Faber and Faber, Ltd., London.) In effect, Mrs. Bergstrom was a pioneer—her book—the first extensive treatise on glass paperweights, the first to cover the whole field of activity—made the collecting world aware of this uniquely fascinating subject. The book was acclaimed by all the foremost collectors of that day. André E. Levy of Mexico City, whose six-hundred-item collection was well known, sent a congratulatory message to her in May, 1941. Several letters from Monsieur Maurice Lindon of Paris during the years 1946 to 1951 revealed his great admiration for her work and her collection. On June 16, 1947, he wrote:

> If I moan after my paperweights which are part of my life, which make me rush from Paris to the provinces, and London and Brussels, often for nothing, and make me spend a lot of money, I believe I have to blame you too, as your wonderful book achieved to tempt me.

An incidental note written early in 1950 is even more revealing:

> . . . there has been news and I promised to myself to let you know of it the first one. You always said, discoveries are constantly made . . . who knows one day a yellow overlay . . . well, Mrs. Bergstrom, I am the lucky "startled" collector and since yesterday I am in possession of a large, perfect yellow overlay, type of your Plate XV. That is, with a bouquet of flowers and the overlay encased in cristal. It is a type that for short, we call "inlay". I have this type in green. Palmer Hart has it in blue. I know you have it in blue and white . . . I have seen it pink, white, and blue-and-pink, but yellow must be unique and gives me the greatest thrill.

Evidently answering her subsequent inquiry, in a letter dated April 18, 1950, he said:

> Yes, my yellow overlay * is an incrusted one with a raising spray of flowers.

---

* This celebrated encased yellow double overlay weight is pictured in Plate 49, page 114, of Jokelson's *One Hundred of the Most Important Paperweights*.

There is no green base, it is lemon color, double overlay of course, with white and encased in cristal . . . it came from a junk shop near London and is not the Italian one.

In 1958, B. H. Leffingwell of Rochester, New York, one of the longtime experts in the field, probably reflected the feelings of many collectors when he said:

If there is any criticism of Mrs. Bergstrom's book, it is that she selected weights which are so far above the average collector's range today, that it is hopeless to try to find weights as good.

Frank Manheim, in his book *A Garland of Weights* (1967), commented:

Mrs. Bergstrom's book paved the role that paperweights play today among sophisticated collectors of art objects. Until that book, uncertainty plagued most would-be collectors who could not distinguish the various types of antique French weights, nor between them and the excellent English and American productions. Fortified with Mrs. Bergstrom's Baedeker, collectors could and did intensify and expand their diffident love affair with confidence and courage.

A question very often put to Mrs. Bergstrom during her lifetime, and one visitors to the museum so frequently ask, is how she happened to start collecting glass paperweights. In a radio interview at the WGN studios in Chicago in 1945, she replied to this query:

Like many collectors—it all started from something my grandmother had and I enjoyed playing with as a child. That paperweight was of the millefiori type, I learned later, and it amused me by the hour to try to find two similar florets. Years later, in St. Petersburg, Florida, at an antique show, I found a weight like the one I loved as a child. It had a B with date 1847, and the dealer told me the B stood for Bristol. I bought it after much deliberation, and also another which took my fancy. The first proved to be Baccarat, of course, and the second an American weight made in Fowlerton, Indiana, although I did not know it at the time. So I started with one French and one American and have been intrigued by them ever since, especially the French ones.

As the interview continued, she said:

What interested me in particular in paperweights was the beautiful color in the canes and flowers, which have a sparkle and brilliancy resembling a precious jewel to me, and the delicate and endlessly varied patterns of the designs which are brought out by the perfect workmanship which was first displayed in the old French weights. Today some of our American ones are becoming just as valuable. Especially the weights made by Nicholas Lutz at the Sandwich factory. He came from the Saint Louis factory in France and understood their art of color and fine workmanship.

When asked if collecting paperweights was a very old hobby, she replied,

It *could* be about one hundred years old. The first weights were made around 1828 and were rather crude in workmanship. It was not until the 1840's that they became pieces of art.

It was Mr. Bergstrom's inspiration that Neenah have a municipal museum, and upon his death in 1951 he left a substantial sum of money for possible museum purposes, to be payable at the time of Mrs. Bergstrom's death. He stipulated that if the legacy had not been so utilized within two years following his death, it would go elsewhere. In 1953, at the request of the Neenah Rotary Club, a committee was named to explore the possibilities of a public museum. The first step toward its realization was also taken in 1953, when the city accepted Mrs. Bergstrom's gift of her extensive lakeshore property and her Tudor residence for ultimate use as an art center and museum. In 1954, The City of Neenah Municipal Museum Foundation was incorporated as a nonprofit organization. Its founding members were Mrs. John Nelson Bergstrom, Mrs. Jessie K. Clark, Mr. and Mrs. Ernst Mahler, J. Russell Ward, Carl E. Loehning (Mayor of Neenah), Mr. and Mrs. S. F. Shattuck, Mr. and Mrs. J. C. Kimberly, Miss Helen E. Babcock, Miss F. Elizabeth Babcock, Mrs. H. E. Babcock, and Arthur P. Remley.

Mrs. Bergstrom lived in the residence until her death in 1958, and in April of the following year the civic museum, operating under the name of The John Nelson Bergstrom Art Center and Museum, was opened. The bequest of her rare accumulation of glass paperweights was and is its most valued permanent collection. Her financial endowment of the museum, along with her husband's legacy and the contributions of other civic-minded citizens, has assured the permanent support of the museum.

In accordance with Mrs. Bergstrom's wishes, the collection of paperweights and related items at the Bergstrom Art Center will remain intact—none of the pieces will ever leave the collection. The same is true of the additions made to the collection and also shown and described in this catalogue. For the most part, these additions are items of fine modern manufacture but in the traditional mode, such as modern Baccarat and the work of Charles Kaziun and Paul Ysart. Others are the work of contemporary artists whose abstract and free forms, though they depart from the traditional, create a new expression in glass paperweights that is distinctively twentieth century in feeling. Thus, the collection is being kept alive and vital, though such is not the only responsibility of those entrusted with its care.

Mrs. Bergstrom, as already mentioned, wanted to share her treasures with posterity, and so the entire collection has been placed on display. Many of the pieces are exhibited in handsome bronze-framed wall cases with built-in lighting on all four sides. To hold the weights at the proper angle for examination, they are cradled in specially designed metal rings, which project from a white formica background. Others are displayed in bronze-framed free-standing cases, but the important fact is that all—the extraordinary as well as the more usual pieces—are available for inspection by the paperweight lover.

A further fulfillment of our responsibility to Mrs. Bergstrom and her achievement has been the establishment of a Research Center for Paperweights. Located on the second floor of the museum, adjacent to a small art-reference library, it provides a workroom to which collectors, dealers, curators, and all persons interested in the study of glass paperweights are invited. They can study the Bergstrom collection itself, read and research in the library sources, and consult with the curator, if desired. Collectors are invited to bring their own weights for study and identification or to write to the Research Center. Thus, the collection has been made available for use as well as for viewing. The Center owes deep gratitude to several contributors who have donated the results of their years of research on paperweights—notes, manuscripts, catalogues, out-of-print books—and also black light equipment. Future contributions of research materials, it is hoped, will make the Center an outstanding depository of paperweight information.

It is also hoped that future contributions to the museum will include fine weights, not only to fill in some of the acknowledged gaps in the collection, but to provide specimens of weights that later research indicates should have been represented. The wonderment is that Mrs. Bergstrom made the collection as representative as it is, with no written word of any importance to guide her. Her intuition and her love of the beautiful were her only guides.

The compilation of this catalogue is the latest step in making the Bergstrom collection accessible to a larger, perhaps an uninitiated, public, and more meaningful to the somewhat smaller but more intensely interested group—those already ensnared in the web of collecting. I have already tried to excuse my presumptuousness in assuming the responsibility, but the work cried out to be done. I admit in advance to faults in attribution and await—without dread—suggestions for correction, even indignant criticism, for it is only by opening channels of communication that our knowledge of paperweights will grow and that more accurate methods of identification will develop. I recall a carefully prepared article by J. Percy Boore entitled "Bergstrom Reviewed" (*Bulletin of the Paperweight Collectors' Association,* June, 1963) in which many misattributions in Mrs. Bergstrom's book were pointed out. In an early paragraph he commented:

> Little printed matter of a reliable nature preceded her effort. Small wonder, then, that the book contains some errors. She herself took cognizance of this, saying "It must be recognized that in assigning certain items to certain classes, the classification is often based upon nothing more substantial than a supposition." The wonder is, not that there were errors, but that they were so few.

If nothing more harsh than that is said about this volume, I shall be reasonably happy.

To quote Mrs. Bergstrom's philosophy of paperweight collecting seems to be an appropriate conclusion to this foreword. In an unpublished article written in 1943, she explained:

> . . . collecting paperweights would not have quite its fascination if all the procedure were cut and dried—and if there were not certain pitfalls along the way, if it were not necessary to exercise your wits at least a little. Now and then you can commit an error that leads to disappointment, and it is by no means impossible to make a foolish mistake that you always feel a little ashamed of—but do we not commit similar follies in every other department of life? Quite possibly, Providence knew what it was about when it did not make life quite perfect!

Perhaps the most valuable asset of the paperweight collector is a consuming interest in the subject. Intense interest—I speak now from personal knowledge!—goes far to make up for what we may lack in native wit. Interest helps us to understand and to remember; to put two and two together, and arrive at new hypotheses and conclusions; to seize every bit of new information and try to fit it in with what we had before; to develop our intuitions to a point where we can often "feel" that something is false or true long before we can demonstrate it by means of air-tight logic. If your interest is strong enough, it will teach you to observe, and to sharpen your perceptions; and perhaps the day will arrive when you see things which escape the notice of others and can echo the Wizard of Baker Street—"Elementary, my dear Watson!"

GLOSSARY

BASE. The bottom portion of a weight, excluding the pedestal or foot (if any).

BASKET. A cuplike ground or sheath for a motif; can be of latticinio or stave canes. *See* LATTICINIO BASKET; STAVE BASKET.

BONBON ANGLAIS. French for "cane." Literally, "English candy."

BOUQUET. Floral motif in paperweights:
Flat Bouquet. Nosegay or floral spray in which the flowers and leaves lie flat.
Upright Bouquet. Compact, three-dimensional grouping of flowers and leaves set vertically. Often, the leaves form a sheath for the flowers, and the flower stems taper to a point.

BOUQUET DE MARIAGE. French term for a motif in tuft form. Strictly speaking, a bouquet de mariage is white, but the term is frequently used of any bouquet in tuft form. *See* MUSHROOM; TUFT.

CANDY. *See* MACÉDOINE.

CANE. Small slice or segment of a glass rod—monochrome, millefiori, filigree, or silhouette.

CARPET GROUND. Ground made of similar canes, arranged compactly.

CHECKER (CHEQUER). A weight with spaced millefiori motif, the individual canes being separated by short pieces of white or colored twisted ribbons or filigree twists, to make a checkered pattern.

CHECKERING. *See* DIAMOND CUTTING.

CHOUFLEUR. French for "cauliflower." Carpet ground of canes that, in shape and color, resembles a cauliflower.

CIRCLET. Small circle of millefiori canes.

CLOSE MILLEFIORI. Type of weight in which the motif consists of many variously patterned canes set closely together.

CLUSTER. A symmetrical grouping of millefiori canes. *See* ROSETTE.

COIL. *See* TORSADE.

COLOR GROUND. Single-color ground that may be translucent, transparent, or opaque. In many weights, the ground is made up of a transparent color laid over opaque white.

CONCENTRIC. Type of millefiori weight in which canes are arranged in circles, one within the other, around a common center.

CRIMP. Metal molding tool used in the formation of three-dimensional flowers— Millville roses, in particular.

CROWN. The glass above the motif.

CROWN WEIGHT. A usually hollow weight in which, radiating from a center cane or rosette positioned high in the crown, there are twisted ribbons and filigree spirals that converge near the base. Variants include MARBRIE WEIGHT and SWIRL WEIGHT.

CRYSTALLO-CÉRAMIE. *See* SULPHIDE.

CULLET. Waste fragments of glass or broken glass that, when cleaned, can be reused in a new melt.

CUSHION. Paperweight ground that resembles a convex pincushion in form.

CUTTING. Type of external decoration done by means of abrasives and various types of wheels. Includes punties, facets, and miter cuts.

DATES. In antique weights, usual dates are between 1845 and 1849, especially in millefiori weights; often the initials of the factory appear along with the date. However, over all, antique weights were rarely dated, and sometimes the dates that appear are not the dates of manufacture.

DESIGN. Synonymous with MOTIF.

DEXTER. Used with reference to sulphide portrait profiles, the word indicates that the subject is turned toward his own right, which is toward the left from the observer's viewpoint. *See also* SINISTER.

DIAMOND CUTTING. Miter cuts, evenly spaced, that cross at oblique angles. Also, flat faceting in diamond form. *See* STRAWBERRY CUTTING.

DOME. The form of some weights—cylindrical, with a slight taper toward the top. (Not to be confused with "crown," which refers to a part of a weight, rather than its shape.)

DOUBLE or TRIPLE OVERLAY. *See* OVERLAY WEIGHT.

ENCASED OVERLAY. An overlay weight that has been given an additional encasement of colorless glass.

END-OF-DAY WEIGHT. *See* MACÉDOINE.

ENGRAVING. Carving done by means of an abrasive such as emery and copper wheels of various sizes. Sometimes the design is polished to remove its frosted appearance. Engraved designs can show variations in depth.

ETCHING. Process of "biting out" a design on the surface of glass by using an acid. Depth of decoration is usually uniform. (Areas not to be etched are protected with an acid-resistant substance.) Etched designs, like engraved ones, have a frosted appearance, but are rarely polished to remove this.

FACET. A flat lapidary-type cutting on the exterior of a weight. Facets are plane cuts; punties are concave cuts.

FACTORY MARKS. Initials or names are sometimes enclosed within the weight, sometimes pressed on the underside. Insignia and/or names of manufacturers and a date are often etched on the underside or near the base. Sticker labels appear occasionally, applied to the base.

FILIGREE. Fine threads or ribbons of opaque white or colored glass, spiraled or twisted. Segments of filigree are often used in a motif or as ground. *See* MUSLIN GROUND.

FLANGED BASE. A base with a circular in-cut.

FLASH. A single-color metallic stain, brushed or sprayed on the exterior of a weight or on the base, and sometimes fired to insure permanence.

FLOATING DESIGN or MOTIF. Flat or three-dimensional motif suspended within the weight, with colorless glass above and below.

FLORET. A single cane or composite cane that, in cross section, even remotely resembles a flower or flower head.

FLOWER WEIGHT. A weight with a natural or stylized flower as the predominant motif. Petals may be smooth, veined, striped, or grooved.

FLUTE CUTTING. Cutting in the form of a round-bottomed groove, usually vertical.

FOOT. An applied formation of glass, usually round and flat, on which a weight rests.

GARLAND. Continuous line, row, or chainlike succession of canes in a design other than a circle; often an intertwined arrangement.

GOLDSTONE. Aventurine of jewel-like appearance in which the gold spangles are close and fine.

GRAVEL GROUND. A single-color, coarse-grained ground.

GROUND. That portion of the inside of a weight between the internal design and the base. *See* CARPET, COLOR, CUSHION, GRAVEL, JASPER, LACE, LATTICINIO, MOSS, MUSLIN, PEBBLE, ROCK, SAND, and STARDUST GROUND.

HAND COOLER. An egg-shaped paperweight.

HONEYCOMB. Type of cane that, in cross section, resembles the cells of a honeycomb.

HONEYCOMB FACETING. Exterior concave cutting in honeycomb form.

INCRUSTATION. Enclosure of a sulphide in colorless glass.

JASPER GROUND. Fine-grained ground composed of two or more colors. (Grain is finer than in gravel ground.)

LACE GROUND. Same as MUSLIN GROUND.

LATTICINIO. Threads or ribbons of opaque white or colored glass so arranged as to produce the effect of intersecting curves, as in latticework.

LATTICINIO BASKET. Usually, a layer of spiral latticinio below the motif, the layer being pulled down in the center to resemble a basket.

MACÉDOINE. Type of weight with its motif made up of a jumble of various canes, often combined with filigree segments, and assembled at random.

MAGNUM. A weight with a diameter of three inches or more.

MANTEL ORNAMENT. Usually, a globular paperweight that is mounted on a standard.

MARBRIE WEIGHT. A type of crown weight. Design is composed of loops or festoons of solid color that decorate a globular monochrome interior.

METAL. Glass in the molten or solid state. (Used interchangeably with the word "glass.")

MILLEFIORI CANE. A segment of a composite glass rod, cut to expose the design in cross section.

MILLEFLEURS. French word for *millefiori,* meaning "thousand flowers."

MINIATURE WEIGHT. One that is two inches or less in diameter.

MITER CUT. A cut of any length that is V-shaped in cross section.

MONOCHROME. Of a single color.

MOSS GROUND. Ground consisting of closely packed green canes resembling blades of grass, sometimes interspersed with small white star canes with pink centers, simulating "prairie flowers." Sometimes called "prairie ground."

MOTIF. The internal design of a weight. *See* SET-UP.

MUSHROOM. Type of motif made up of a sheaf of millefiori canes narrow at the base and spreading into a tuft shape as it rises into the crown. "Tuft" is an alternate term. *See also* BOUQUET DE MARIAGE.

MUSLIN GROUND. Ground made up of segments of spiraled opaque threads (usually white) or filigree rods, assembled at random. Sometimes called "upset muslin."

OLIVE CUT. *See* THUMBPRINT.

OVERLAY WEIGHT. One with the exterior covered with one layer (single overlay), 2 layers (double overlay), or 3 layers (triple overlay) of opaque or transparent glass. Decorative cutting through outer layer or layers reveals the interior design. Innermost layer is usually white, which reflects light and illuminates the motif.

PAPERWEIGHT (GLASS). An object made of glass, usually with a decorative motif enclosed.

PASTRY MOLD. Type of cane that flares at the base and usually has deep and rounded serrations, giving the effect of having been formed in a jelly mold.

PATTERNED MILLEFIORI. Weight with motif of millefiori canes set in a symmetrical design other than concentric circles.

PEBBLE GROUND. Same as GRAVEL GROUND.

PELL-MELL WEIGHT. Same as MACÉDOINE.

PIEDOUCHE WEIGHT. Weight supported by a column (sometimes drawn, sometimes applied) that frequently encloses staves, latticinio designs, or torsades.

PINCHBECK WEIGHT. One with motif, in relief, that is a metal alloy such as Pinchbeck gold and that is set under a lens-type colorless glass crown; usually base is pewter or marble.

PONTIL MARK. A rough mark or scar left on the underside of a weight, where it was broken off from the pontil rod.

PONTIL ROD. Solid metal rod on which glass is gathered from the pot and worked.

PRINTY. Alternate term for punty, especially in British usage. A circular concave cut on the exterior of a weight.

PUNTY. Circular or oval (thumbprint) concave cut on the exterior of a weight. Synonymous with "window." (Glassworkers often call the pontil rod the "punty," and the pontil mark the "punty mark.")

QUATREFOIL. Type of cane found in Baccarat weights that portrays, in cross section, a 4-leaf design. Also, a garland of canes in a 4-leaf pattern.

RIBBON. A flattened cane, usually opaque, in one or a combination of colors and frequently twisted, as in crown and checker weights.

ROCK GROUND. Ground made up of glass fragments having a quartzlike, sandy appearance, often with mica flakes and green glass chips. Used as ground for reptiles and sometimes as a complete motif.

ROSETTE. Circular cluster of closely set canes at center of motif.

SAND GROUND. Same as ROCK GROUND.

SCRAMBLED WEIGHT. Same as MACÉDOINE.

SET-UP. Paperweight makers refer to design or motif of a paperweight as the set-up.

SILHOUETTE CANE. A segment of a rod that, in cross section, portrays a silhouette or undetailed outline of an animal or other figure.

SINGLE OVERLAY. *See* OVERLAY WEIGHT.

SINISTER. Used with reference to sulphide portrait profiles, the word indicates that the subject is turned toward his own left side, which is toward the right from the observer's viewpoint. *See also* DEXTER.

SPACED MILLEFIORI.   (Sometimes erroneously called "scattered millefiori.") Type of weight in which the canes are distributed over the ground with spaces intervening.

STAIN. *See* FLASH.

STAR CUT. Miter cut made in star shape of five or more points.

STARDUST GROUND. Carpet ground composed of tiny star-shaped rods, sometimes with colored dot at center.

STAVE BASKET. Outer circle of flattened, opaque canes (usually of alternating colors) in a concentric or close millefiori, drawn to the base to simulate a basket.

STAVE CANE. Flattened and usually opaque cane that often is used for the outer circle in a close millefiori, concentric, or mushroom motif.

STRAWBERRY CUTTING. Embellished version of the diamond cut in which each diamond is further cut with lines bisecting the points; usually seen on underside of weight. (Called "strawberry diamond" in cut glass and pressed glass terminology.)

STYLIZED FLOWER. A flower design made up of canes, not lampwork parts.

SULPHIDE. A ceramic bas-relief portrait or medallion to be incrusted in glass and used for ornamentation of various glass objects.

SULPHIDE WEIGHT. Type of weight in which the principal motif is an incrusted sulphide.

SWIRL WEIGHT. Weight with motif consisting of opaque colored rods of alternating colors radiating from a central cane or group of canes in pinwheel or swirl formation. A type of crown weight.

THUMBPRINT. Cutting in the form of an elongated punty (concave oval); also called "olive cut."

TORSADE. Spiral of fine ribbons, rods, or filigree (often a combination of these) encircling the motif, sometimes near the base. Also called "coil."

TREFOIL. Type of cane found in Baccarat weights portraying, in cross section, a 3-leaf design. Also, a garland of canes in 3-leaf pattern.

TUFT. Synonymous with MUSHROOM. *See also* BOUQUET DE MARIAGE.

WHORL. Type of design in spiral formation; term is usually used in reference to the design of a cane. Sometimes called "pinwheel" or "swirl."

WINDOW. Circular flat or concave cut on the exterior of a weight. *See* PUNTY and FACET.

1
FRENCH
WEIGHTS

Though the making of glass artifacts had been an art, a craft, and a science for hundreds of years, it reached its zenith of compact excellence in the middle of the nineteenth century in France, when an artisan enclosed a colored, preformed element within a small sphere of clear glass and named it a paperweight. The era of this amazing accomplishment has been called "the golden age of colored glass, the most colorful the industry has ever known," and the accomplishment itself, "the art of glassmaking in its highest degree of perfection." Thus, by implication, a definition of the term "paperweight" is suggested—the only one acceptable to purists among collectors, though objectionable perhaps to those collectors who include among paperweights objects with exterior or applied decoration. It will be obvious to the reader that the preponderance of the Bergstrom collection consists of the enclosed type, but whatever one's attitude toward the definition, most collectors will surely agree that the exquisite mid-nineteenth-century French weights are the ultimate.

Who first introduced a "glass embedded within glass" weight? Craftsmen, no matter the nationality, did not arrive at the perfection of such a weight without much experimentation. Among the earliest dates actually enclosed in known paperweights are "1845" in weights of the Venetian craftsman Pietro Bigaglia; "1845" in a paperweight vase of Saint Louis (229, Plate 25); "1846" in a Baccarat weight (151, Plate 5); and "1848" both in a Bohemian-Silesian piece (337, Plate 38) and an English Whitefriars weight (23, Plate 35). These dates would indicate that the Venetians, the French, and probably the Bohemians and the English must have arrived at successful millefiori enclosures in paperweights at about the same time. Whether or not we agree that Bigaglia was the first to introduce a millefiori paperweight, there is little doubt that the showing of his weights at the Vienna industrial

27

From 1831 to 1857, the two factories employed as their sales agent the firm of Launay, Hautin & Compagnie with offices at 50, rue Paradis-Poissonnière, in Paris. Much of the information known today about their paperweight production, especially during the years 1847 to 1851, was revealed in the correspondence of this firm with the management of the factories.

Although the career of the Clichy factory was brief in comparison to that of Baccarat and Saint Louis, Clichy ranked equally in the quality of the glass paperweights produced. The factory, known as Clichy-la-Garenne, was established about 1840 in Clichy, a northwest suburb of Paris that is now absorbed within the city. The tremendous success of the factory in manufacturing paperweights gave keen competition to both Baccarat and Saint Louis. Its height of prosperity was reached at the time of the international exhibition in London in 1851, when reports became widespread about the remarkable quality of Clichy glass displayed there. Today, some connoisseurs prefer Clichy weights above all others.

The "trademark"—and as good as a signature—is the "Clichy rose." This is a cane made up of many thin leaflets of glass, tightly clustered; it appears in pink, white, purple, blue, yellow, and green, sometimes with an outer leaflet of a contrasting color. The letter "C" often appears in a cane, and in rare pieces the entire word "Clichy" is found. No cane bearing a date is known to be in a Clichy weight. Pastry-mold canes, which flare at the base and usually have deep serrations, were profusely used. Clichy weights were often made of what has been termed "boracic" glass rather than lead glass; the best of them are white and sparkling, and their colors are brilliant and pure. Little is known of Clichy production after 1860, although the factory continued until about 1880, when it was absorbed by the Cristalleries de Sèvres.

After 1860, there is little evidence of the manufacture of the finer millefiori weights. Imbert and Amic, in their book *Les Presse-Papiers Français* (1948), state that in the 1880's and later, weights in high relief (458, Plate 7) and reptiles on gray and green rocklike ground (230, Plate 21 and 261, Plate 7) were made; and they say further that this type continued at least through 1907, since price lists for 1907 indicated these as well as pansy weights.

Information is sparse, too, on French paperweight production during the first half of the twentieth century. But the 1950's marked what might be termed a renaissance of weight making in both the Baccarat and Saint Louis factories. At the time of the coronation of Queen Elizabeth II, Baccarat began to issue in limited editions a series of sulphide weights in overlay and nonoverlay portraying famous persons, and new models have continued to appear every year. Also, since 1957, some weights in the millefiori technique have been made. Colors are in paler hues, and the designs lack the artistry found in antique Baccarat examples. A 1957 Baccarat price list included thirteen weights that were produced in an unlimited edition, and four of these were in the millefiori technique.

The weights made at the Saint Louis factory since 1950 have been of superior quality. Examples include the coronation sulphide of Queen Elizabeth II (593 and 594, Plate 32) and copies of Saint Louis antique weights, including a double overlay millefiori mushroom (711, Plate 32), vegetable and fruits, and concentric millefiori piedouche weights. Dates of 1952 and 1953 are often found. More recently, in 1967, a sulphide of King Saint Louis was issued to commemorate the bicentenary of the Saint Louis factory. Also, in connection with the bicentenary celebration, a detailed history of the factory, entitled "Saint Louis, Cristal de France," with a preface by André Maurois, was published.

Today, these renowned French factories, Baccarat and Saint Louis, have their spacious salesrooms side by side at 30, rue de Paradis, in Paris.

NOTE TO THE READER: *In some instances, there is a difference between the color described in a caption and that which appears in the illustration. This variation results largely from the necessity of using a common background for sizable groups of variously colored objects. Lighting also influences color tones. For example, in Plate 30, the base of the John F. Kennedy weight (715) appears to be black. Its true color, when it is held to the light, is ruby-red.*

The numbers used to identify the illustrations and their captions are the Bergstrom acquisition numbers. The information that follows the □ device in a caption is Mrs. Bergstrom's attribution of that item and other data about it from her records. Her spellings are retained.

Plate 1

154. Baccarat. Dated 1848. Spaced millefiori canes; set in star-dust ground (white stars with red dot centers). "B 1848" appears in one cane; an elephant, flower, arrow, and butterfly appear in various others. $3\frac{3}{16}$" (8.1 cm.) diam.

□ Baccarat; acquired Oct., 1938.

368. Baccarat. Dated 1848. Spaced millefiori canes on white muslin ground; occasional twists of colored ribbons. "B 1848" appears in one cane; others contain squirrel, elephant, bird, flower, butterfly, and arrow. $3\frac{5}{16}$" (8.4 cm.) diam.

□ Baccarat; acquired Oct., 1940.

9. Baccarat. Dated 1848. Spaced millefiori canes on white muslin ground; occasional twists of colored ribbons. "B 1848" appears in one cane; butterfly cane is in center; other canes include squirrel, white lovebirds, and man with rifle. $3\frac{3}{16}$" (8.1 cm.) diam.

□ Baccarat; acquired May, 1936.
(Illus. 14, 1940 Bergstrom book; Illus. 15, subsequent editions.)

102. Baccarat. Mid-19th century. Double overlay, turquoise over opaque white. The millefiori mushroom consists of 4 concentric circles of canes. The center cane as well as the circle of canes near the periphery resembles Clichy roses. Outer circle of blue-and-white canes is drawn down to base to form tuft. Punty on top and 5 punties on curve. A 24-pointed star is cut in a punty on the underside of the weight. $3\frac{3}{16}$" (8.1 cm.) diam.

□ Clichy; acquired Dec., 1937.

178. Baccarat. Mid-19th century. Double overlay, royal blue over opaque white. Motif—a floating, patterned millefiori design—consists of 7 circlets of varicolored canes, each circlet surrounding a single cane; 4 of these center canes are arrow canes and 3 are white stars. Punty on top and on underside, 6 punties on curve; 12 oval cuts near base. $3\frac{1}{16}$" (7.8 cm.) diam.

□ Baccarat; acquired Dec., 1938.

106. Baccarat. Mid-19th century. Double overlay, turquoise over opaque white, encloses floating, patterned millefiori design on clear ground. Two garlands of varicolored canes intertwine, enclosing single canes of animals and birds. Center motif is circlet of white star and red canes surrounding butterfly cane. Punty on top, 6 punties on curve, and 12 oval cuts near base. A 24-pointed star is cut on the underside. $3\frac{1}{8}$" (7.9 cm.) diam.

□ Baccarat; acquired Dec., 1937.

526. Baccarat. Mid-19th century. Full-length sulphide figure of Madonna wearing crown and with a cherub at her feet, on translucent cobalt blue ground. Slightly concave top and rectangular cuttings on curve. Flat base. $3\frac{1}{4}$" (8.3 cm.) diam.

□ Unrecorded.

387. Attributed to Baccarat. Mid-19th century. Full-length sulphide figure of Madonna with crown, and child holding bird, on translucent cranberry ground. Flat top and base; rectangular faceting on curve. 3" (7.6 cm.) diam.

□ English; acquired March, 1941.

216. Baccarat. Mid-19th century. Hunter and dog sulphide on translucent cobalt blue ground. Flat top; diamond-shaped faceting on curve. $3\frac{1}{4}$" (8.3 cm.) diam.

□ Baccarat; acquired Feb., 1939.
(Illus. 39, 1940 Bergstrom book; Illus. 37, subsequent editions; Fig. 48, p. 54, Jokelson *Sulphides*.)

104. Baccarat. Dated 1848. Spaced millefiori canes, including "B 1848" cane, are set in carpet ground of green, red, and white canes. Animal, butterfly, arrow, and flower canes appear. $3\frac{1}{4}$" (8.3 cm.) diam.

□ Baccarat; acquired Dec., 1937.

145. Baccarat. Dated 1848. Spaced millefiori canes on white star-dust ground. "Butterfly" cane is in center; "B 1848" cane appears also, as well as elephant, monkey, dove, and swan canes. $2\frac{7}{8}$" (7.3 cm.) diam.

□ Baccarat; acquired Oct., 1938.

132. Baccarat. Dated 1848. Spaced millefiori canes are set in unusual carpet ground of red-and-white canes with blue star centers. "B 1848" cane appears, as well as animal, bird, arrow, and other canes. An unusual cane is white bird set in red with 2 small green shamrocks. 3" (7.6 cm.) diam.

□ Baccarat; acquired June, 1938.

Plate 1

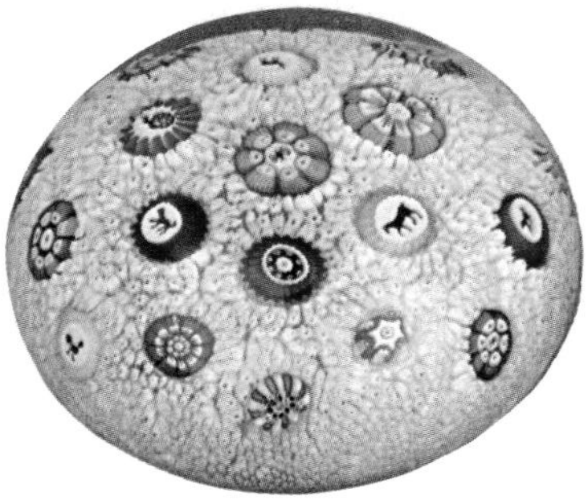

154

368

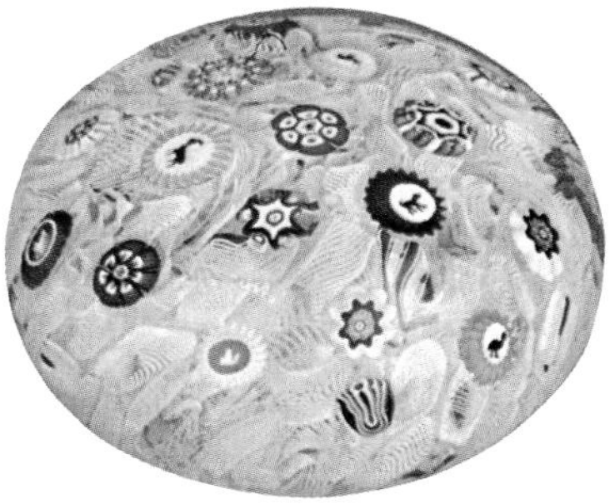

9

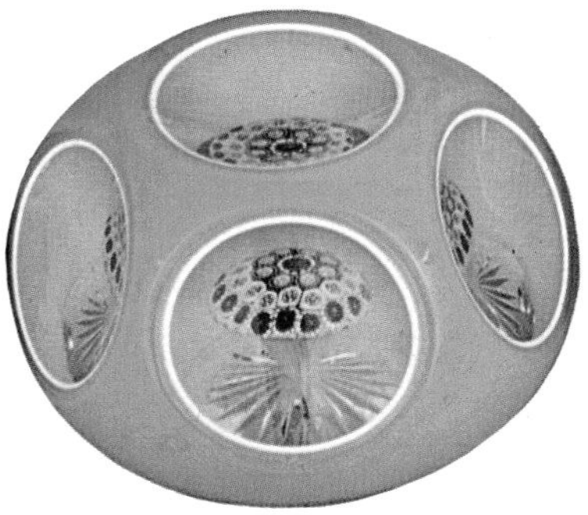

102

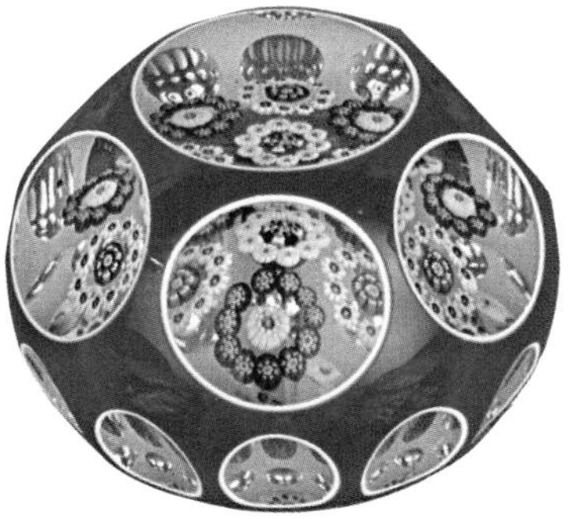

178

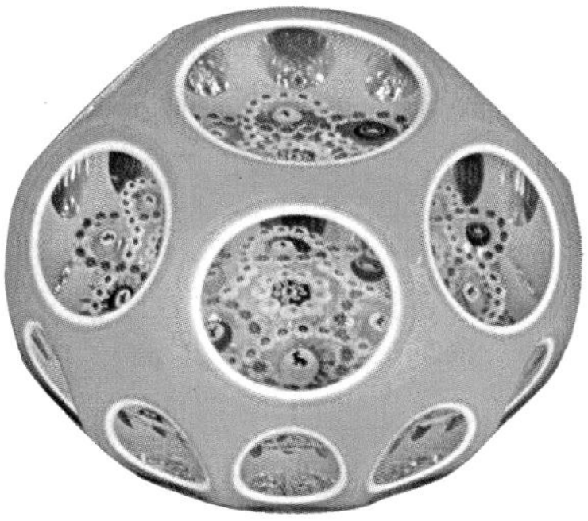

106

526

387

216

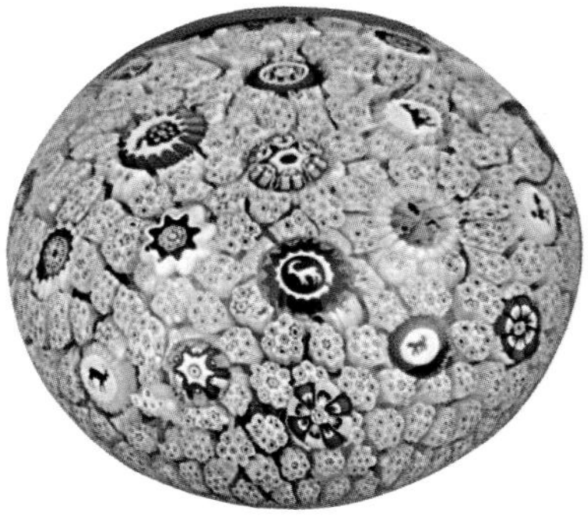

104

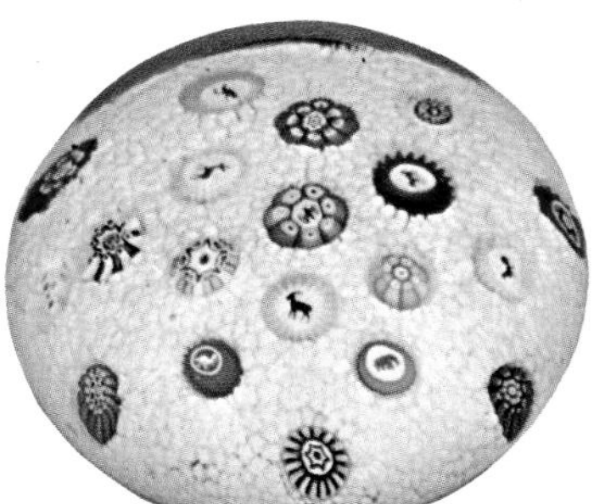

145

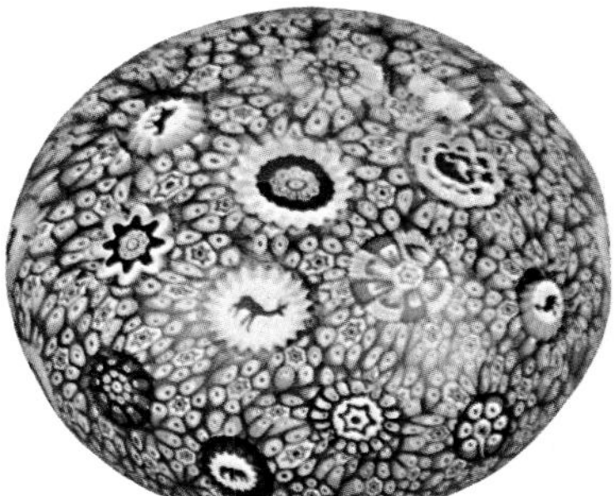

132

Plate **2**

224. Baccarat. Mid-19th century. Floating motif consists of copper-tone camomile flower with petals of crescent-shaped canes and yellow stamen center; 2 buds and 7 leaves, with lower 2 leaves on stem. At periphery is a circle of millefiori canes, green alternating with white. Six punties on curve. Convex top. Underside is cut with 24-pointed star. 3¼″ (8.3 cm.) diam.

☐ Baccarat; acquired Feb., 1939.

71. Origin unknown, possibly Dorflinger, White Mills, Pa. *Ca.* 1863–1915. Large, heavy weight with floating motif of 4 concentric circles, not contiguous, of rose-colored, blue-and-white, and red-and-white canes. Large central cane is green "wagon wheel" with green rim, opaque white spokes, and green stamen center. Most prevalent are 5-pointed star canes. Allover geometric faceting. A 32-pointed star is cut on the underside. 3⅞″ (9.9 cm.) diam. (The canes are similar to those in weight 283, Plate 43; 445, Plate 44; and 254, Plate 62.)

☐ Unidentified; acquired Sept., 1937.

503. Baccarat. Mid-19th century. Floating motif consists of galloping horse painted in various shades of blue on opaque white glass disk. Narrow band of dark blue outlines the disk; then comes a circle of white canes alternating with red-and-white canes. Punty on top and 6 punties on curve. Underside is flat. 3⅜″ (8.6 cm.) diam.

☐ Baccarat; acquired Sept., 1942.
(Plate 19, Jokelson, *One Hundred of the Most Important Paperweights.*)

476. Baccarat. Dated 1848. Spaced millefiori on star-dust ground (white stars with red dot in center). In addition to "B 1848" cane, others include silhouettes, such as an elephant, squirrel, and swan. Punty on top and 2 circles of punties on curve. 2¹¹⁄₁₆″ (6.8 cm.) diam.

☐ Baccarat; acquired Jan., 1942.

295. Attributed to Baccarat. Mid-19th century. Fruit weight. Cluster of 5 red cherries with thin, translucent, pink stems, which are attached to a sturdy, orange-colored main stem. Four large green leaves. Bubble at blossom end of each cherry and occasional bubbles on leaves. Colorless base. 3⅛″ (7.9 cm.) diam.

☐ Baccarat; acquired Jan., 1940.
(Illus. 19, Bergstrom book.)

479. Baccarat. Mid-19th century. Floating flat bouquet motif with red camomile center flower, white star-cane center, surrounded by 4 stylized flowers (arrow cane petals),

each with bud, leaves, and stem. The arrow canes in 2 of the smaller flowers are similar to those which make up lower pansy petals of early Baccarat manufacture. Top punty is large, possibly making the weight a wafer tray. Alternating punties and vertical oblong cuts on curve. A 16-pointed star is cut on the underside. 3⅜″ (8.6 cm.) diam.

☐ Baccarat; acquired Jan., 1942.

278. Baccarat. Mid-19th century. Floating bellflower motif: Three flat white flowers with grooved pointed petals, white bud, 7 green leaves, hang from a central stem. Colorless base. 3″ (7.6 cm.) diam.

☐ Baccarat; acquired Nov., 1939.

340. Bohemian. Mid-19th century. A type of crown weight with central cluster of 8 canes from which radiate alternating deep blue and opaque white ribbons, not contiguous, converging at center of base. There are 2 white monkey silhouette canes. 2¹¹⁄₁₆″ (6.8 cm.) diam. (See Hollister, *The Encyclopedia of Glass Paperweights,* p. 33 and Fig. 10.)

☐ Baccarat; acquired June, 1940.

417. Origin unknown, probably French. Green and brown striped coiled snake with large red eyes lies on translucent, sparsely-covered base of green over white with many tiny bubbles. Pontil mark on underside. 2⅞″ (7.3 cm.) diam. (Ground is similar to that in weight 305, Plate 61, and the snake has a similarity to the duck figures in the "Ducks in a Pond" weight, 571 in Plate 8.)

☐ English; acquired May, 1941.

428. Baccarat. Mid-19th century. Floating motif: In center, a sulphide portrait, profile to sinister, of Josephine is encircled by 5 separated but identical large canes. Circle of canes at periphery. Colorless ground. 2⁷⁄₁₆″ (6.2 cm.) diam.

☐ Baccarat; acquired Aug., 1941.

199. Attributed to Baccarat. *Ca.* 1900. Miniature "Sand Dunes" weight of sparkling colorless glass. Green, gray, and buff-colored sand ground is drawn. up into 2 peaks. 1¹³⁄₁₆″ (4.7 cm.) diam.

☐ Unidentified; listed as "Sand Dunes of Cape Cod"; acquired Dec., 1938.

183. Baccarat. Flat bouquet weight with colorless glass base. Floating motif includes dark blue clematis with furrowed petals, red and white striped petaled flower, and an opaque white flower; all have cane centers, blue stems. There are 18 green leaves. 2½″ (6.3 cm.) diam.

☐ Unidentified; acquired Dec., 1938.

Plate 2

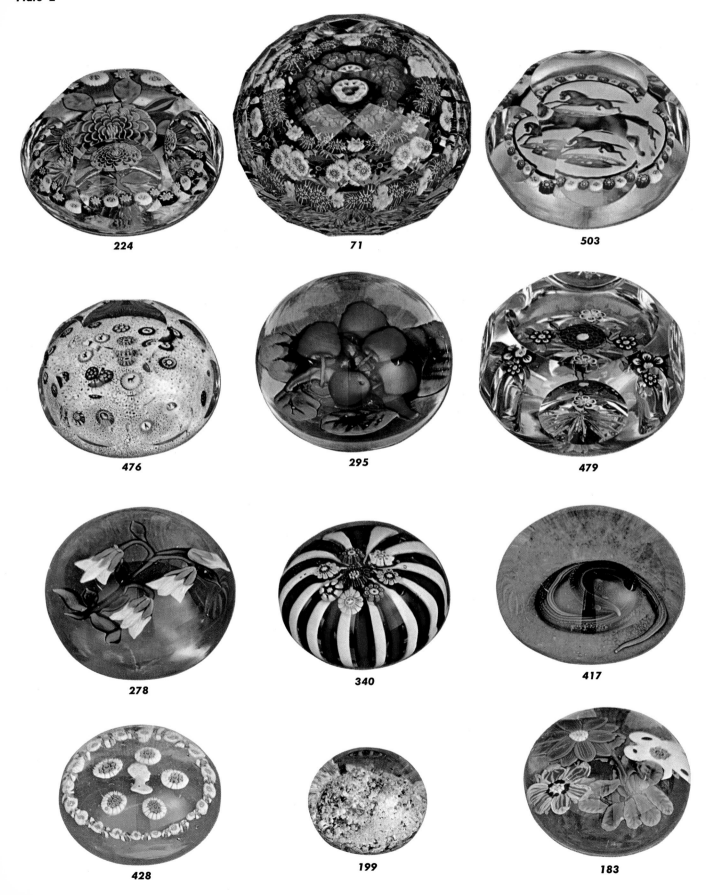

224

71

503

476

295

479

278

340

417

428

199

183

Plate 3

335. Baccarat. Mid-19th century. Floating pansy motif, of early Baccarat manufacture. Upper 2 purple petals have velvet texture; lower 3 petals are serrated white canes with white veining on translucent blue centers. Pale yellow honeycomb center cane. Red bud, 7 green leaves, and stem. A 24-pointed star is cut on the underside. $3\frac{1}{16}$" (7.8 cm.) diam.

☐ Baccarat; acquired May, 1940.
(Illus. 13, 1940 Bergstrom book; Illus. 14, subsequent editions.)

223. Baccarat. Mid-19th century. Patterned millefiori motif. Red-and-white center cane is encircled by 7 green shamrock canes, then a circle of canes similar to the center cane, and beyond this a circle of deep blue and red arrow canes—all on white muslin ground. Spaced butterfly canes appear at periphery. Motif is close to encasing glass. 3" (7.6 cm.) diam.

☐ Baccarat; acquired Feb., 1939.

144. Baccarat. Mid-19th century. Floating flat bouquet consists of 4 flowers (pansy with 2 purple upper petals, 3 lower yellow petals, and white star-cane center; blue and white primrose with cane center; yellow wheat flower with black dots; full-blown pink rose), a red bud, blue bud, 11 green leaves, and 2 stems that cross. Base is colorless. $3\frac{3}{16}$" (8.1 cm.) diam.

☐ Baccarat; acquired Oct., 1938.
(Illus. 29, Bergstrom book.)

184. Baccarat. Mid-19th century. Floating dark red clematis has 10 furrowed pointed petals and a yellow, 5-sided honeycomb center cane. Motif also includes a red bud, 7 green leaves, a green stem, and a circle of predominantly red and white canes at the periphery. A 24-pointed star is cut on the underside. $2\frac{7}{8}$" (7.3 cm.) diam.

☐ Unidentified; acquired Dec., 1938.

450. Baccarat. Profile view of brick-red dahlia flower, floating on colorless glass ground. The 20 veined petals have pinpoint bubbles interspersed. Four narrow, pointed green leaves and stem. A 32-pointed star is cut on the underside. $2\frac{3}{4}$" (7.0 cm.) diam.

☐ Baccarat; acquired Sept., 1941.

8. Baccarat. *Ca.* 1855. Floating pansy motif also includes one bud, 7 green leaves, and stem. Upper 2 petals of pansy are purple with velvet texture; lower 3 are yellow with purple tips and fine black applied veining. Center cane of white stars with red center. Circle of red-and-white and blue-and-white canes surrounds pansy. Weight is hexagonal, the crown cut into pyramid form. A 24-pointed star is cut on the underside. $2\frac{1}{2}$" (6.3 cm.) diam.

☐ Sandwich; acquired May, 1936.

233. Baccarat. Mid-19th century. Floating red flower has round petals and a white star center cane; a red bud, 6 green leaves, and stem also appear. Small 24-pointed star is cut on the underside. $2\frac{1}{2}$" (6.3 cm.) diam.

☐ Baccarat; acquired May, 1939.

186. Attributed to Baccarat. *Ca.* 1900. Sulphide fish, white with red sword, floats very close to top of crown, above a predominantly blue and white jasper ground. $2\frac{3}{4}$" (7.0 cm.) diam. (Weight has characteristics of both Sandwich and Saint Louis.)

☐ Baccarat; acquired Jan., 1939.
(Illus. 37, 1940 Bergstrom book; Illus. 35, subsequent editions.)

386. Baccarat. *Ca.* 1855. Floating pansy with bud, 12 green leaves, and stem. Upper 2 petals are purple with velvet texture; lower 3 are yellow over opaque white with purple tips and fine applied veining. Center is white star cane with red center. A 24-pointed star is cut on the underside. $2\frac{13}{16}$" (7.2 cm.) diam.

☐ Baccarat; acquired Dec., 1940.

67. Baccarat. *Ca.* 1855. Floating pansy with bud, 7 green leaves, and stem. Upper 2 petals are purple with velvet texture; lower 3 are yellow over opaque white with purple tips and applied black veining. White star center cane with red center. Small 16-pointed star is cut on the underside. $2\frac{5}{8}$" (6.6 cm.) diam.

☐ Cambridge; acquired Sept., 1937.

Plate 3

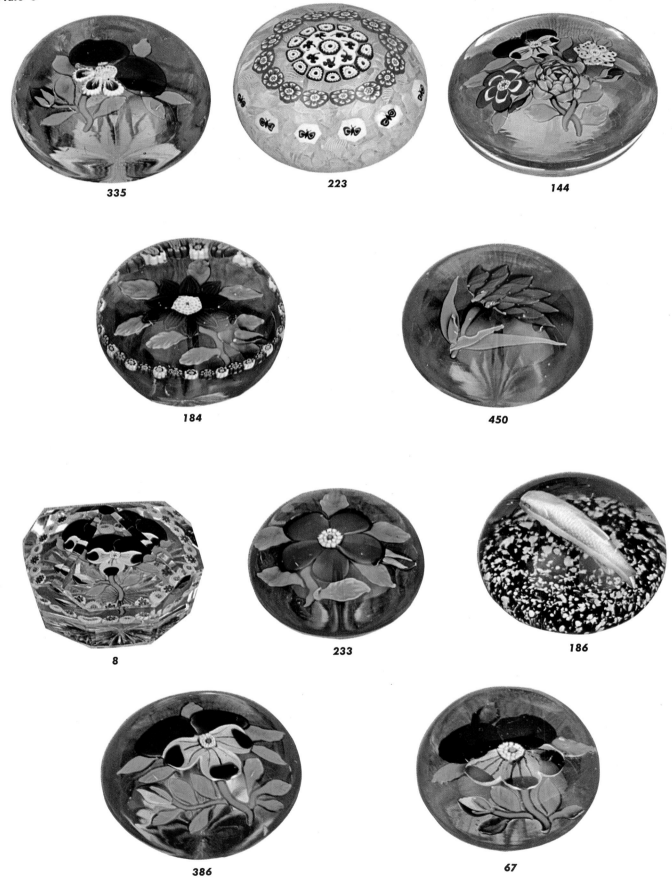

335

223

144

184

450

8

233

186

386

67

Plate 4

95. Baccarat. Mid-19th century. Patterned millefiori on translucent ruby ground. A garland of white-and-red canes intertwines with a garland of blue-and-white canes, forming double trefoil design. Each loop encloses a single cane; among them are bird, animal, and butterfly canes. At center, a circlet of white-and-green star canes surrounds a pink-and-white cane. 3³⁄₁₆″ (8.1 cm.) diam.

☐ Baccarat; acquired Nov., 1937.

472. Origin unknown; possibly Baccarat. *Ca.* 1900. "Rock" weight, sometimes called "Sand Dunes" weight. Emerald green and light gray sand ground is drawn up into 3 peaks. Some of the sand in the ground moves when weight is tipped. 3¹³⁄₁₆″ (8.1 cm.) diam.

☐ Unidentified; acquired Dec., 1941.

226. Baccarat. Mid-19th century. Floating patterned millefiori on colorless ground. Center of design is 2 concentric circles with single cane center, surrounded by canes in 4 groups and a garland in quatrefoil design. Weight is footed, the foot enclosing a torsade of red ribbon twist around which white filigree strands are coiled. 3⅛″ (7.9 cm.) diam.

☐ Baccarat; acquired May, 1939.

508. Baccarat. Mid-19th century. Millefiori mushroom of chalk-white star canes with center cane of arrows in red, white, and blue. Torsade has tubular core of white filigree about which is coiled a strand of cobalt blue. A small 32-pointed star is cut on the underside. 3¼″ (8.3 cm.) diam.

☐ Baccarat; acquired Oct., 1942.

152. Baccarat. Dated 1848. Spaced millefiori canes are set in carpet ground of blue-and-white canes with star centers. "B 1848" appears in one cane; others contain animals, shamrocks, butterflies, arrows, and so on. 3″ (7.6 cm.) diam.

☐ Baccarat; acquired Oct., 1938.

146. Baccarat. Mid-19th century. Concentric millefiori in mushroom form is made up of 4 circles of white star with red dot, deep red with stamen of ocher, and white-and-green canes. At center is large, opaque white, serrated cane with blue-and-white star center. Torsade is tubular white filigree core around which is coiled a dark blue strand. A 16-pointed star is cut on the underside. 3¼″ (8.3 cm.) diam.

☐ Baccarat; acquired Oct., 1938.

299. Baccarat. Mid-19th century. Floating motif: Large butterfly with deep purple filigree body, turquoise eyes, and multicolored wings. Circle of arrow canes alternates with white-and-red canes at periphery. A 24-pointed star is cut on the underside. 3⅛″ (7.9 cm.) diam.

☐ Baccarat; acquired Feb., 1940.
(Plate XIII, Bergstrom book.)

127. Baccarat. Mid-19th century. Butterfly, with purple filigree body, turquoise eyes, dark blue head, 2 antennae, and wings of flattened colored canes over opaque white, hovers over white flower, which has 12 furrowed, pointed petals and a cane center. Eight pale green leaves, stem, and a white bud surround flower. A 24-pointed star is cut on the underside. 3¹⁄₁₆″ (7.8 cm.) diam.

☐ Baccarat; acquired May, 1938.
(Plate V, Bergstrom book.)

549. Baccarat. Mid-19th century. Butterfly, with purple filigree body, turquoise eyes, and wings of flattened vari-colored canes over opaque white, hovers over large white flower, which has 12 grooved pointed petals and pale yellow honeycomb cane center. Five pale green leaves surround the flower. White bud and 3 leaves are supported by stem. On underside 12 radial oval cuts alternate with 12 small miter cuts. 3³⁄₁₆″ (8.1 cm.) diam.

☐ Unrecorded.

215. Baccarat. Mid-19th century. Floating motif: Figure of horse is painted in various shades of pink on opaque white glass disk that is edged with narrow pink band. Encircling the disk are white star canes with green centers alternating with blue arrow canes. Punty on top and 6 punties on curve. Flat colorless base. 3¼″ (8.3 cm.) diam.

☐ Baccarat; acquired Feb., 1939.
(Illus. 24, Bergstrom book.)

437. French. Oval-shaped plaque enclosing sulphide bust, front view slightly to sinister, of Louis Philippe on translucent cobalt blue ground is framed in a metal band. Edge of glass is beveled on both sides. 3″ × 3¼″ (7.6 cm. × 8.3 cm.).

☐ Unidentified; acquired Sept., 1941.

157. Baccarat. Dated 1847. Close millefiori includes unusual canes, among them a squirrel cane and a "B 1847" cane. Allover faceting in geometric cuts. 2¹⁵⁄₁₆″ (7.4 cm.) diam.

☐ Baccarat; acquired Oct., 1938.
(Illus. 15, 1940 Bergstrom book; Illus. 16, subsequent editions.)

Plate 4

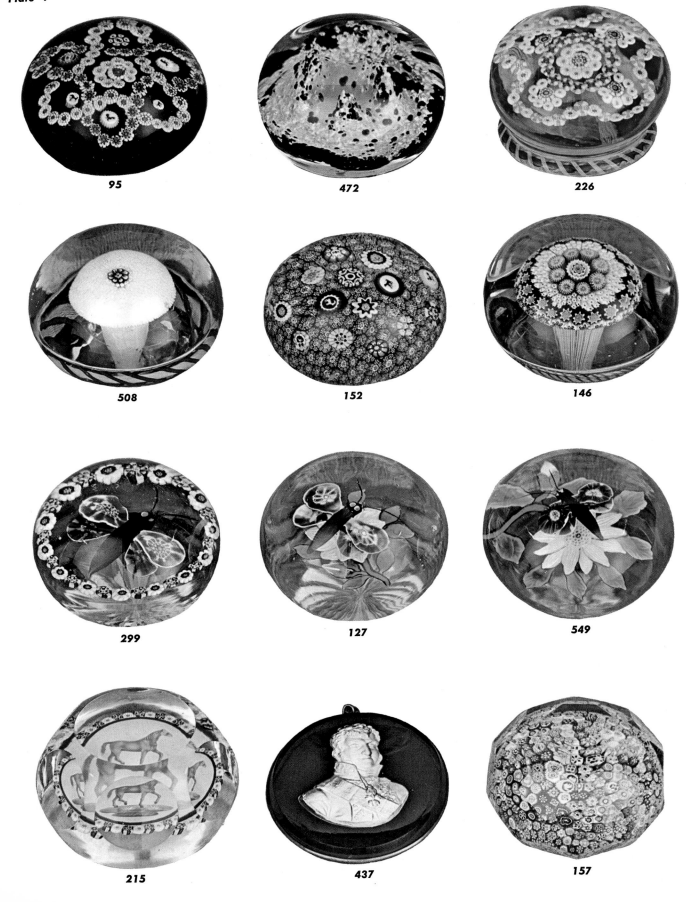

95

472

226

508

152

146

299

127

549

215

437

157

Plate 5

509. Clichy. Mid-19th century. Unusual Clichy weight with pink, blue, and white millefiori mushroom motif. Outer circle of canes is drawn to a point at base to form uneven tuft. Tubular white latticinio torsade. Clear base. 2¾″ (7.0 cm.) diam.

☐ Baccarat; acquired Oct., 1942.

339. Baccarat. Mid-19th century. Floating flat bouquet with pale green leaves and double crossed stems. Spray consists of white flower with grooved pointed petals, red and white primrose, and 5 small blue flowers on one stem; all have cane centers. Large punty on top and 6 punties on curve. A 24-pointed star is deeply cut on the underside. 3⅜″ (8.6 cm.) diam.

☐ Baccarat; acquired June, 1940.
(Plate XII, Bergstrom book.)

78. Baccarat. Mid-19th century. Patterned millefiori weight. Floating design is made up of 7 circlets of canes, each circlet enclosing a single cane; 4 of these singles, including the center one, are arrow canes. Colors are predominantly white and red. Colorless base. 3″ (7.6 cm.) diam.

☐ Baccarat; acquired Sept., 1937.

407. Baccarat. Mid-19th century. Floating motif: Blue and white, deeply cupped primrose flower with yellow star-cane center. Green stem supports 3 green leaves and blue bud; 5 green leaves surround flower. White canes alternate with green in the circle at periphery. A 16-pointed star is cut on the underside. 3″ (7.6 cm.) diam.

☐ Baccarat; acquired May, 1941.

303. Baccarat. Mid-19th century. Floating motif consists of pale yellow camomile flower with green arrow cane center, 6 green leaves, a red bud, and a sturdy green stem. In the circle of canes at periphery, blue-and-white canes alternate with red-and-white ones. There is a deeply cut 24-pointed star on the underside, with the points extending to the curve. 2½″ (6.3 cm.) diam.

☐ Baccarat; acquired March, 1940.

258. Baccarat. Mid-19th century. Floating motif: Single pale yellow buttercup-type flower has cup-shaped petals and white star center cane; there are also 8 pale green leaves,

a sturdy stem, and red bud. A 24-pointed star is cut on the underside. 3″ (7.6 cm.) diam.

☐ Baccarat; acquired Sept., 1939.

151. Baccarat. Dated 1846. Close millefiori motif. Typical Baccarat canes are placed over segments of white filigree. "B 1846" appears in one cane. 3″ (7.6 cm.) diam.

☐ Baccarat; acquired Oct., 1938.

2. Baccarat. Dated 1847. Close millefiori motif including —besides "B 1847" cane—dog, kangaroo, and devil canes. 2⁹⁄₁₆″ (6.5 cm.) diam. This is believed to be the first weight that Mrs. Bergstrom acquired.

☐ Baccarat; acquired March, 1935.

439. Saint Louis. *Ca.* 1840–45. One of the early weights. Close millefiori motif. The small, tightly packed canes extend to the encasing glass. Colors are pale, with a predominance of blue. Lining of blue and white jasper covers the inside ends of canes, visible from underside of weight. 2¹⁵⁄₁₆″ (7.4 cm.) diam.

☐ Baccarat; acquired Sept., 1941.

123. Baccarat. Dated 1848. Close millefiori motif over white muslin segments. Five animal canes are included; "B 1848" appears in one cane. 2¼″ (5.7 cm.) diam.

☐ Baccarat; acquired May, 1938.

302. Baccarat. Mid-19th century. High-crowned colorless glass weight encloses replica of French Legion of Honor medal in gold leaf with applied enamel coloring. Medal is a 5-armed cross in white against a green laurel wreath background, hanging from a jeweled crown and ribbon enameled in translucent red. Gilt male profile is set against dark blue circular ground at center of cross. Medal rests on the colorless base, which protrudes downward from the underside of the weight. 3³⁄₁₆″ (8.1 cm.) diam.

☐ Unidentified; acquired Feb., 1940.

221. Baccarat. Dated 1849. Close millefiori motif, the millefiori canes being placed over segments of white filigree. The date "1849" appears in one cane. 2⁹⁄₁₆″ (6.5 cm.) diam.

☐ Baccarat; acquired Feb., 1939.

Plate 5

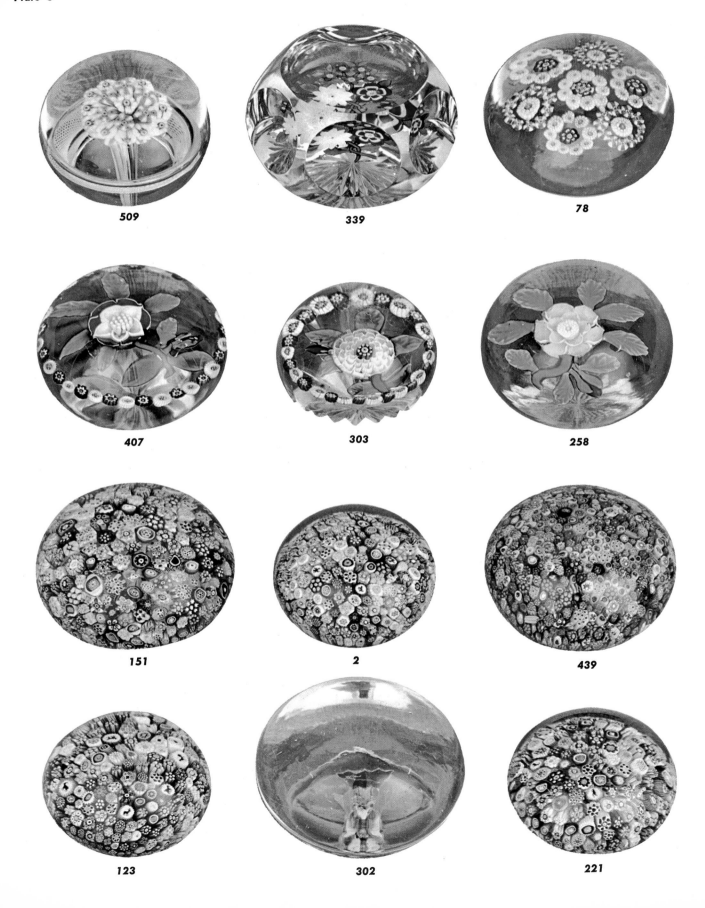

509

339

78

407

303

258

151

2

439

123

302

221

Plate 6

149. Baccarat. Mid-19th century. Cup-shaped floating primrose flower has cobalt blue petals with white edges; flower center is white star cane with red center. There are also 11 dark green leaves and a stem. A small 16-pointed star is cut on the underside. 2¹³⁄₁₆″ (7.2 cm.) diam.

☐ Unidentified; acquired Oct., 1938.

140. Baccarat. Mid-19th century. Concentric millefiori motif consists of 3 circles of pastel-colored canes, not contiguous, encircling a center sulphide, profile to dexter, of Queen Victoria. 2¹⁵⁄₁₆″ (7.4 cm.) diam.

☐ Baccarat; acquired Oct., 1938.
(Illus. 40, 1940 Bergstrom book; Illus. 38, subsequent editions.) (Ex collection of Oscar Wilde.)

72. Baccarat. Mid-19th century. Floating primrose flower has white recessed petals with red edges and pointed tips, a white star center cane, 11 green leaves, and stem. A 16-pointed star is deeply cut on the underside. 2¾″ (7 c.m.) diam.

☐ Baccarat; acquired Sept., 1937.

7. Baccarat. Mid-19th century. Floating butterfly with purple filigree body has wings of flattened varicolored canes over opaque white. Blue-and-white canes alternate with arrow canes in circle at periphery. Punty on top and 6 punties on curve. A 24-pointed star is cut on the underside. 2⅞″ (7.3 cm.) diam.

☐ Sandwich; acquired May, 1936.

361. Baccarat. Mid-19th century. Floating motif on translucent amber base consists of sulphide profile to dexter of Queen Victoria in center, surrounded by 5 large spaced canes in red, white, and blue, and a circle of yellow alternating with blue canes at periphery. "Victoria" is inscribed in blue on the sulphide. 2⁹⁄₁₆″ (6.5 cm.) diam.

☐ Baccarat; acquired Aug., 1940.

47. Baccarat. Mid-19th century. Floating motif of white flower with 10 furrowed petals and center cane of green arrows around red star center; 6 green leaves and white bud. Circle of green canes alternating with white is at periphery. Punty on top and 6 punties on curve. Large 24-pointed star is deeply cut on the underside, extending to curve. 2⁹⁄₁₆″ (6.5 cm.) diam.

☐ Unidentified; acquired Aug., 1937.

457. Baccarat. Dated 1849. Close millefiori motif includes "1849" cane and typical Baccarat canes: squirrel, arrow, trefoil, quatrefoil, shamrock, honeycomb, and so on. 2⅞″ (7.3 cm.) diam.

☐ Baccarat; acquired Oct., 1941.

60. Baccarat. Mid-19th century. Blue primrose flower has opaque white petals bordered with cobalt blue, a yellow honeycomb center cane, sturdy dark green stem, and 6 paler green leaves. White-and-green canes alternate with red canes in circle at periphery. A small, 24-pointed star is cut on the underside. 2½″ (6.3 cm.) diam.

☐ Unidentified; acquired Aug., 1937.

10. Baccarat. Mid-19th century. Close millefiori weight with mushroom motif. Torsade is tubular white filigree around which a deep blue strand is coiled. A small, 32-pointed star is cut on the underside. 3″ (7.6 cm.) diam.

☐ Baccarat; acquired May, 1936.

273. Baccarat. Mid-19th century. Butterfly with purple filigree body, turquoise eyes, dark blue head, and 2 antennae floats over white muslin ground. Wings are flattened colored canes over opaque white. White star canes alternate with red-and-green arrow canes in circle at periphery. 2¼″ (5.7 cm.) diam.

☐ Unidentified; acquired Nov., 1939.

188. Baccarat. Mid-19th century. Pale blue clematis with white star-cane center has pointed, furrowed petals. Motif also includes 2 blue buds, 5 green leaves, and 3 stems, one of which crosses the other two. A 16-pointed star is cut on the underside. 2¹³⁄₁₆″ (5.5 cm.) diam.

☐ Unidentified; acquired Jan., 1939.

403. Baccarat. Mid-19th century. Butterfly with purple filigree body, turquoise eyes, dark blue head, and 2 antennae hovers over a flower with white star-cane center and furrowed, opaque white petals with red centers. Butterfly wings are flattened colored canes over opaque white. Flower has green stem and is surrounded by 7 green leaves. A 16-pointed star is cut on the underside. 2¼″ (5.7 cm.) diam.

☐ Baccarat; acquired May, 1941.

Plate 6

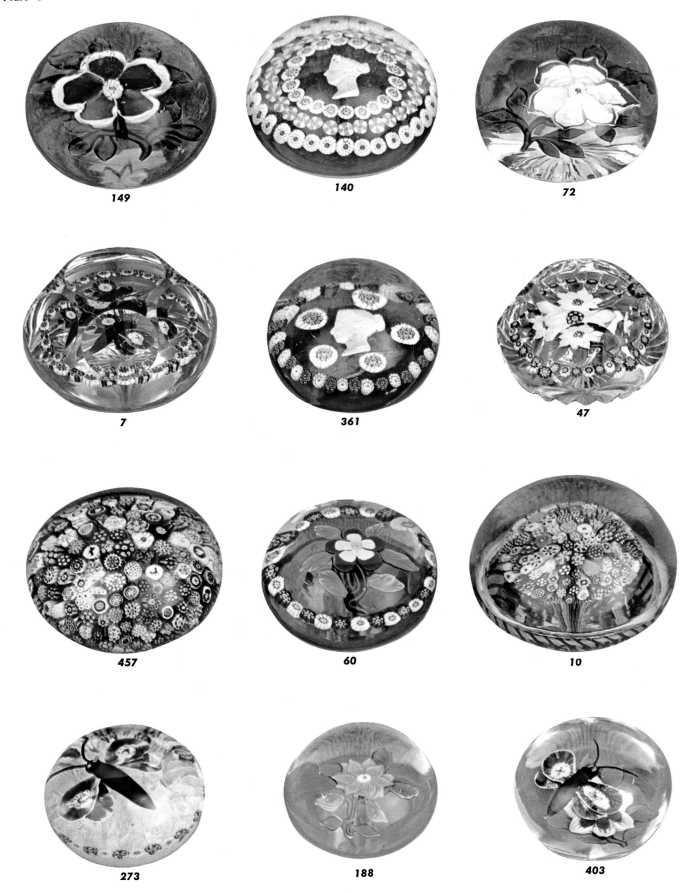

149

140

72

7

361

47

457

60

10

273

188

403

Plate 7

247. Baccarat. Mid-19th century. Floating on a colorless glass ground is a primrose flower with 5 red petals with cupped white edges and a star-cane center, 10 green leaves, and a stem. The high crown has a slightly gray tinge. A small 16-pointed star is cut on the underside. 3¼″ (8.3 cm.) diam.

☐ Baccarat; acquired July, 1939.

261. French. *Ca.* 1900. Large reptile weight. Motif represents the earth of the Mesozoic era. Three plants with green leaves and various colored blossoms grow from sandy base, which is green and buff over opaque white. In center stands red-eyed, black dinosaur spotted with white. 4⅛″ (10.5 cm.) diam.

☐ Baccarat; acquired Sept., 1939.

259. Baccarat. Mid-19th century. Colorless glass encloses floating flat spray of 6 pink clematis buds arranged in symmetrical tiers; also green vertical stems and 6 green leaves, 2 of which are large. A small 16-pointed star is cut on the underside. 3¹⁄₁₆″ (7.8 cm.) diam.

☐ Baccarat; acquired Sept., 1939.

159. Baccarat. Mid-19th century. In floating spray of 4 flowers and red bud, the center flower is a deeply cupped white buttercup type with yellow star stamen center. Two flowers are pansies of early Baccarat manufacture, the upper petals deep purple, the lower ones translucent blue with white veining and white serrated edges; centers are yellow honeycomb cane. Fourth flower is red clematis with deeply furrowed petals and honeycomb center. Motif includes 10 pale green leaves and darker green stem. Punty on top and 6 smaller punties on curve. A 24-pointed star is cut on the underside. 3¼″ (8.3 cm.) diam.

☐ Unidentified; acquired Oct., 1938.

438. Baccarat. *Ca.* 1855–60. Floating pansy motif includes

7 green leaves, darker green stem, and purple bud. Upper 2 petals are purple; lower 3 are yellow and manganese enamel over opaque white glass with purple tips and purple veining. Center cane is of yellow stars. Circle of alternating white star and blue canes surrounds the motif. A 24-pointed star is cut on the underside. 3⅝″ (9.2 cm.) diam.

☐ Baccarat; acquired Sept., 1941.

366. Baccarat. Mid-19th century. Pale yellow camomile with blue arrow cane center is surrounded by 7 green leaves and stem; 2 red buds. Circle of canes at periphery is predominantly white and red. Punty on top, and 5 of equal size on curve. A 24-pointed star is cut on the underside. 3⅛″ (7.9 cm.) diam.

☐ Baccarat; acquired Sept., 1940.

458. Attributed to Baccarat. *Ca.* 1900. "Sand Dunes" weight. Sparkling glass encloses sand ground of green, gray, and buff-colored glass that is drawn up in 3 peaks. 2¹⁵⁄₁₆″ (7.4 cm.) diam.

☐ Unidentified; acquired Oct., 1941.

308. Baccarat. Mid-19th century. Floating dark red, full-blown rose is surrounded by 5 green leaves. There are 3 additional leaves, and a red bud on a green stem. A small 24-pointed star is cut on the underside. 3″ (7.6 cm.) diam.

☐ Unidentified; acquired April, 1940.

245. Baccarat. Mid-19th century. Upright bouquet of small, varicolored flowers is surrounded by green leaves, with stems drawn to a point at center of the colorless base. The lavender and white flowers have star-cane centers. Torsade is tubular core of white filigree about which is coiled a deep blue strand. A 24-pointed star is cut on the underside. 2⅞″ (7.3 cm.) diam.

☐ Baccarat; acquired July, 1939.

Plate 7

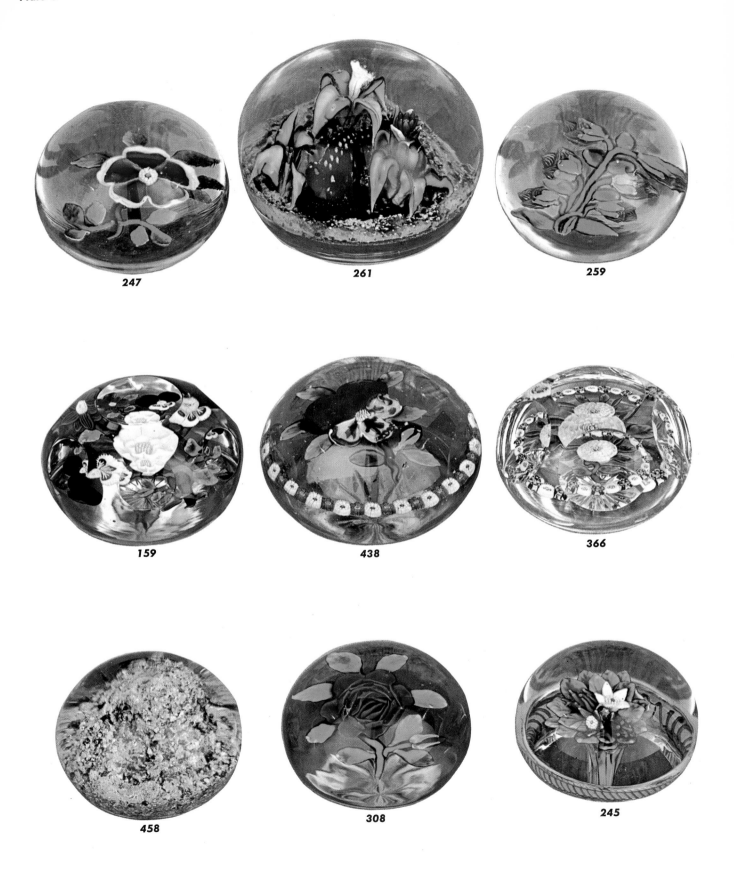

247

261

259

159

438

366

458

308

245

Plate 8

426. Baccarat. Dated 1849. Spaced millefiori canes appear against white muslin ground; among them are an "1849" cane and animal canes. 2⁹⁄₁₆″ (6.5 cm.) diam.

☐ Baccarat; acquired Aug., 1941.

400. Baccarat. Mid-19th century. Patterned millefiori in 3 tiers. In top (smallest) tier is white upright flower, which has grooved petals with blue dots, a center cane, and green leaves. Middle tier has 3 concentric circles of varicolored millefiori canes, including arrow and star canes around a central serrated cane. Lowest tier has spaced canes on white muslin base, including animal, bird, and devil silhouettes. Five small punties on curve of bottom tier. 2½″ (6.3 cm.) diam. of base tier; 3¹⁄₁₆″ (7.8 cm.) height.

☐ Baccarat; acquired May, 1941.

367. Baccarat. Dated 1848. Eight-sided vase or penholder with paperweight base. The edges of the scalloped and flared rim and the edges of side panels are flashed with emerald green. Colorless collar joins vase and paperweight base, which encloses spaced millefiori canes set in white muslin ground. "B 1848" appears in one cane. Animals, pair of birds, and other typical Baccarat canes appear also. 2½″ (6.3 cm.) diam. of base; 5⅛″ (13.1 cm.) overall height.

☐ Baccarat; acquired Oct., 1940.

372. Baccarat. Mid-19th century. Spaced millefiori canes on white muslin ground. Unusual weight, as it has both Clichy canes, including a pink Clichy rose, and Baccarat animal canes. Punty on top of weight and 10 smaller punties on curve. 2⁹⁄₁₆″ (6.5 cm.) diam. (Black light tests more Baccarat than Clichy.)

☐ Clichy; acquired Nov., 1940.

568. Baccarat. Mid-19th century. Double overlay, geranium red over opaque white, with floating, patterned millefiori motif. Garland of cobalt blue canes intertwines with garland of red-and-white canes forming double trefoil design. A single cane is enclosed in each of the 6 loops; the center arrow cane is surrounded by circlet of white star canes. Punty on top, 5 punties on curve, and 12 thumbprint cuts near colorless base. 3³⁄₁₆″ (8.1 cm.) diam.

☐ Unrecorded.

571. Origin unknown; probably French. "Ducks in a Pond" weight. Three opaque, pale yellow ducks with stripes of brown, red, and green, and brown bills, sit on colorless glass simulating a pond, surrounded by circle of green and white jasper, under a hollow crown. The fused flat base forms a flange. Circular facet on top and 5 punties on curve. A 32-pointed star is cut on the underside. There is a similarity in the duck figures to the snake in weight 417, Plate 2. 3⅛″ (7.9 cm.) diam.

☐ Saint Louis and Baccarat.
(Illus. 16, 1940 Bergstrom book [Baccarat]; Illus. 12, subsequent editions [Saint Louis].)

474. Baccarat. Mid-19th century. Double overlay is pink over opaque white. (Both overlays are unusually thin, giving a delicate effect.) Floating, patterned millefiori design includes garland of blue canes intertwined with garland of white canes to form double trefoil pattern. Each loop encloses a single cane; center arrow cane is encircled by white star canes. Punty on top, 5 punties on curve, and 12 thumbprint cuts near base. 3¹⁄₁₆″ (7.8 cm.) diam.

☐ Baccarat; acquired Jan., 1942.

499. Baccarat. Mid-19th century. Double overlay, blue over opaque white, has applied gilt tracery. Motif is a millefiori tuft with white star center cane and 3 concentric circles of arrow, white star with red dot, and ocher-colored canes. White star canes at periphery of tuft are pulled down to base to form the mushroom. Punty on top and 5 punties on curve. A small 24-pointed star is cut on the underside. 3⅛″ (7.9 cm.) diam.

☐ Clichy; acquired July, 1942.

142. Baccarat. Mid-19th century. Single overlay is transparent emerald green. Floating motif of patterned millefiori canes is made up of 7 circlets of canes, each circlet enclosing an arrow cane. Punty on top, 6 punties on curve, and 12 thumbprint cuts near base, underside of which is cut with a small 24-pointed star. 2⅞″ (7.3 cm.) diam.

☐ Baccarat; acquired Oct., 1938.

326. Baccarat. Mid-19th century. Single overlay is transparent red. Floating motif of patterned millefiori canes is arranged in 7 circlets, each with a single center cane. Punty on top, 6 punties on curve, and 12 thumbprint cuts near base. A 24-pointed star is cut on the underside. 3⅛″ (7.9 cm.) diam.

☐ Baccarat; acquired May, 1940.
(Plate IV, Bergstrom book.)

241 and **242.** Saint Louis. *Ca.* 1848. Pair of colorless glass plates, each with 16 spaced millefiori canes, thinly sliced, encased in rim. A 32-pointed star is cut on the underside of the plates. 6″ (15.3 cm.) diam.

☐ Unidentified; acquired June, 1939.

420. Baccarat. Mid-19th century. Lady's hand cooler, hollow and egg-shaped, is colorless glass with blue over opaque white, double overlay. There are 4 circles of punties on curve; 8-pointed star cut on top. 2″ (5.1 cm.) diam.; 2⅝″ (6.6 cm.) height.

☐ Baccarat; acquired July, 1941.

Plate 8

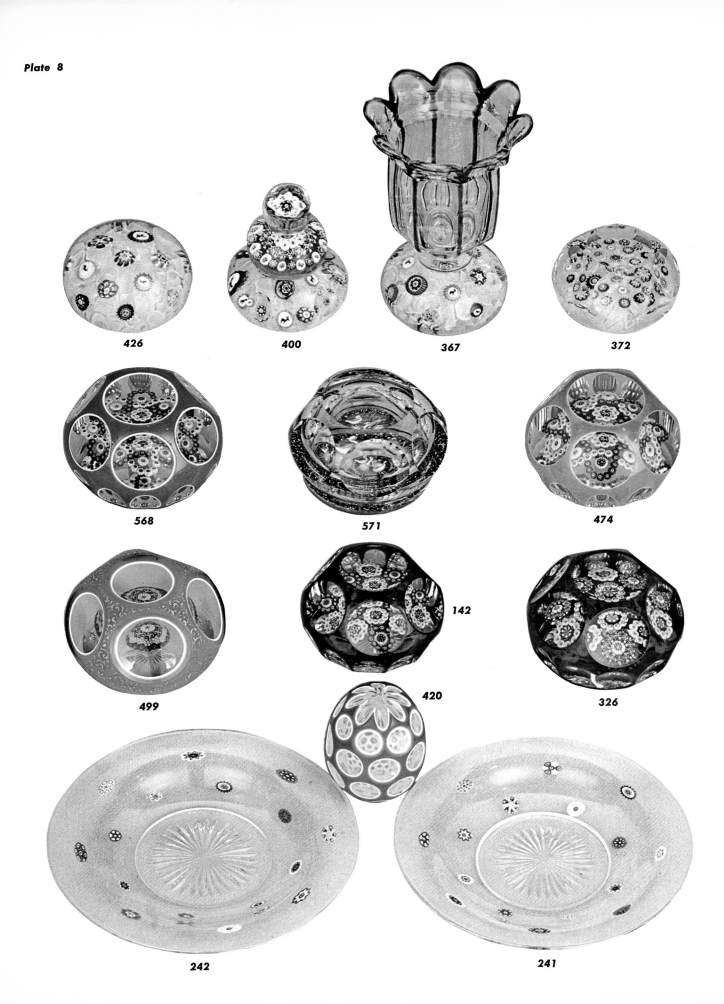

426

400

367

372

568

571

474

499

142

420

326

242

241

Plate 9

442. Baccarat. Round patch box of colorless glass. The screw-on cover is faceted in star design and encloses enamel-over-gilt design of flowers in basket. Underside of box is faceted in square and radial cuts, which extend to threaded gold ring on curve. 2⁹/₁₆″ (6.5 cm.) diam.

☐ Unidentified; acquired Sept., 1941.

336. Baccarat. Thick glass tumbler has vertical panel cuttings. Near rim is an incrusted medallion picturing, in colored enamel over gold leaf, a cupid emerging from pink rose, a green stem, 4 leaves, and a pink bud. Sixteen deep radial cuts on underside. 2⅞″ (7.3 cm.) diam.; 2⅜″ (6.1 cm.) height.

☐ Unidentified; acquired May, 1940.

298. Baccarat. 1812–40. Heavy glass tumbler has incrustated sulphide of Louis XVIII (1755–1824), profile to sinister. "Andrieu" appears on the sulphide. Tumbler is faceted in squares with strawberry-cut centers. Underside, finely cut in "rays" at outer edge, has smooth, slightly concave center. 2⅞″ (7.3 cm.) diam.; 3⅜″ (8.6 cm.) height.

☐ Unidentified; acquired Jan., 1940.

378 and **379.** Origin unknown. Pair of tall, tapered, colorless glass wig stands enclose varicolored nodules of glass in "string" extending from base to top. Each has footed, colorless, circular base. 14½″ (36.8 cm.) height.

☐ Bristol; acquired Dec., 1940.

510. Baccarat. Mid-19th century. Patterned millefiori motif. Canes, predominantly blue, white, and terra-cotta-colored, are arranged in a flowerlike design of 6 "petals" and set on a carpet ground of closely packed blue-and-white canes. A small 32-pointed star is cut on the underside. 3¹/₁₆″ (7.8 cm.) diam.

☐ Baccarat; acquired Oct., 1942.

524. Baccarat. Dated 1847. Millefiori canes, including a "B 1847" cane and animal silhouettes of monkey and

squirrel, are spaced among segments of white and colored filigree spirals, opaque colored rods, and fragments of canes. Occasional spots of goldstone. 3⅛″ (7.9 cm.) diam.

☐ Unrecorded.

497. Baccarat. Dated 1848. Magnum close millefiori weight. Sparkling glass encloses closely set millefiori canes, including animal, bird, arrow, quatrefoil, trefoil, honeycomb, and so on, and "B 1848" cane. Segments of filigree twists in white and colors are below the canes. A peripheral circle of miter cuts, crisscrossed, is on underside of flat base. 4″ (10.2 cm.) diam.

☐ Baccarat; acquired May, 1942.

113. Baccarat. Mid-19th century. Small sulphide portrait of Queen Victoria, profile to dexter. "Victoria" is inscribed in blue on the sulphide. Half-wreath of green leaves, with red rose, appears below sulphide. Small punty on top; 3 circles of punties on curve, becoming larger toward base. 2⁹/₁₆″ (6.5 cm.) diam.

☐ Unidentified; acquired Feb., 1938.

727. French. Round, covered box of ruby glass overlaid with opaque white is decorated in gilt. Faceting on top of cover is an 8-petaled design, with 8-petaled gilt design in center. Circular concave cuts outlined in gilt appear on curve of cover and sides of box. 3¹⁵/₁₆″ (10.1 cm.) diam.

☐ Unrecorded.

401. Attributed to Baccarat. Solid, colorless glass weight has flower motif engraved on the slightly concave underside and decorated in applied colored enamel. The design consists of a single pansy encircled by a wreath of pink flowers and green leaves. Large punty on top and 6 punties on curve. 3⅛″ (7.9 cm.) diam. See comments on this weight in Hollister, *Encyclopedia of Glass Paperweights*, p. 78 and Col. Fig. 22.

☐ Unidentified; acquired May, 1941.

Plate 9

378

442

336

298

379

510

524

497

113

727

401

Plate 10

346.   Attributed to Baccarat. Colorless glass bottle stopper encloses sulphide male portrait, profile to sinister. Sulphide —signed "P D & R"—is on an octagonal green plaque outlined with red line. On reverse side of plaque is small sulphide portraying reclining nude female figure. Stopper is flat with deep cuttings on edge. 2⅝" × 2" (6.6 cm. × 5.1 cm.).

☐ Unidentified; acquired June, 1940.
(Fig. XIX, Jokelson, *Sulphides*.)

332.   French. Mid-19th century. Sulphide double male portraits, profiles to dexter, on translucent cobalt blue ground. Slightly concave top; triangular facets on curve; clear base. 3⅝" (9.2 cm.) diam.

☐ Unidentified; acquired May, 1940.

427.   French. Round patch box of colorless glass has screw-on cover. Octagonal medallion on cover encloses sulphide portrait, front-view bust, of Prince of Orange. "S K H de Prins van Oranje" is inscribed on base of sulphide in blue script. Edge of cover is faceted in twisted rope design. An 8-pointed star is deeply cut on the underside of box, extending on curve to threaded metal ring. 2⅜" (6.1 cm.) diam.

☐ Unidentified; acquired Aug., 1941.

362.   Attributed to Clichy. Mid-19th century. Sulphide bust of Queen Victoria, profile to dexter, on black ground. Curve of weight has 4 raised oval facets with vertical flute cuts between facets. Colorless base. 2¹³⁄₁₆" (7.2 cm.) diam.

☐ Unidentified; acquired Aug., 1940.

190.   Attributed to Clichy. Mid-19th century. Sulphide portrait of Louis Philippe, profile to dexter, on translucent cobalt blue base. Punty on top and 6 punties on curve. 2¹⁵⁄₁₆" (7.4 cm.) diam.

☐ Unidentified; acquired Jan., 1939.

512.   Attributed to Clichy. Mid-19th century. Sulphide bust portrait of Pope Pius IX, profile to dexter. Sulphide rests on amber flashed base. 2¹⁵⁄₁₆" (7.4 cm.) diam.

☐ Unidentified; acquired Nov., 1942.

353.   Baccarat. *Ca.* 1824. Sulphide doorknob. One of a pair of sparkling glass doorknobs encloses sulphide portrait of Lafayette, profile to sinister. Matching knob (353A) encloses sulphide portrait of Benjamin Franklin. 2" (5.1 cm.) diam.

☐ Baccarat; acquired July, 1940.
(Illus. 57, 1940 Bergstrom book; Illus. 55, subsequent editions.)

353A.   Baccarat. *Ca.* 1824. Sulphide doorknob. One of a pair of sparkling glass doorknobs encloses sulphide portrait of Benjamin Franklin, profile to dexter. What looks like the letters "BRICHT" appears on the sulphide. Matching knob (353) encloses sulphide of Lafayette. 2" (5.1 cm.) diam.

☐ Baccarat; acquired July, 1940.

279.   Origin unknown. Colorless glass weight encloses round sulphide medallion, on translucent cobalt blue ground, of the London Crystal Exposition. The words "The Building for the International Exhibition" appear near perimeter of medallion, at top. The initials "A & M" (Allen & Moore) and "London 1851" are below. Colorless base. 2¹⁄₁₆" (5.3 cm.) diam.

☐ Unidentified; acquired Nov., 1939.

485 and **485A.**   Baccarat. *Ca.* 1824. A pair of sparkling glass drawer knobs. Each encloses sulphide portrait of Benjamin Franklin, profile to dexter. What looks like the letters "BRICHT" appears on the sulphide. (Same Franklin sulphide as 353A.) 1¾" (4.5 cm.) diam.

☐ Unidentified; acquired March, 1942.

343.   Attributed to Creusot factory. *Ca.* 1830. Octagonal clear glass plaque, with beveled edges on both sides, encloses sulphide portrait of Josephine, profile to sinister. 3⅛" × 2¾" (7.9 cm. × 7.0 cm.).

☐ Baccarat; acquired June, 1940.
(Illus. 41, 1940 Bergstrom book; Illus. 39, subsequent editions.)

627.   Montcenis (French). Octagonal glass lavaliere plaque, with beveled edges on both sides, encloses sulphide portrait of Louis XVIII, profile to sinister. "Andrieu F." appears on the sulphide; "Montcenis" is impressed on the reverse. (Montcenis was the name of the Manufactory Royale de Montcenis in France.) A bronze acorn and oak leaf mounting supports a ring at top of plaque. 2½" × 1⅞" (6.3 cm. × 4.8 cm.).

☐ Unrecorded.

396.   Desprez (French). Ca. 1800. Round colorless glass plaque encloses sulphide portrait of George Washington, profile to sinister, probably after medal by Duvivier. "Washington" and "Desprez, Rue des Récolets, No. 2 à Paris" are impressed on back of sulphide. Edge of plaque is faceted on both sides. 3¼" (8.3 cm.) diam.

☐ Unidentified; acquired March, 1941.

344.   Attributed to Creusot factory. *Ca.* 1830. Octagonal colorless glass plaque with beveled edges on both sides encloses sulphide portrait of Napoleon, profile to dexter, probably after Andrieu, although sulphide is not signed. 3" × 2¼" (7.6 cm. × 5.7 cm.).

☐ Baccarat; acquired June, 1940.
(Illus. 41, 1940 Bergstrom book; Illus. 39, subsequent editions.)

Plate 10

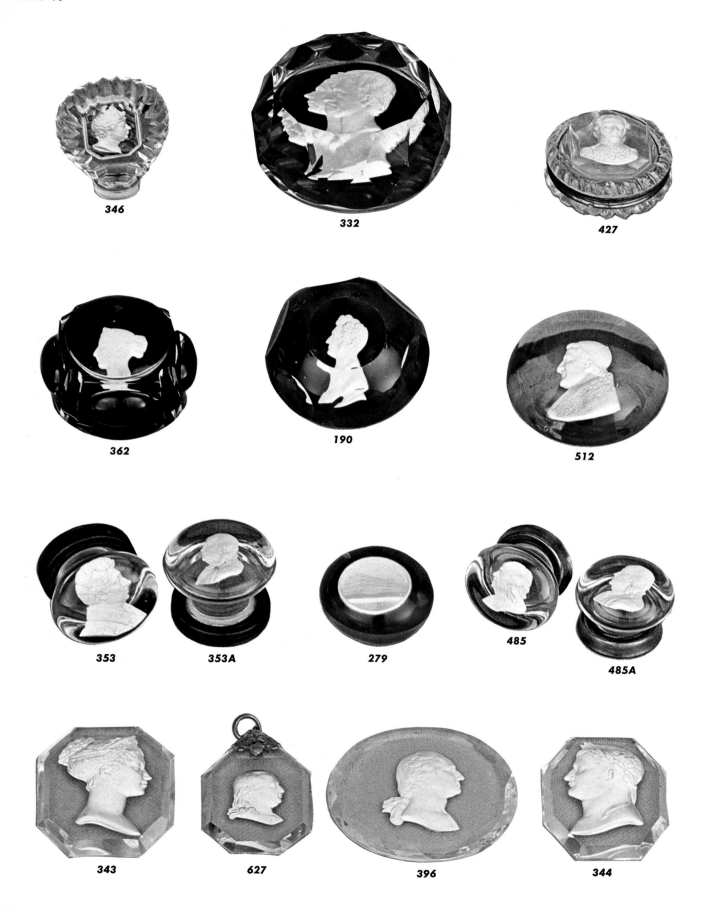

346

332

427

362

190

512

353

353A

279

485

485A

343

627

396

344

Plate 11

347. French. Cut glass cologne bottle of mallet form. Stopper encloses, facing upward, a sulphide bust portrait, profile to dexter, probably of Benjamin Franklin. Both bottle and stopper edge are cut in 12 panels of square facets, each square cut with sunburst design. Faceted raised collar circles neck of bottle; flared neck rim is 12 sided. A 24-pointed star is cut on the underside of bottle. 2¾″ (7.0 cm.) diam.; 7¼″ (18.4 cm.) overall height.

☐ Unidentified; acquired June, 1940.

397. Origin unknown. Mantel ornament in shield form is of colorless cut glass with gray tinge. Center oval medallion encloses sulphide bust, probably of George Washington, profile to dexter. Reverse is diamond cut. Shoulders of the ornament are cut in fine horizontal grooves; sides, diamond cut with centers of grid cutting. A knob at top, mushroom form, is finely faceted. Waisted stem is faceted in 8 panels, above flat circular foot; a large 32-pointed star is cut on the underside of the foot. 4″ (10.2 cm.) diam. of foot; 8″ (20.3 cm.) height.

☐ Unidentified; acquired March, 1941.

348. French. Cut glass cologne bottle in flattened ovoid form has thin, faceted stopper. Diamond-shaped medallion on obverse encloses sulphide portrait of Napoleon I in uniform of Colonel of the Guard, profile to sinister. Reverse is faceted in star design, with strawberry cuts on alternate rays, honeycomb facets along sides and across shoulders of bottle. Oval base. A 32-pointed star is cut on the underside. 3½″ (8.9 cm.) width; 8″ (20.3 cm.) overall height.

☐ Unidentified; acquired June, 1940.

634. Origin unknown; probably Sèvres. Porcelain cup and saucer. Interior sides of cup are lined with gold; exterior is dark blue with gilt decoration. On obverse is gilt shield design with monogram "F A" and leaf motif. On reverse are 2 gilt designs portraying music and painting. Applied gilt handle extends above rim of cup. Clear glass bottom of cup encloses, facing upward, sulphide bust portrait, probably of George Washington, profile to dexter. Saucer has a dark blue band near rim, with 4 gilt motifs and gilt edge. Letter "F" in blue appears on underside of saucer under the glaze. 3¹³⁄₁₆″ (9.7 cm.) diam. of saucer; 2³⁄₁₆″ (5.5 cm.) height of cup.

☐ Unrecorded.
(Fig. XIV, Jokelson, *Sulphides.*)

430. Apsley Pellatt. 1819–40. Cut glass scent bottle. On obverse, rectangular medallion encloses sulphide male portrait, profile to sinister, which is signed "Apsley Pellatt" (English, 1791–1863). Reverse is faceted in diagonal squares; the sides, in horizontal grooves. Top of mushroom-shaped stopper is faceted with deep radial cuts, strawberry cutting on alternate rays. 2½″ (6.3 cm.) width; 4″ (10.2 cm.) overall height.

☐ Unidentified; acquired Aug., 1941.

383. Baccarat. *Ca.* 1820. Heavy glass cylindrical tumbler bears incrusted sulphide portrait of Napoleon with crown, from a medal by Andrieu. Tumbler is faceted in 10 gothic panels, with circle of knobs at base edge. Underside is cut in star design, the 12 rays extending to the edge between the knobs. 3⅛″ (7.9 cm.) diam.; 3⅞″ (9.9 cm.) height.

☐ Unidentified; acquired Dec., 1940.

431. Attributed to Apsley Pellatt. *Ca.* 1819–40. Cut glass, flattened bottle, with stopper. Obverse encloses sulphide bust of George III, profile to dexter. Diagonal cuts appear on reverse, and horizontal grooved cuts along sides and shoulders. Flat top of stopper is cut with deep radial facets. 2½″ (6.3 cm.) width; 3⅞″ (9.9 cm.) overall height.

☐ Unidentified; acquired Aug., 1941.

298. Baccarat. *Ca.* 1820. Cut glass cylindrical tumbler. On obverse an octagonal clear glass medallion encloses sulphide of Louis XVIII, profile to sinister, signed "Andrieu" (made between 1812 and 1840). Tumbler has 10 panels of square facets with strawberry-cut centers. Underside is slightly concave, and finely cut in "rays" at outer edge. 2⅞″ (7.3 cm.) diam.; 3⅜″ (8.6 cm.) height.

☐ Unidentified; acquired Jan., 1940.

275. Baccarat. Mid-19th century. Flat weight. Colorless glass encloses sulphide replica of medal, signed "Gayrard" and portraying female portrait, profile to dexter, with the lettering "Marie Rabutin de Sévigné" at periphery. Sulphide floats over slightly larger, circular, translucent cobalt blue base. Strawberry cutting on curve alternates with smooth cuts in raised swirl design. 2¹⁵⁄₁₆″ (7.4 cm.) diam. (See Hollister reference to this weight, p. 258.)

☐ Saint Louis, acquired Nov., 1939.
(Illus. 38, 1940 Bergstrom book; Illus. 36, subsequent editions.)

434. French, probably Desprez. Round, colorless glass plaque with faceted edge encloses sulphide portrait of George Washington, after Duvivier, profile to sinister. Plaque is placed on blue background and framed in round, recessed mahogany frame with a circle of bronze rosebuds around the inner edge. (Sulphide is same as in 396, Plate 10, on which "Washington" and "Desprez Rue des Récoltes No. 2 à Paris" are impressed on back.) 6¹⁄₁₆″ (15.4 cm.) diam., including frame.

☐ Unidentified; acquired Aug., 1941.
(Fig. XVII, Jokelson, *Sulphides.*)

345. French. Round, flat tortoiseshell box has cover on which an oval, colorless glass medallion, framed in a narrow gold band, encloses sulphide male portrait of warrior with helmet, profile to dexter. 3″ (7.6 cm.) diam.

☐ Unidentified; acquired June, 1940.

Plate 11

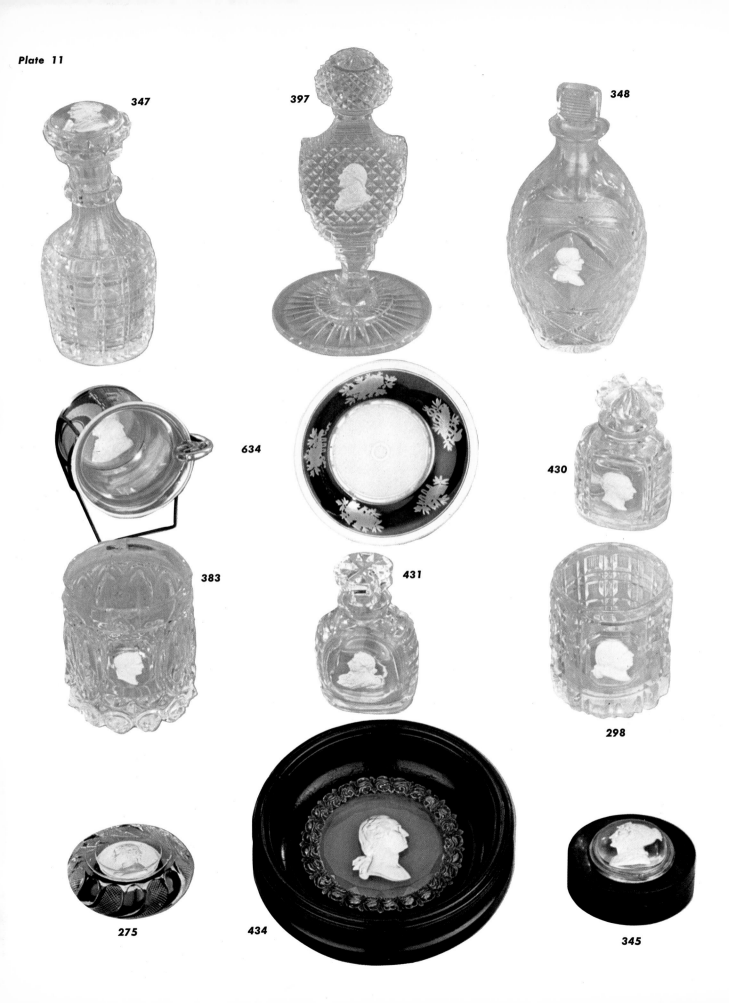

347

397

348

634

430

383

431

298

275

434

345

Plate 12

559. Probably Clichy; possibly Sandwich, Mass. (American.) *Ca.* 1860. Colorless glass with gray cast encloses floating sulphide portraits, profiles to sinister, possibly of Maximilian, Emperor of Mexico (1864–67), and Princess Charlotte. There is a slight circular depression on outside at sulphide level. (Similar to 79 and 58, this plate.) 3³⁄₁₆″ (8.1 cm.) diam.

☐ Unrecorded.

580. Attributed to Clichy. Mid-19th century. Colorless glass with gray cast encloses floating sulphide portraying death mask of Napoleon on cushion, profile to dexter, from a medal by Depaulis. 3⁵⁄₈″ (9.2 cm.) diam.

☐ Unrecorded.

85. Origin unknown. 19th century. Sulphide bust portrait of Lord Melbourne, Queen Victoria's first prime minister, profile to dexter, floats midway in weight. 3½″ (8.9 cm.) diam.

☐ Unidentified; acquired Oct., 1937.

263. Baccarat. Mid-19th century. Sulphide portrait, profile to sinister, of Romanesque head of Napoleon and star overhead. Sulphide is signed "Andrieu" (French medalist) and placed on ground of transparent turquoise glass over opaque white. Colorless base. 3⅛″ (7.9 cm.) diam.

☐ Baccarat; acquired Sept., 1939.
(Illus. 34, 1940 Bergstrom book; Illus. 32, subsequent editions.)

79. Probably Clichy; possibly Sandwich, Mass. (American.) *Ca.* 1860. Colorless glass with gray cast encloses, near top, a floating sulphide bust portrait of Zachary Taylor, 12th President of the United States. The name "Taylor" appears on back of sulphide in blue script. There is a circular depression on the outside of the weight at the level of the sulphide. 2¾″ (7.0 cm.) diam. Weight is similar to 58 and 559, this plate. (See *The American Story Recorded in Glass* by Tracy Marsh, p. 206.)

☐ Unidentified; acquired Sept., 1937.

212. Baccarat. Mid-19th century. Sulphide portrait of George Washington, profile to dexter, on ground of transparent turquoise glass over opaque white. Colorless base. 3¹⁄₁₆″ (7.8 cm.) diam.

☐ Baccarat; acquired Feb., 1939.

480. Baccarat. Mid-19th century. Colorless glass encloses full-length figure of Joan of Arc and a wreath of oak and laurel leaves. Transparent green flash on the underside extends to the level of sulphide on sides of weight. Flat top; diamond-shaped faceting on curve. 3¹⁵⁄₁₆″ (8.4 cm.) diam.

☐ Unidentified; acquired Jan., 1942.

58. Probably Clichy; possibly Sandwich, Mass. (American.) *Ca.* 1860. Colorless glass with a gray cast encloses, near top, a floating sulphide bust portrait of Lajos Kossuth, Hungarian general and patriot, front view slightly to sinister, possibly cast after a medal by V. M. Borel, in 1851. Colorless ground and base. A circular depression appears at level of sulphide on the outside of the weight. (Similar to 79 and 559, this plate.) 2⁹⁄₁₆″ (6.5 cm.) diam.

☐ Unidentified; acquired Sept., 1937.

488. Baccarat. Mid-19th century. Sulphide portrait of Queen Victoria as a young girl, head and bare shoulders in profile to dexter. The words "Victoria I Reine de la Grande Bretagne" encircle the sulphide. Base is translucent cranberry-red. Diamond faceting on curve; slightly concave top; circular groove is cut between base and crown on exterior. 3¼″ (8.3 cm.) diam.

☐ Unidentified; acquired March, 1942.

464. Baccarat. Mid-19th century. Sulphide male portrait, profile to sinister, floats in colorless glass. "L'n Bonaparte" appears in blue script at base of sulphide. Circle of white canes alternating with red canes surrounds portrait. Flat top and 3 circles of geometric facets on curve. 2¼″ (5.7 cm.) diam.

☐ Unidentified; acquired Oct., 1941.

561. Baccarat. Mid-19th century. Sulphide bust portrait, almost front view, with "St. Augustin" in blue script on the sulphide, floats in colorless glass weight. Circle of arrow canes alternating with white-and-red canes surrounds portrait. Flat top; curve is faceted in diamond-shaped cuts. Twelve radial oval cuts alternate with 12 small miter cuts on underside. 2⅝″ (6.6 cm.) diam.

☐ Unrecorded.

191. French. Mid-19th century. Small sulphide portrait of Napoleon III, profile to dexter. Sulphide rests on transparent green flanged base. Slightly concave top; geometric facets on curve. 2⅜″ (6.1 cm.) diam.

☐ Unidentified; acquired Jan., 1939.

Plate 12

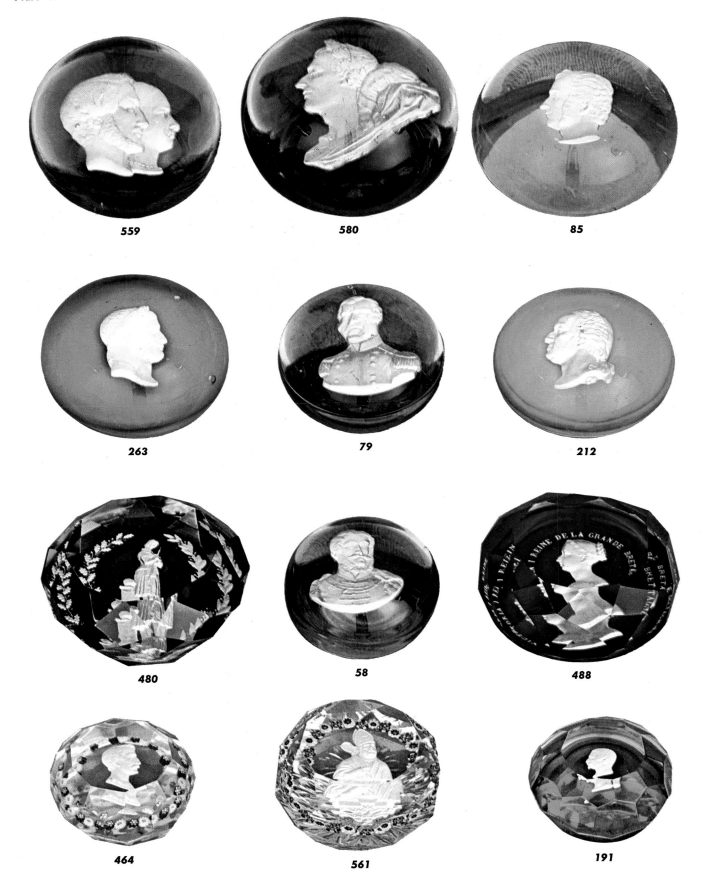

559

580

85

263

79

212

480

58

488

464

561

191

Plate 13

467. Clichy. Mid-19th century. Patterned millefiori on white muslin ground. Five looped garlands of canes surround a large pastry-mold center cane. One loop is pink-and-green Clichy roses; others are green, mauve, red, and blue canes. Large punty on top and 2 circles of punties on curve. Under the muslin ground, segments of white filigree are laid parallel. 3" (7.6 cm.) diam.

☐ Clichy; acquired Nov., 1941.

369. Attributed to Clichy. Mid-19th century. Motif of a reclining doe and tree is etched in gilt on amber-flashed, concave underside. Faceted with punty on top and 6 punties on curve. 3³⁄₁₆" (8.1 cm.) diam.

☐ Clichy, possibly Bohemian; acquired Oct., 1940.

506. Clichy. Mid-19th century. Double overlay is cobalt blue over opaque white. Mushroom-shaped bouquet of close millefiori has outer circle of opaque pink canes alternating with opaque white canes drawn down to a point at base. Circular flat cut on top and 5 punties on curve. Twelve radial oval cuts alternate with 12 small miter cuts on underside. 2⁹⁄₁₆" (6.5 cm.) diam.

☐ Clichy; acquired Oct., 1942.

514. Clichy. Mid-19th century. Concentric millefiori with 7 circles of canes. Outside circle is of opaque lavender and opaque white hollow canes that are elongated to a point near the center of the base, following the curve of the weight, to form a stave basket. 2⁹⁄₁₆" (6.5 cm.) diam.

☐ Clichy; acquired April, 1943.

405. Clichy. Mid-19th century. Floating "Johnny-jump-up" pansy. Two upper petals are purple; 3 lower ones are yellow with purple tips; center of flower has purple veining. Motif also includes thick dark green stem, 5 leaves, and a purple bud bent downward on end of a second stem. A 16-pointed star is cut on the underside. 2½" (6.3 cm.) diam.

☐ Unidentified; acquired May, 1941.

234. Clichy. Mid-19th century. Checker weight. Cobalt blue and opaque white ribbon twists, around which are coiled white filigree threads, are laid between spaced millefiori canes in checkered pattern; all are set on white muslin ground. A white-and-green Clichy rose and the letter "C" cane appear. 2⁹⁄₁₆" (6.5 cm.) diam.

☐ Clichy; acquired June, 1939.

582. Clichy. Mid-19th century. Swirl weight. Opaque lavender alternating with opaque white ribbons radiate from a central white pastry-mold cane, with red and green center, in pinwheel design. Colorless base. 2⁹⁄₁₆" (6.5 cm.) diam.

☐ Unrecorded.

484. Clichy. Mid-19th century. Flat motif of single pansy. Upper 2 petals are purple; lower 3 petals are yellow with purple tips; applied veining appears in center. Motif also includes 6 green leaves, green stem, and a bud turned down on a second stem. Weight is ¾" (1.9 cm.) high; top is flat, and there is a narrow flange on the flat base. 2⅜" (6.1 cm.) diam.

☐ Unidentified; acquired Feb., 1942.

389. Clichy. Mid-19th century. Swirl weight. Opaque blue alternating with opaque white ribbons radiate from central pink Clichy rose cane with green outer leaflet, in pinwheel design. Colorless base. 2⅝" (6.6 cm.) diam.

☐ Clichy; acquired March, 1941.

156. Clichy. Mid-19th century. Swirl weight. Opaque green alternating with opaque white ribbons radiate from a large, dark red and green pastry-mold cane, in pinwheel design. Colorless base. 2⁵⁄₁₆" (5.8 cm.) diam.

☐ Clichy; acquired Oct., 1938.
(Illus. 28, Bergstrom book.)

429. Clichy. Mid-19th century. Miniature weight. Patterned millefiori design (all canes of pastry-mold design) floats in colorless glass. Pink, blue, and green canes are spaced in 2 concentric circles around a large center cane. 1¾" (4.5 cm.) diam.

☐ Baccarat; acquired Aug., 1941.

211. Clichy. Mid-19th century. Swirl weight. Opaque pink alternating with opaque white ribbons radiate from green pastry-mold center cane, in pinwheel design. Colorless base. 2¹⁄₁₆" (5.3 cm.) diam.

☐ Clichy; acquired Feb., 1939.

Plate 13

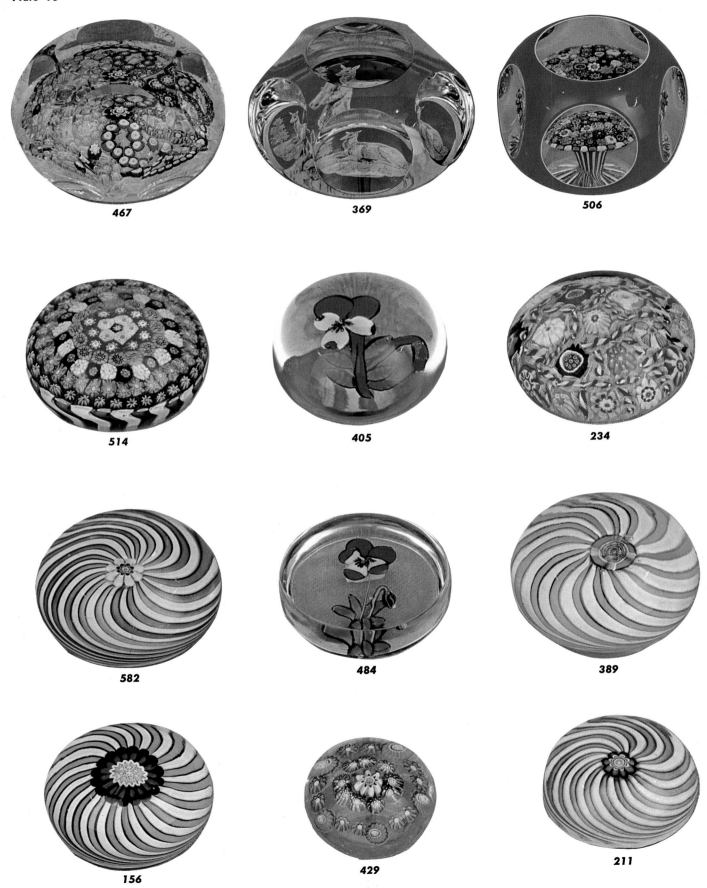

467

369

506

514

405

234

582

484

389

156

429

211

Plate 14

197. Clichy. Mid-19th century. Double overlay is deep rose over opaque white. Millefiori tuft is made up of 6 concentric circles of canes in white, pink, green, and blue. Outer circle consists of smooth opaque white canes, flattened and drawn to base to form the mushroom. Overlay is cut with large circular facet on top and 5 punties on curve. Strawberry cutting appears on underside. $3\frac{1}{16}$" (7.8 cm.) diam.

☐ Saint Louis; acquired Jan., 1939.
(Plate I, Bergstrom book.)

198. Clichy. Mid-19th century. Patterned millefiori canes float in colorless glass. Toward periphery is a garland of blue and buff-colored canes; 5 pink-and-green Clichy roses are placed between loops of garland. Between loops, toward the center, are 5 large white star canes. Central motif is 2 concentric circles of green and pink canes enclosing a single blue center cane. Flat top and 5 large punties on curve. Twelve radial oval cuts alternate with 12 small miter cuts on underside. 3" (7.6 cm.) diam.

☐ Clichy; acquired Jan., 1939.

505. Clichy. Mid-19th century. Double overlay is dark green over opaque white. Millefiori tuft has a pink Clichy rose in center and 6 concentric circles of canes, one of which is purple Clichy roses. Outside circle is flattened opaque white staves drawn down to base to form mushroom. Overlay is cut with circular facet on top and 5 slightly concave punties on curve. Strawberry cutting appears on underside. $3\frac{1}{16}$" (7.8 cm.) diam.

☐ Clichy; acquired Oct., 1942.

551. Clichy. Mid-19th century. Patterned millefiori design on translucent cobalt blue ground over opaque white. Loops of green, white, and pink canes are set around 2 center concentric circles of predominantly white canes. Colorless base. 3" (7.6 cm.) diam.

☐ Unrecorded.

116. Clichy. Mid-19th century. Close millefiori (in 2 pieces, showing cross section) includes a pink Clichy rose and a "C" cane. $3\frac{3}{16}$" (8.1 cm.) diam.

☐ Clichy; no record of acquisition. "Broken in handling." (Illus. 4, Bergstrom book.)

100. Clichy. Mid-19th century. Patterned millefiori on moss ground. Two garlands of millefiori canes, pink and white-and-blue, intertwine to form double trefoil design. In center, circle of white canes surrounds a large blue pastry-mold cane. Moss ground is somewhat translucent and resembles blades of grass. Colorless base. $3\frac{1}{16}$" (7.8 cm.) diam.

☐ Unidentified; acquired Nov., 1937.

175. Clichy. Mid-19th century. Sulphide portrait of Count de Chambord or possibly Alfred de Musset, profile to sinister, rests on translucent green ground. At periphery is circle of white star canes with green centers interspersed with larger pastry-mold canes with yellow stamen centers. Colorless uncut base. $3\frac{1}{16}$" (7.8 cm.) diam.

☐ Unidentified; acquired Nov., 1938.

228. Clichy. Ca. 1852. Sulphide profiles of Napoleon III and Empress Eugénie, to dexter (possibly by Apsley Pellatt), rest on cobalt blue ground lined with opaque white. Six pink Clichy roses and smaller white canes between the roses encircle the portraits. Colorless base. On underside is engraved the Imperial Eagle of Napoleon III and Eugénie. According to Mrs. Bergstrom's notes, this weight was made especially for the royal family. 3" (7.6 cm.) diam.

☐ Clichy; acquired May, 1939.
(Plate IX, Bergstrom book; Illus. 36, 1940 Bergstrom book; Illus. 34, subsequent editions.)

493. Clichy. Mid-19th century. Colorless glass weight encloses sulphide portrait bust, profile to sinister, of a Madonna on green oval plaque with white border; plaque is centered on cobalt blue ground with undercoating of opaque white. At periphery is a circle of pink-and-green canes interspersed with large, pink, pastry-mold canes. Colorless base. 3" (7.6 cm.) diam.

☐ Clichy; acquired May, 1942.

174. Clichy. Mid-19th century. Nineteen spaced millefiori canes with unusual pink Clichy rose in center (6 tiny stars in center of rose). Near edge, another unusual cane has a minute Clichy rose on stem with leaves in white crimped casing. Ground is translucent cobalt blue over opaque white. Colorless base. $2\frac{13}{16}$" (7.2 cm.) diam.

☐ Clichy; acquired Nov., 1938.

69. Clichy. Mid-19th century. Macédoine, or candy design. Fragments of large-sized canes, including 2 pink Clichy roses, are assembled at random. Motif is lined with varicolored jasper ground. Colorless base. $2\frac{1}{2}$" (6.3 cm.) diam.

☐ Clichy; acquired Sept., 1937.

44. Clichy. Mid-19th century. Patterned millefiori design. Two concentric circles of canes, one of pink Clichy roses and the other of blue canes, enclose a large red pastry-mold cane. Near periphery are 5 varicolored groups of canes, each group in the form of letter "C." Under the white muslin ground, segments of filigree are laid parallel. $2\frac{13}{16}$" (7.2 cm.) diam.

☐ Clichy; acquired June, 1937.

Plate 14

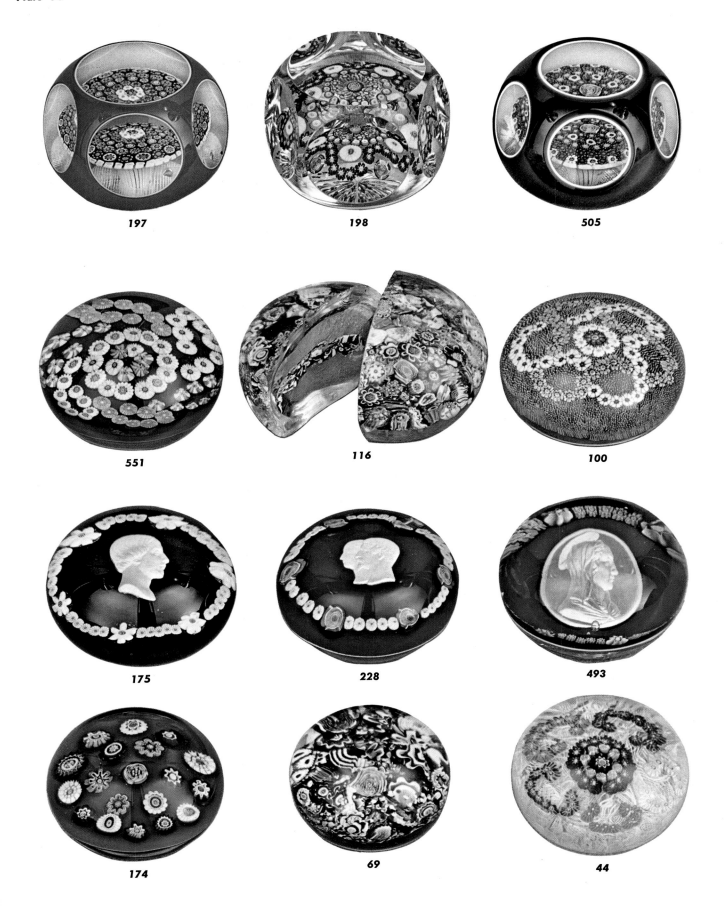

197

198

505

551

116

100

175

228

493

174

69

44

Plate 15

623. Attributed to Saint Louis. *Ca.* 1840–50. Glass plate has double overlay, applegreen over opaque white. On upper side, near rim, overlay is faceted in heart-shaped cuts (each with 2 concave sections) with connecting stems, and at underside center 12 radial oval cuts alternate with 12 miter cuts. Underside is clear glass. 6¼" (15.9 cm.) diam.

☐ Unrecorded.

624. Attributed to Saint Louis. *Ca.* 1840–50. Ovoid scent bottle has double overlay, cobalt blue over opaque white, and gilt decoration. Leaf- and stem-design facets encircle the bottle; there are 4 circular cuttings on the shoulder and oblong cuts on the elongated neck. Top of flat neck rim shows opaque white below clear glass. Colorless stopper is 8-sided and pointed. 1¹³⁄₁₆" (4.7 cm.) diam. of bottle; 5½" (13.9 cm.) overall height.

☐ Unrecorded.

193. Clichy. Mid-19th century. Piedouche weight. Motif is made up of 7 concentric circles of varicolored millefiori canes with a pink Clichy rose in the center. Outside circle of canes (alternating opaque blue and opaque white flattened rods) is extended in base to form a pedestal with a colorless square foot. 2½" (6.3 cm.) diam.

☐ Clichy; acquired Jan., 1939.
(Illus. 31, Bergstrom book.)

86. Clichy. Mid-19th century. Sixteen spaced millefiori canes, one a pink Clichy rose, are arranged on white filigree ground. Segments of white filigree twists are placed between canes to resemble a checker pattern, above a layer of parallel filigree twists. Colorless concave base. 2⅝" (6.6 cm.) diam.

☐ Clichy; acquired Oct., 1937.

73. Clichy. Mid-19th century. Piedouche weight. Seven concentric circles of blue, white, green, purple, and red canes surround center cane of white stars and stamens. Outside circle of cobalt blue alternating with opaque white flattened rods extends in base to form a pedestal with colorless, round, flat foot. 2¾" (7.0 cm.) diam.

☐ Saint Louis; acquired Sept., 1937.

352. Clichy. Mid-19th century. Miniature weight of close millefiori has 3 pink Clichy roses among the canes. Outside circle of canes is alternating turquoise blue and opaque white flattened rods, which are drawn to base, following the curve of the weight, to form a stave basket. Weight is mounted on marble rectangular base carved at edges and corners. 1¾" (4.5 cm.) diam. of weight; 3½" × 2½" (8.9 cm. × 6.3 cm.) marble base.

☐ Clichy; acquired June, 1940.

98. Clichy. Mid-19th century. Sparkling glass encloses 7 concentric circles of varicolored canes with pink Clichy rose at center. Circle at periphery is alternating opaque white and pink canes, drawn to the base, following the curve of the weight, to form a stave basket. 2³⁄₁₆" (5.5 cm.) diam.

☐ Clichy; acquired Nov., 1937.

196. Clichy. Mid-19th century. Verre opaline weight is rectangular in shape. Centered on the flat top is an oval, clear glass medallion encasing a flat bouquet consisting of a pink flower with round petals, and tiny rose in center; pink bud, green stem, and 7 green leaves. Petals and leaves show "waffle" pattern. 2⅝" × 2⅜" × ¾" (6.6 cm. × 6.1 cm. × 1.8 cm.).

☐ Baccarat; acquired Jan., 1939.

Plate 15

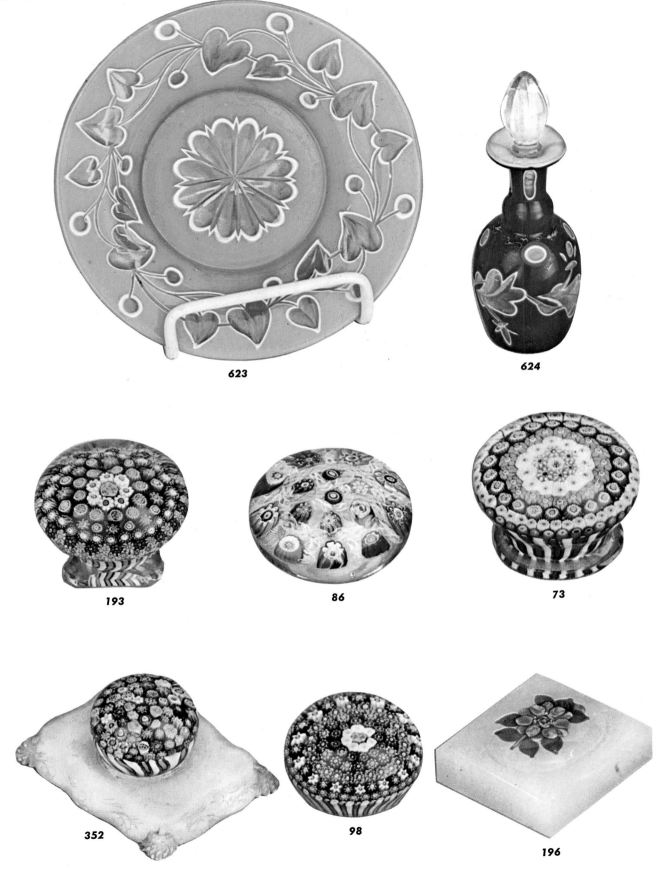

623

624

193

86

73

352

98

196

Plate 16

341. Attributed to Saint Louis. *Ca.* 1840–50. Double overlay, rose color over opaque white, footed tumbler of conical form. Encircling the bowl are spaced cuttings (in 3- and 4-concave sections) simulating hearts and diamonds. The stepped colorless base of the bowl is supported by a short, 6-sided stem above the circular, low conical foot. The double overlay of the foot is cut on underside with 12 radial cuts that alternate with 12 small miter cuts. 2⅞″ (7.3 cm.) diam. of foot; 4⅜″ (11.1 cm.) overall height. (A pair with 342.)

☐ Clichy; acquired June, 1940.

128. Attributed to Boston and Sandwich Glass Co., Sandwich, Mass., or New England Glass Co., East Cambridge, Mass. (American.) *Ca.* 1853–88. Five-petaled, opaque white flower with blue central cane rests on a cross in the center of the weight. Cross is composed of overlapping tiers of smooth, pointed green leaves. Ground is white latticinio, over a colorless concave base. Allover geometric faceting. 3¼″ (8.3 cm.) diam.

☐ Baccarat; acquired May, 1938.
(Illus. 21, Bergstrom book.)

342. Attributed to Saint Louis. *Ca.* 1840–50. Double overlay is cobalt blue over opaque white. In all other respects except color this tumbler matches 341, and it was bought at the same time.

570. Clichy. Dated 1848. Sulphide portrait head of Czar Nicholas I, profile to sinister, appears against a translucent cobalt blue ground, with circle of chartreuse and red canes at periphery. Large date "1848" in blue numerals on white disk (cracked) is on the underside of the blue ground, within the colorless casing. Slight circular depression on exterior at motif level. 3¾″ (9.6 cm.) diam.

☐ Unrecorded.

507. Clichy. Mid-19th century. Checker weight. Sixteen large millefiori canes, including a white Clichy rose and a "C" cane, are spaced on white filigree segments laid parallel. Between canes are opaque red-and-white ribbon twists and white filigree threads forming a checkered design. Colorless base. 3″ (7.6 cm.) diam.

☐ Clichy; acquired Oct., 1942.

504. Clichy. Mid-19th century. Concentric millefiori tuft. Center cane, a large pink Clichy rose, is surrounded by 5 concentric circles of varicolored canes. Pink Clichy roses alternate with purple canes in one circle. Outside circle is opaque white, flattened rods drawn to base to form the mushroom. Flat top; 6 punties on curve. Base is colorless; underside is cut in combination of 12 radial cuts alternating with 12 small miter cuts. 3⅜″ (8.6 cm.) diam.

☐ Clichy; acquired Sept., 1942.

54. Clichy. Mid-19th century. Patterned millefiori motif. A garland of pink-and-white canes intertwines with garland of blue-and-white canes to form double trefoil design, which circles a large red pastry-mold central cane. Transparent emerald-green ground is lined with opaque white, over a colorless base. 2¹¹⁄₁₆″ (6.8 cm.) diam.

☐ Baccarat; acquired June, 1939.

264. Clichy. Mid-19th century. Concentric millefiori mushroom motif has 6 circles of millefiori canes. One circle is of purple Clichy roses. Another is white-and-green Clichy roses alternating with red-and-white canes. Outside circle (cobalt blue rods alternating with opaque white) is drawn to a point at base to form the tuft. Flat top, 6 punties on curve. Colorless base. A small 32-pointed star is cut on the underside. 3³⁄₁₆″ (8.1 cm.) diam.

☐ Clichy; acquired Sept., 1939.

Plate 16

341

128

342

570

507

504

54

264

Plate 17

218. Clichy. Mid-19th century. Patterned millefiori motif consists of 6 circlets of varicolored millefiori canes; each circlet encloses a large cane. In center is a large white, crimped-edge rod surrounded by 3 red canes. Ground is transparent purple over opaque white. Colorless base. 2$\frac{15}{16}$" (7.4 cm.) diam.

☐ Clichy; acquired Feb., 1939.

486. Clichy. Mid-19th century. Patterned millefiori motif is arranged on green moss ground dotted with stars. At center is pink-and-green Clichy rose surrounded by 2 concentric circles of blue canes and white-star canes. Intertwining garlands of pink canes and purple canes make a double quatrefoil design. Colorless base. 3$\frac{1}{4}$" (8.3 cm.) diam.

☐ Clichy; acquired March, 1942.

76. Clichy. Mid-19th century. Floating, patterned millefiori motif is made up of 6 circlets of varicolored canes. Each circlet encloses a single cane, one of which is a large pink-and-green Clichy rose. Single canes also appear at periphery between the circlets. 3" (7.6 cm.) diam.

☐ Clichy; acquired Sept., 1937.

160. Clichy. Mid-19th century. Concentric millefiori has 7 circles of pink, blue, and green canes. Pink Clichy roses surround the large center cane, and also appear near periphery alternating with white canes. Outside circle is green, stamen-like canes. Colorless ground. 2$\frac{5}{8}$" (6.6 cm.) diam.

☐ Clichy; acquired Oct., 1938.

301. Clichy. Mid-19th century. Spaced millefiori canes, predominantly pastel colors, and a "C" cane are set between and on strips of white filigree segments. Delicacy of filigree gives gauzelike appearance. 2$\frac{7}{8}$" (7.3 cm.) diam.

☐ Clichy; acquired Feb., 1940.
(Illus. 25, Bergstrom book.)

475. Clichy. Mid-19th century. Close millefiori motif has a small, pink Clichy rose in the center. A "C" cane, 2 blue Clichy roses, and 3 purple Clichy roses are among the canes. At periphery are alternating opaque white and turquoise blue staves in form of basket. 2$\frac{7}{16}$" (6.2 cm.) diam.

☐ Clichy; acquired Jan., 1942.

436. Clichy. Mid-19th century. Checker weight. Spaced millefiori canes include a pink-and-green Clichy rose and a white-and-red Clichy rose. Twists of opaque white-and-green ribbons, within spirals of white filigree, separate the canes in a checker design. Parallel segments of white filigree form the ground over a colorless base. 2$\frac{5}{8}$" (6.6 cm.) diam.

☐ Clichy; acquired Sept., 1941.

158. Clichy. Mid-19th century. Nineteen spaced millefiori canes are arranged on transparent royal blue over opaque white ground. Among the canes are 2 bearing the letter "C" and one white-and-green Clichy rose. Colorless base. 2$\frac{5}{8}$" (6.6 cm.) diam.

☐ Clichy; acquired Oct., 1938.
(Plate VII, Bergstrom book.)

164. Clichy. Mid-19th century. Patterned millefiori motif is on an unusual color ground of transparent orange-red over opaque white. Center pink-and-green Clichy rose is encircled by 9 small green serrated canes. Five circlets of varicolored canes, one of which is white-and-green Clichy roses, surround the center circlet; each circlet encloses a large single cane. Colorless base. 2$\frac{5}{8}$" (6.6 cm.) diam.

☐ Clichy; acquired Oct., 1938.

316 and **316A.** Clichy. Mid-19th century. Pair of colorless glass doorknobs, not identical, encloses patterned millefiori canes on white muslin ground. Pink-and-green Clichy rose in center is surrounded by 2 circles of canes. White filigree rods below the muslin ground are laid parallel. 2$\frac{1}{8}$" (5.4 cm.) diam.

☐ Clichy; acquired April, 1940.
(Illus. 56, 1940 Bergstrom book; Illus. 54, subsequent editions.)

204. Clichy. Mid-19th century. Footed wafer tray. The bowl is decorated with white filigree swirl and has red-and-white ribbon twist applied to the rim. Colorless stem joins bowl to a flat circular foot, which encloses 3 concentric circles of millefiori canes, including 6 pink-and-green Clichy roses. In center of foot is large green cane with yellow stamen center. 3$\frac{1}{4}$" (8.3 cm.) diam. of tray at rim; 2$\frac{1}{16}$" (5.3 cm.) diam. of foot.

☐ Clichy; acquired Feb., 1939.
(#13, p. 41, 1940 Bergstrom book; p. 42, subsequent editions.)

Plate 17

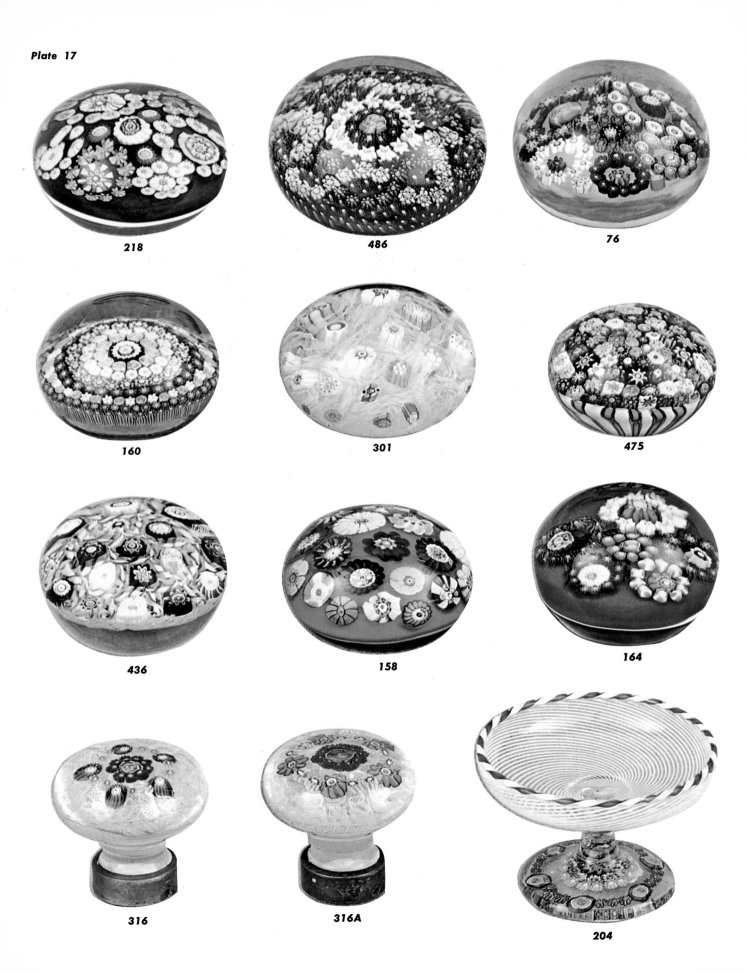

218

486

76

160

301

475

436

158

164

316

316A

204

Plate 18

246. Clichy. Mid-19th century. Flat floating bouquet on colorless base consists of deep blue clematis and mauve clematis, each with furrowed petals and cane centers; and a large pink Clichy rose. A bud is attached to each of the 3 stems; 2 groups of 3 green leaves. Stems, ending in points, are crossed by pink ribbon. 3³⁄₁₆″ (8.1 cm.) diam.

☐ Clichy; acquired July, 1939.
(Illus. 27, Bergstrom book.)

163. Clichy. Mid-19th century. Sulphide of the Emperor Napoleon, standing full-length in characteristic pose, is set against translucent cobalt blue ground lined with opaque white, and within a circlet of pink and green canes. Large circular facet on top and 5 punties on curve. Colorless base. 3¼″ (8.3 cm.) diam.

☐ Clichy; acquired Oct., 1938.
(Plate VIII, Bergstrom book.)

300. Clichy. Mid-19th century. Fruit weight. Two russet-colored pears with sturdy gray stems rest on 3 deep green leaves; all on ground of tubular twists of white filigree, laid parallel. Dewdrop bubbles can be seen on the leaves, and bubble at blossom end of pears. Colorless base. 3⁹⁄₁₆″ (9.1 cm.) diam.

☐ Clichy; acquired Feb., 1940.
(Plate XI, Bergstrom book.)

547. Clichy. Mid-19th century. Two concentric circles of spaced varicolored millefiori canes surround a center pink Clichy rose. White filigree segments divide the individual canes. Ground is of white filigree rods that are laid parallel above colorless base. Punty on top and 2 circles of punties on curve. 3″ (7.6 cm.) diam.

☐ Unrecorded.

253. Clichy. Mid-19th century. Spherical newel post is mounted on ebony stand. Spaced millefiori canes are set in white muslin ground near encasing glass. There are 3 concentric circles of large spaced canes, one of which is a pink Clichy rose. White filigree segments are laid between canes. 3⁹⁄₁₆″ (9.1 cm.) diam.

☐ Clichy; acquired Sept., 1939.
(#12, p. 41, 1940 Bergstrom book; p. 42, subsequent editions.) (Ex collection of Oscar Wilde.)

277. Clichy. *Ca.* 1845. Probably one of the early weights. Close millefiori motif includes approximately 25 Clichy roses in varying shades of pink. All canes are small; underside shows their uneven ends. Punty on top and 2 circles of punties on curve. Colorless base. 3¼″ (8.3 cm.) diam.

☐ Clichy; acquired Nov., 1939.
(Illus. 26, Bergstrom book.)

360. Clichy. Mid-19th century. Spaced millefiori canes are arranged in 2 concentric circles around a center white cane. Segments of tubular pink filigree between the canes form a checkered pattern over a ground of white filigree rods laid parallel. In colorless base is unusual swirl of white latticinio strands in pinwheel design. 3³⁄₁₆″ (8.1 cm.) diam.

☐ Clichy; acquired Aug., 1940.

96. Clichy. Mid-19th century. Patterned millefiori. Two intertwining garlands of varicolored canes surround a center motif of 2 concentric circles of pink and green canes with a deep blue cane in center. The same deep blue cane appears several times in garlands. All are sunk into opaque chalk-white ground. Colorless base. 3³⁄₈″ (8.6 cm.) diam.

☐ Bristol, 1845; acquired Nov., 1937.

487. Clichy. Mid-19th century. Thirty-seven large varicolored individual canes, predominantly pastry-mold, are spaced on transparent cranberry base. The red letter "C" in center of one cane and an all-white Clichy rose appear. 3³⁄₁₆″ (8.1 cm.) diam.

☐ Clichy; acquired March, 1942.

202. Clichy. Mid-19th century. Close millefiori motif includes 2 pink Clichy roses, one white-and-green Clichy rose, and an all-white Clichy rose. At periphery are flattened opaque white rods alternating with green canes drawn toward colorless base, following curve of weight, to form a stave basket. 3³⁄₁₆″ (8.1 cm.) diam.

☐ Clichy; acquired Feb., 1939.

201. Clichy. Mid-19th century. Patterned millefiori motif is set into transparent pink over opaque white ground. Garland of pastel-colored pastry-mold canes is arranged in trefoil design, with individual larger canes interspersed. Center cane is green. Colorless base. 3⅛″ (7.9 cm.) diam.

☐ Clichy; acquired Feb., 1939.

143. Clichy. Mid-19th century. Patterned millefiori. Two garlands of pink-and-green canes and white-and-green canes intertwine to form double quatrefoil design. The garlands surround a center motif of 2 concentric circles of red, white, and green canes, which surround a white center cane. Pattern is slightly off center on the translucent cobalt blue base. 3³⁄₁₆″ (8.1 cm.) diam.

☐ Unidentified; acquired Oct., 1938.

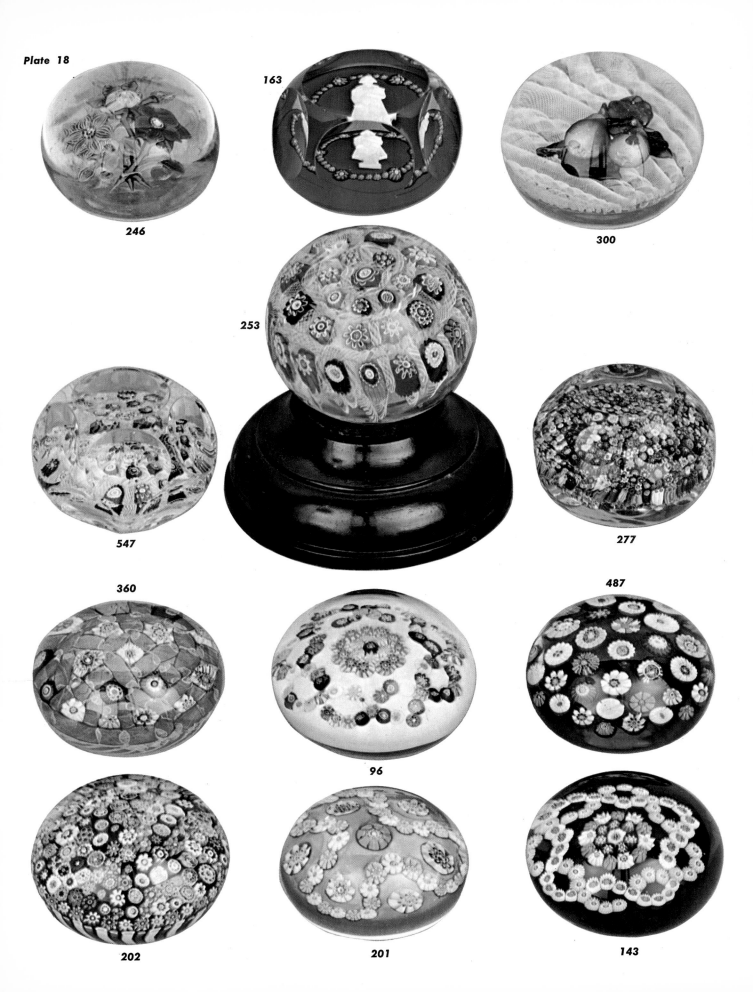

Plate 18

246

163

300

253

547

277

360

487

96

202

201

143

Plate 19

181. Saint Louis. Mid-19th century. Open red and blue fuchsia flower with long stamens has a pink stem. Motif also includes a narrow red bud, 2 small red buds, and 4 green leaves all on orange stalk. White latticinio ground over colorless base. 3 1/16″ (7.8 cm.) diam.

☐ Sandwich; acquired Dec., 1938.

(Illus. 52, 1940 Bergstrom book; Illus. 50, subsequent editions.)

93. Saint Louis. Mid-19th century. Pink camomile flower, chiffon type, has yellow cane center. Motif also includes 4 green leaves, pointed stem, and a pink bud. White latticinio ground over colorless base. Six punties on curve; convex top. 3 1/8″ (7.9 cm.) diam.

☐ Baccarat; acquired Nov., 1937.

462. Saint Louis. Mid-19th century. White camomile flower, chiffon type, has pale yellow and red cane center. Motif also includes 4 green leaves, stem, and a white bud. White, lined with red, latticinio ground over colorless base. 3 1/16″ (7.8 cm.) diam.

☐ Baccarat; acquired Oct., 1942.

81. Saint Louis. Mid-19th century. Large, pinkish mauve dahlia has 42 furrowed, pointed petals; 6 green leaves are visible at periphery. Center cane is yellow, serrated, with blue center. Colorless base. A 24-pointed star is cut on the underside. 2 15/16″ (7.4 cm.) diam.

☐ Unidentified; acquired Sept., 1937.

402. Saint Louis. Mid-19th century. Cobalt blue clematis has 15 striped pointed petals, 4 pale green leaves, and a short stem. Center of flower is ocher-colored serrated cane with blue and white center. Motif floats midway in colorless glass. A 24-pointed star is cut on the underside. 3″ (7.6 cm.) diam.

☐ Saint Louis; acquired May, 1941.

365. Baccarat. Mid-19th century. Salmon pink clematis has 10 grooved petals, white star-cane center. Motif also includes 5 pale green leaves, stem, and red bud. Circle of alternating white and green canes is at periphery. White filigree ground extends to the base. 2 7/8″ (7.3 cm.) diam.

☐ Saint Louis; acquired Sept., 1940.

5. Saint Louis. Mid-19th century. Rose-colored anemone has 5 smooth petals and 5 narrow green leaves between petals; 2 narrow green leaves are on green stem. Center of flower is opaque yellow dots; applied black veining appears on petals. White latticinio ground over colorless base. 2 3/4″ (7.0 cm.) diam.

☐ Unidentified; acquired April, 1936.

390. Saint Louis. Mid-19th century. Crown weight. Two red-and-blue ribbon twists with white edges, alternating with white filigree spiral, radiate from center cane of chartreuse-and-white and converge at a point on base. 2 3/4″ (7.0 cm.) diam.

☐ Saint Louis; acquired March, 1941.

220. Saint Louis. Mid-19th century. Upright bouquet is arranged in white latticinio basket, which is rimmed with yellow and white spiral. Bouquet is made up of a center flower of deep blue, a white flower, a pink flower, and 2 canes simulating flower heads, all surrounded by green leaves. Basket floats midway in colorless glass. 3″ (7.6 cm.) diam.

☐ Saint Louis; acquired Feb., 1939.

(Illus. 11, Bergstrom book.)

232. Saint Louis. Mid-19th century. Fruit weight. Cluster of 3 yellow, shading to white, fruit pieces and 4 red berries with thin yellow stems is set amid 10 green leaves, in white latticinio basket over colorless base. 2 11/16″ (6.8 cm.) diam.

☐ Unidentified; acquired May, 1939.

103. Saint Louis. Mid-19th century. White camomile flower, chiffon type, has pale green center cane, 4 green leaves, and stem; a white bud also appears. The white, lined with red, latticinio ground is drawn to a point on the colorless base to form a tuft. Six punties on curve; convex top. 2 9/16″ (6.5 cm.) diam.

☐ Baccarat; acquired Dec., 1937.

(Illus. 20, Bergstrom book.)

66. Saint Louis. Mid-19th century. Fruit weight. Floating near base is cluster of 8 cranberries attached to thin yellow stems in parallel position and bound with a fine opaque white twist simulating a cord. Four pale green narrow leaves are set near end of stems. A 24-pointed star is cut on the underside. 2 15/16″ (7.4 cm.) diam.

☐ Unidentified; acquired Sept., 1937.

Plate 19

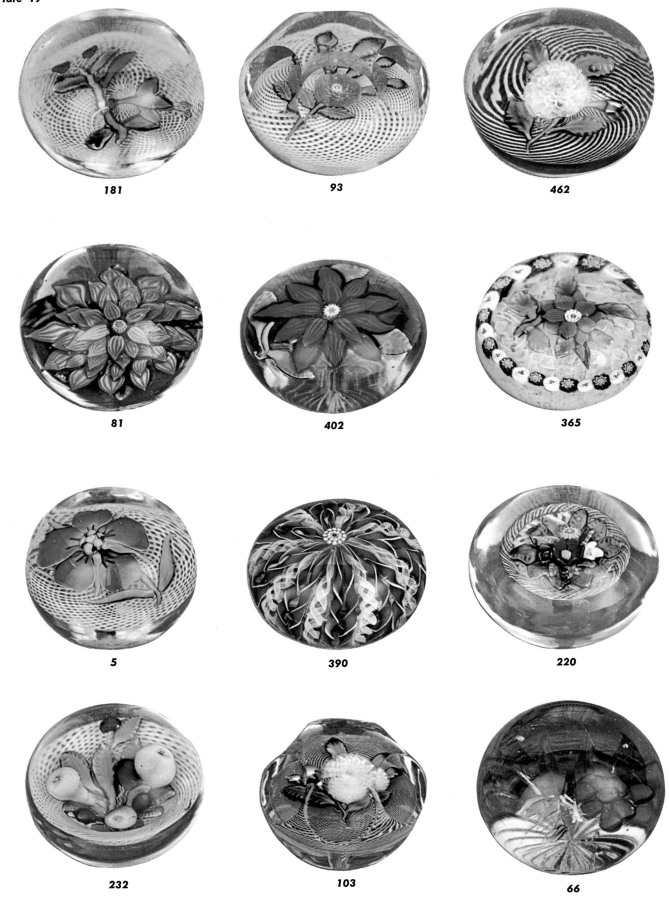

181

93

462

81

402

365

5

390

220

232

103

66

Plate 20

130.   Saint Louis. Mid-19th century. Floating flat bouquet consists of 4 millefiori canes centered on 5 green leaves with stems ending in a point. At periphery is a circle of canes: white-and-blue alternating with yellow-and-blue. Underside is flashed with amber; there is allover honeycomb faceting on the exterior, the cuts becoming larger near the base. 3″ (7.6 cm.) diam.

☐   Unidentified; acquired June, 1938.

414.   Saint Louis. Mid-19th century. Upright bouquet with white center flower, 2 deep blue flowers, 2 salmon-pink flowers, and 4 millefiori canes is surrounded by 10 pale green leaves. Torsade has no core; narrow band of white threads separates the red strands in the coil. Curve is cut with honeycomb facets that become larger near the colorless base. Convex top. 4⅟₁₆″ (10.3 cm.) diam.

☐   Baccarat; acquired May, 1941.

74.   Saint Louis. Mid-19th century. Small upright bouquet is made up of salmon-pink center flower, a white flower, a blue flower (all with opaque yellow centers), 2 florets, and green leaves ending in a point. A coil of opaque white strands encircles motif and rests on the colorless base. Geometric facets become larger near base. 2¹⁵⁄₁₆″ (7.4 cm.) diam.

☐   Baccarat; acquired Sept., 1937.

354.   Saint Louis. Mid-19th century. Crown weight. White-edged red-and-green ribbon twists and white-edged deep blue-and-chartreuse twists alternate with white filigree spirals, and radiate from central cane of deep blue and white, converging at center of base. 3¼″ (8.3 cm.) diam.

☐   Saint Louis; acquired Aug., 1940.
(Illus. 12, 1940 Bergstrom book; Illus. 13, subsequent editions.)

119.   Saint Louis. Mid-19th century. Upright bouquet consists of red, white, and blue flowers and 2 canes. Four pale green leaves are drawn to a point at the colorless base. Torsade has no core; a narrow band of white threads separates red strands in the coil. Punty on top, 6 punties on curve. 3″ (7.6 cm.) diam.

☐   Baccarat; acquired May, 1938.

6.   Saint Louis. Mid-19th century. Crown weight, thickly encased. White-edged red-and-green ribbon twists alternate with white filigree spiral twists, and radiate from center green-and-blue cane, converging at center of base. 3³⁄₁₆″ (8.1 cm.) diam.

☐   Sandwich; acquired May, 1936.

207.   Saint Louis. Mid-19th century. Encased white single overlay. Small upright bouquet of colored flowers and canes is surrounded by green leaves. Center flower is coral-red with bubble center. Opaque overlay is cut with 7 circular windows and further encased with colorless glass. A small 24-pointed star is cut in the encasing glass on the underside. 2⅝″ (6.6 cm.) diam.

☐   Baccarat; acquired Feb., 1939.

495.   Saint Louis. Mid-19th century. Marbrie weight. Rare crown type. Near encasing glass are 4 series of concentric loops in red and green on opaque white, globular ground, with a blue and white floret in center. When viewed from the top, motif resembles quatrefoil design or stylized flower. 3⅟₁₆″ (7.8 cm.) diam.

☐   Baccarat; acquired May, 1942.

219.   Saint Louis. Mid-19th century. Encased double overlay. The small upright bouquet rests on the base. Overlay is a "stencil-like" design of 8 vertical panels following curve of weight: cobalt blue-over-opaque white alternating with all-white; panels are cut with circles and stars. The whole is further encased in colorless glass. 3″ (7.6 cm.) diam.

☐   Baccarat; acquired Feb., 1939.
(Plate XV, Bergstrom book.)

282.   Saint Louis. Mid-19th century. White clematis has 10 deeply furrowed, pointed petals; center simulates a sulfur-tipped "match head." There are 3 green leaves and a darker green, pointed stem. Base is green and white jasper. 2⁷⁄₁₆″ (6.2 cm.) diam.

☐   Sandwich; acquired Nov., 1939.

388.   Saint Louis. Mid-19th century. White camomile flower (chiffon type) with pale yellow stamen center, a white bud, 4 green leaves, and stem make up the motif. White, lined with red, latticinio ground above a colorless base. 2½″ (6.3 cm.) diam.

☐   Baccarat; acquired March, 1941.

468.   Attributed to Bohemian-Silesian manufacture. Crown weight. Tubular white filigree rods radiate from center millefiori cane of a red monkey silhouette. The filigree rods enclose ribbon twists of alternating red, white, and blue. Encasing glass is thicker than in usual crown weight. Light in weight. 2⁷⁄₁₆″ (6.2 cm.) diam.

☐   Saint Louis; acquired Dec., 1941.

Plate 20

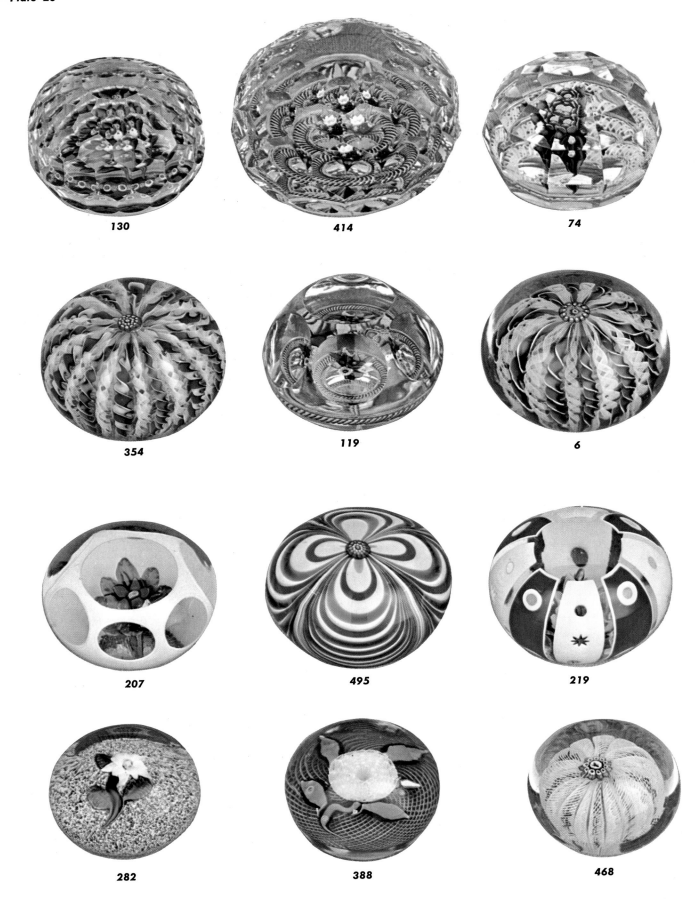

130

414

74

354

119

6

207

495

219

282

388

468

Plate 21

357.   Baccarat. Mid-19th century. Opaque red snake, with green markings along its spine of linked ovals interspersed with dots, is coiled on a white filigree base. Single bubbles appear on either side of snake's head and between the coils. 3¹⁄₁₆″ (7.8 cm.) diam.

☐ Baccarat; acquired Aug., 1940.
(Plate VI, Bergstrom book.)

230.   French. Green and yellow salamander appears to be crawling on rock ground of sand-colored and green glass. Motif also includes striped bug with transparent wings, near the head of the lizard, and a white flower with yellow center, growing out of dark green, upright leaves. Pinprick bubbles can be seen on leaves and lizard. Flat base is colorless. 4⅛″ (10.5 cm.) diam. The white flower in this weight has similarities to flowers in 136, Plate 27, and to the center of flowers in 137, Plate 24.

☐ Saint Louis; acquired May, 1939.
(Illus. 6, Bergstrom book.)

99.   Baccarat. Mid-19th century. Opaque green snake, with brown markings along its spine of linked ovals interspersed with dots, is coiled on white filigree base. 3¹⁄₁₆″ (7.8 cm.) diam.

☐ Unidentified; acquired Nov., 1939.

209.   Saint Louis. Ca. 1848. Molded lizard weight. Hollow, blown sphere of translucent white glass overlaid with pink glass is crowned with coiled lizard. Faceting on curve is in floral design. Hole in center of underside of weight. 3⁷⁄₁₆″ (8.7 cm.) diam.

☐ Saint Louis; acquired Feb., 1939.
(Illus. 7, Bergstrom book.)

322.   Saint Louis. Last half 19th century. Snake weight. Frosted, opaque white sphere with bluish cast has applied cobalt blue snake, decorated with gilt tracery, coiled around the outside. 3⅛″ (7.9 cm.) overall diam.

☐ Saint Louis; acquired April, 1940.
(Illus. 8. Bergstrom book.)

177.   Saint Louis. Ca. 1848. Molded lizard weight. Hollow blown sphere is crowned with coiled lizard decorated with

gilt. Sphere is green and white jasper encased in clear glass. 3³⁄₁₆″ (8.1 cm.) diam.

☐ Saint Louis; acquired Nov., 1938.

449.   Saint Louis. Mid-19th century. Fruit weight. Floating motif consists of a bunch of purple grapes on pale yellow, thin stem and 2 green leaves attached to sturdy orange stem. Slightly concave punty on top; 2 circles of punties on curve, the lower one of larger-size cuts. Colorless base. Strawberry cutting on underside. 3¹⁄₁₆″ (7.8 cm.) diam.

☐ Saint Louis; acquired Sept., 1941.

416.   Attributed to Saint Louis. Mid-19th century. Opaque emerald-green snake with red eyes and nostrils is coiled on red and white jasper ground. Flat top; curve is faceted in diamond-shaped cuts, the edges of which are beveled. Colorless base. 2¹⁵⁄₁₆″ (7.4 cm.) diam.

☐ Baccarat; acquired May, 1941.

147.   Saint Louis. Mid-19th century. Fruit weight. Cluster of 3 yellow and red fruit pieces, 4 red berries with thin yellow stems, and 8 green leaves are arranged in white latticinio basket over colorless base. Slightly concave punty on top; 6 oval cuts on curve. 2¹⁵⁄₁₆″ (7.4 cm.) diam.

☐ Unidentified; acquired Oct., 1938.

148.   Saint Louis. Mid-19th century. Cobalt blue clematis has 15 striped, pointed petals and a dark red center. Motif includes 5 pale green leaves and a stem. White latticinio ground over colorless base. 2⅝″ (6.6 cm.) diam.

☐ Unidentified; acquired Oct., 1938.

424.   Saint Louis. Mid-19th century. Pale pink clematis has 28 furrowed and striped, pointed petals, a blue-and-white cane center, 3 green leaves, and stem. White latticinio ground over colorless clear base. 2¾″ (7.0 cm.) diam.

☐ Saint Louis; acquired Aug., 1941.

150.   Saint Louis. Mid-19th century. Red clematis with 15 faintly striped, pointed petals has the initial "B" on opaque yellow, square center. Motif includes 5 pale green leaves and stem. White latticinio ground over colorless base. 2⅝″ (6.6 cm.) diam.

☐ Baccarat; acquired Oct., 1938.

Plate 21

357

230

99

209

322

177

449

416

147

148

424

150

Plate 22

293. Saint Louis. 1840–50. Vase of ovoid form tapers toward flared, scalloped rim. It is decorated with white filigree threads alternating with opaque white strands, spiraling from base to rim. Flange at base encloses coral-colored ribbon and white filigree twist, matching the applied encased twist at scalloped rim. 11½″ (29.2 cm.) height.

☐ Saint Louis; acquired probably 1939.

413. Saint Louis. Mid-19th century. Colorless glass vase, round-bottom conical form with flared rim, has paperweight base. Base encloses small upright bouquet consisting of central white flower, 2 deep blue flowers, 2 red flowers, and 4 florets, surrounded by 10 pale green leaves. Torsade is a coil of white filigree threads and red strand (no core). Waisted stem with 5 sides joins the paperweight base to the vase. At rim is applied coil of white filigree threads and red strand, matching torsade in base. Allover honeycomb facets become larger toward vase rim and toward base of weight. 4⅛″ (10.5 cm.) diam. of base; 13″ (32.9 cm.) overall height.

☐ Baccarat; acquired May, 1941.

Plate 22

293

413

Plate 23

334. Baccarat. Heavy colorless glass ring is decorated with 3 incrustated medallions: bust portrait of "Escalupe" in colored enamel over gold leaf; a running dog with letter in mouth, in colored enamel; and a gilt monogram. Faceting in loops appears between the medallions. 2⅞" (7.3 cm.) diam.; 2⅜" (6.1 cm.) height.

☐ Unidentified; acquired May, 1940.
(Fig. XXII, Jokelson, *Sulphides*.)

284. Saint Louis. Wineglass has 4 concentric circles of pastel-colored millefiori canes enclosed in the bottom of the flared bowl. Outer circle is pink serrated canes with white centers. Ball-knopped stem, above a flat circular foot, has been applied to underside of bowl. (The bowl is similar to 311, 312, 313, 314, and 315 in Plate 26.) 4" (10.2 cm.) height.

☐ Sandwich; acquired Nov., 1939.
(#7, page 41, 1940 Bergstrom book; page 42, subsequent editions.)

443. Bohemian. *Ca.* 1850. Colorless glass seal. The knob end, faceted in diamond cuts, encloses 7 spaced floating millefiori canes, 2 of which are dog silhouettes. Stem of seal is 4-sided, enclosing a dark blue ribbon twist around which are coiled white filigree threads. 3⁷⁄₁₆" (8.7 cm.) length.

☐ Baccarat; acquired Aug., 1941.

615. Baccarat. Colorless glass seal. Mushroom-shaped top encloses round sulphide disk on which a flower spray and leaves are painted in colors. The stem of the seal is 6-sided above a knop, with circular groove cuts below the knop. Strawberry cutting appears on edge of mushroom top and on knop. The seal end, mounted in a brass fitting, is onyx with an incised portrait of Chateaubriand. 2¾" (7.0 cm.) length.

☐ Unrecorded.

517. Saint Louis. Mid-19th century. White clematis flower has pointed, grooved petals and center cane; tips of 5 very pale green leaves are visible surrounding flower, which is centered on unusual cushion of deep green aventurine. Torsade is of flattened white filigree twist around which is coiled a pink strand. Colorless base. 2¾" (7.0 cm.) diam.

☐ Saint Louis; acquired April, 1943.
(Illus. 10, Bergstrom book.)

115. Saint Louis. Mid-19th century. Thin, pale green snake has darker spots and line running down its back; red eyes and nostrils. Snake is coiled on white muslin ground, the muslin extending to the encasing glass at the bottom of the weight. Flat top; geometric faceting on curve. 3" (7.6 cm.) diam.

☐ Baccarat; acquired Feb., 1938.

92. Saint Louis. Mid-19th century. Cluster of 7 vegetables, probably turnips and radishes, in opaque lavender, white, and yellow, is arranged in a circle with the green tops at periphery, on a white latticinio basket over colorless base. High, clear crown. 3¹⁄₁₆" (7.8 cm.) diam.

☐ Baccarat; acquired Nov., 1937.
(Illus. 18, Bergstrom book.)

274. Clichy. Mid-19th century. Single flower has pink and white striped, narrow, pointed petals (raised); central floret is cobalt blue with yellow star center. Dewdrop bubbles appear on petals; translucent purple base. The 4 sides of the weight are squared; convex top. 2⁵⁄₁₆" (5.8 cm.) diam.

☐ Unidentified; acquired Nov., 1939.

15. Saint Louis. Mid-19th century. Flat flower spray contains 4 florets centered among 4 pale green leaves; leaf stems are drawn to a point. Colorless base has strawberry cutting on underside. 2³⁄₁₆" (5.5 cm.) diam.

☐ Cambridge; acquired May, 1936.

543. Saint Louis. Mid-19th century. Center motif of 2 concentric circles of canes surrounding a floret is impressed in pink and white jasper ground. 2¹⁵⁄₁₆" (7.4 cm.) diam.

☐ Unrecorded.

231. Origin unknown; possibly Pantin (French). *Ca.* 1878. Fruit weight. Large brown pear, 2 red berries with translucent yellow stems, 3 dark green leaves, 2 blue leaves, and a blue stem are arranged on opaque, light gray ground. Concave underside; colorless base. Light in weight. (Similar to 558.) 2¾" (7.0 cm.) diam.

☐ Unidentified; acquired May, 1939.

90. Clichy. Mid-19th century. Patterned millefiori weight. Colorless glass of grayish hue encloses floating design of varicolored canes arranged in "C" patterns surrounding a central grouping of pink canes. 2¾" (7.0 cm.) diam.

☐ Unidentified; acquired Nov., 1937.

558. Origin unknown; possibly Pantin (French). *Ca.* 1878. Full-blown pink rose, 3-dimensional, with yellow stamen center, a red bud, 3 emerald-green leaves, 2 olive-green leaves, and a sturdy stem are set on an opaque, light gray ground. Concave underside; colorless base. Light in weight. (Similar to 231.) 2¹¹⁄₁₆" (6.8 cm.) diam.

☐ Unrecorded.

Plate 23

334

284

443

615

517

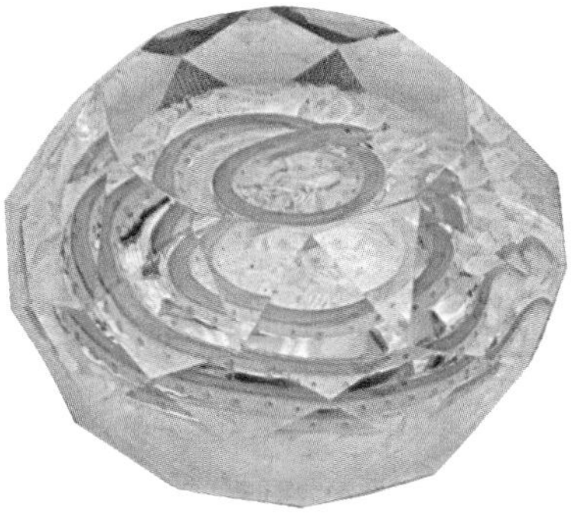

115

92

274

543

15

231

90

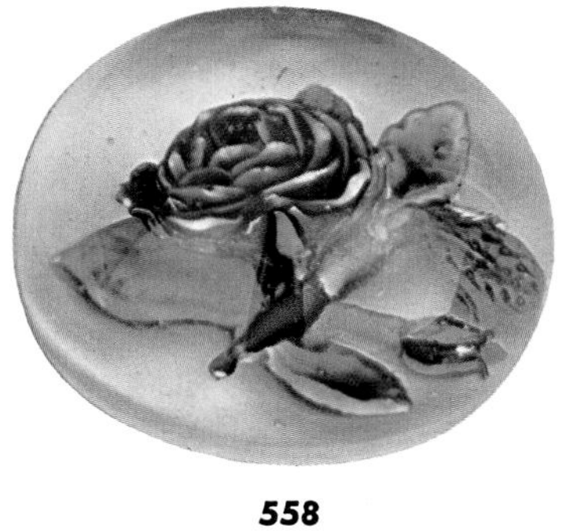

558

Plate 24

213. Saint Louis. Mid-19th century. Large mauve dahlia with striped and pointed petals has serrated, ocher-colored central cane with blue center. Tips of 5 green leaves are visible at periphery. A 24-pointed star is cut on the underside. Colorless base. 3 1/16″ (7.8 cm.) diam.

☐ Saint Louis; acquired Feb., 1939.
(Illus. 9, Bergstrom book.)

521. Saint Louis. Mid-19th century. Large macédoine weight (a true end-of-day weight). Near center is a group of 7 slurred silhouette canes with a white dog cane in center. Filigree segments, some in color, and ribbon twists and canes, all small, are assembled at random. Punty on top; curve faceted with 3 circles of punties increasing in size toward base. 3¾″ (9.6 cm.) diam.

☐ Saint Louis; acquired April, 1943.

500. Saint Louis. Mid-19th century. Coral-pink clematis with 10 striped, pointed petals and center blue-and-white cane has 3 dark green leaves and a stem that ends in a point. Green and white jasper base. 3 1/16″ (7.8 cm.) diam.

☐ Baccarat; acquired July, 1942.

167. Saint Louis. Mid-19th century. Patterned millefiori, carpet ground. Five silhouette canes, including a camel, each encircled by hollow pale pink rods, are spaced in a circle on carpet ground of white, serrated hollow canes lined with green. Center motif is group of hollow rods encircled by white-and-pale-blue canes. 3″ (7.6 cm.) diam.

☐ Saint Louis; acquired Nov., 1938.

11. Saint Louis. Mid-19th century. Concentric millefiori weight with 5 circles of millefiori canes in blue, white, green, pink, and dark green. The letters "SL" appear in a white cane. Center is large, opaque white, serrated rod containing blue flower, stem, and leaves. The outer circle of canes (green exterior and opaque white interior) extends, following curve of weight, to center of flat base. 3 3/16″ (8.1 cm.) diam.

☐ Saint Louis; acquired May, 1936.
(Illus. 5, Bergstrom book.)

269. Saint Louis. Mid-19th century. Ocher-colored single large dahlia has brown-striped petals surrounding white central floret with red center. Tips of 5 green leaves are visible at periphery. Colorless base. A 24-pointed star is cut on the underside. 2⅞″ (7.3 cm.) diam.

☐ Saint Louis; acquired Aug., 1939.

481. Saint Louis. Mid-19th century. Floating flat spray of 5 stylized flower heads made up of varicolored rods is set on 6 curled and serrated leaves, the stems ending in a point. Circle of pink and green canes is at periphery. Flat, amber-flashed underside has strawberry cutting. 3 1/16″ (7.8 cm.) diam.

☐ Saint Louis; acquired Feb., 1942.

137. French. Spray of dark gentian-blue flowers has 2 in full bloom and 3 partly opened. Centers are opaque yellow dots on green. Motif also includes 5 pale green leaves and 3 stems, one crossing the other two. White latticinio ground over colorless base. (Centers of flowers are similar to centers in weight 136, Plate 27. Mrs. Bergstrom purchased both from same source and at same time. There is also a similarity to the center of the white flower in the salamander weight 230, Plate 21.) 2 13/16″ (7.2 cm.) diam.

☐ Unidentified; acquired Aug., 1938.
(Plate #53, Jokelson, *One Hundred of the Most Important Paperweights*.)

45. Saint Louis. Mid-19th century. Coral pink clematis with deeper pink stripes on petals and a center of opaque yellow is set on spray of 4 green leaves and stem, which ends in a point. White latticinio ground over colorless base. 2⅛″ (5.4 cm.) diam.

☐ Unidentified; acquired Aug., 1937.

81. Saint Louis. Mid-19th century. Large pink dahlia has 42 striped and pointed petals. Tips of 6 green leaves are visible at periphery. Serrated, ocher-colored central cane has blue center. Colorless base. A 24-pointed star is cut on the underside. 2 15/16″ (7.4 cm.) diam.

☐ Unidentified; acquired Sept., 1937.

22A. Saint Louis. Mid-19th century. Pink dahlia with striped, pointed petals has pink-and-white serrated cane center. Five green leaves surround flower. Colorless base. A 24-pointed star is cut on the underside. 2¼″ (5.7 cm.) diam.

☐ Unrecorded.

Plate 24

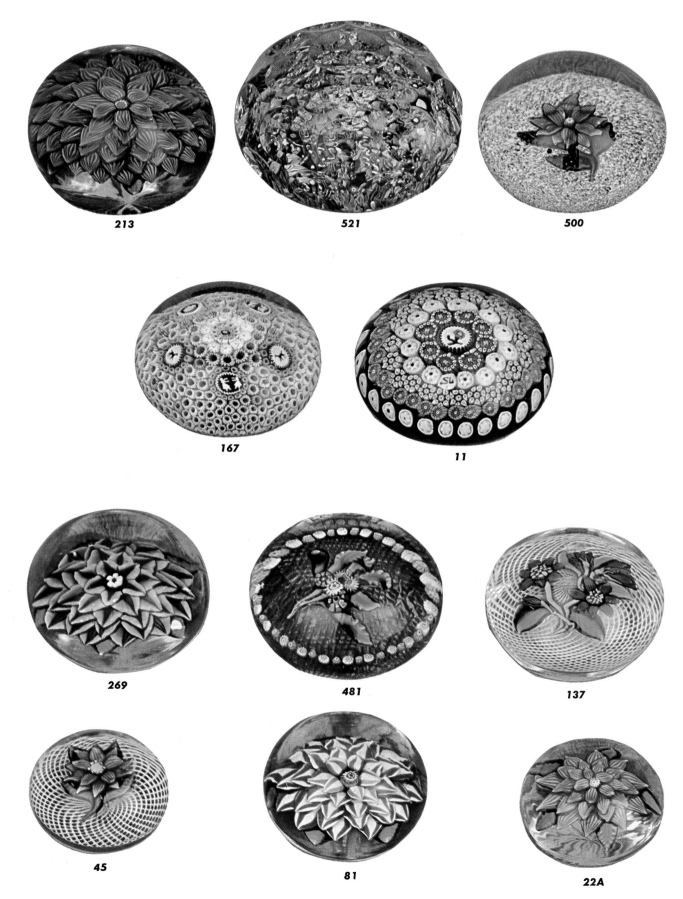

213

521

500

167

11

269

481

137

45

81

22A

Plate 25

229. Saint Louis. Dated 1845. Trumpet-shaped paper-weight vase of colorless glass has 10 vertical flutes on exterior above the small spherical base of the bowl, which is diamond cut. Rim edge is cobalt blue over opaque white. An applied colorless paperweight base encloses close mille-fiori motif of predominantly pink and blue canes, and one cane with "SL 1845" in reverse. 2 1/16" (5.3 cm.) diam. of base; 5¾" (14.6 cm.) overall height.

□ Saint Louis; acquired May, 1939.
(#14, p. 41, 1940 Bergstrom book; p. 42, later editions.)

222. French, probably Saint Louis. Mid-19th century. Glass bowl and cover have overall honeycomb faceting with gold vermiculation design; gilt band appears at rim and on protruding base of bowl. On obverse is translucent white oblong medallion in relief on which 2 birds on branches are painted in soft colors. Colorless, faceted, spherical finial encloses upright bouquet of 3 flowers (red, white, and blue), 2 florets, and green leaves. Colorless base. A 32-pointed star is cut on the underside. 4½" (11.4 cm.) diam.; 5⅝" (14.3 cm.) overall height.

□ Baccarat; acquired Feb., 1939.
(#10, p. 41, 1940 Bergstrom book; p. 42, later editions.)

227. Saint Louis. Mid-19th century. Colorless glass vase with concentric millefiori paperweight base. Conical-form vase, flaring to 4¼" (10.8 cm.) diam. at rim, is decorated with a 2" (5.1 cm.) band of white filigree thread swirls; both rim and base of bowl are bordered by salmon-pink-and-white ribbon twist. The 6-sided clear stem is waisted and faceted. Paperweight base encloses 7 concentric circles of millefiori canes, predominantly blue, green, and white, encircling a large red serrated central cane. Outer circle of canes (salmon-pink exterior) is drawn to the center of flat base. 6⅝" (16.8 cm.) overall height.

□ Saint Louis; acquired May, 1939.
(#9, p. 41, 1940 Bergstrom book; p. 42, later editions.)

118. Saint Louis. Mid-19th century. Colorless glass vase, bell-shaped, with candy-type paperweight base. Lower half of bowl is 11-sided; upper half has circular engraving of flowers and leaves; circular groove cuts appear between the halves. Applied at rim is an encased cobalt blue strand coiled around a white filigree flat twist. Varied canes, ribbons, and filigree strands are assembled at random in paperweight base. 2¾" (7.0 cm.) diam. of base; 5¾" (14.6 cm.) overall height. □ Baccarat; acquired April, 1938.
(#16, p. 41, 1940 Bergstrom book; p. 42, later editions.)

569. Saint Louis. Mid-19th century. Pink over white double overlay. Upright bouquet consists of a central rose-colored flower with grooved petals and cane center, and 2 blue, 2 white, and 2 ocher-colored flowers each with bubble center. Bouquet is surrounded by green foliage. Overlay, cut with punty on top and 6 punties on upper curve, is further

encased in colorless glass. A small 24-pointed star is cut on the underside. 3⅛" (7.9 cm.) diam.

□ Unrecorded.

155. Saint Louis. Mid-19th century. Lady's hand cooler, egg-shaped, blown, and ribbed. Spiraled white filigree threads alternate with red-and-white ribbon twists edged in white. 2⅞" (7.3 cm.) long; 2" (5.1 cm.) diam.

□ Saint Louis; acquired Oct., 1938.
(Illus. 22, Bergstrom book.)

257. Saint Louis. Mid-19th century. Lady's hand cooler, egg-shaped and 10-sided (rectangular facets). Colorless glass encloses joined upright bouquets, one facing upward, the other downward, of red, white, and blue single flowers among green leaves. Flat top and bottom. 1 15/16" (4.9 cm.) diam.; 2 5/16" (5.8 cm.) height.

□ Baccarat; acquired Sept., 1939.
(Illus. 22, Bergstrom book.)

206. Saint Louis. Last half 19th century. Patterned mille-fiori weight. Blue and white alternating with red and white jasper ground is divided by 8 segments of opaque white cable radiating from large central devil-silhouette cane. Between cables and near center are individual large varicolored canes. A layer of green and white jasper ground lines the underside of design. At periphery, visible only from sides, is rose ribbon twist around which are coiled strands of white filigree. Colorless base. 3 3/16" (8.1 cm.) diam.

□ Saint Louis; acquired Feb., 1939.

306. French, probably Saint Louis. Mid-19th century. Colorless glass doorknob with flat top encloses a single lemon or lime, yellow shading to green, with yellow stem and 2 green leaves. White latticinio ground. 2" (5.1 cm.) diam. □ Unidentified; acquired March, 1940.

648. Saint Louis. Mid-19th century. Stylized flower spray consists of 4 millefiori canes set on 5 green leaves, and a stem. White muslin ground extends to encasing glass at bottom of weight. Circle of canes, alternating chartreuse and blue, is at periphery. 2⅞" (7.3 cm.) diam.

Gift of Mrs. Gordon Mahlke in memory of her mother, Mrs. William A. Hall, 1959.

448. Saint Louis. Mid-19th century. Carpet ground is made up of opaque white, serrated, millefiori canes with red-white-and-blue interiors. Central motif is a single pink-and-blue cane encircled by small green rods. Punty on top, 3 circles of smaller punties on curve. 2 11/16" (6.8 cm.) diam.

□ Saint Louis; acquired Sept., 1941.

187. Saint Louis. Mid-19th century. Colorless glass door-knob encloses red fuchsia flower with blue center, a pink stem, purple stalk, 4 green leaves, and 2 red buds. White latticinio ground. 2 13/16" (7.2 cm.) diam.

□ Unidentified; acquired June, 1939.

Plate 25

229

222

227

118

569

155

257

206

306

648

448

187

Plate 26

519. Saint Louis. Mid-19th century. Small, transparent ruby glass vase with waisted form is joined to paperweight base by collar of colorless glass. Encased white filigree twist is applied to the slightly flared rim of the vase. Base encloses spaced millefiori canes on white muslin ground— large serrated center cane surrounded by 5 red-white-and-green spaced canes. Circle of blue alternating with chartreuse canes is at periphery. 2″ (5.1 cm.) diam. of base; 5″ (12.6 cm.) overall height.

☐ Saint Louis; acquired April, 1943.

609. Saint Louis. 1840–50. Cylindrical, colorless glass vase has narrow neck, flared rim. Spiral design from base to rim is of red-over-opaque white cane alternating with white filigree threads. Exterior is finely ribbed horizontally. 2⅛″ (5.4 cm.) diam.; 4⁵⁄₁₆″ (10.9 cm.) height.

☐ Unrecorded.

307. Saint Louis. 1840–50. Colorless glass scent bottle with stopper has long tapering neck. White filigree strands swirl from base to top of neck, becoming finer toward top. Applied red, white, and opaque blue glass twist encircles bottle at shoulder and at rim. Steeple stopper encloses same white filigree swirl and colored twist. 7¼″ (18.4 cm.) overall height.

☐ Saint Louis; acquired March, 1940.
(#1, p. 41, 1940 Bergstrom book; p. 42, subsequent editions.)

520. Saint Louis. 1845–50. Colorless glass, ovoid scent bottle has ball-shaped stopper and macédoine paperweight base. Base contains variety of canes, ribbon twists, and white filigree twists arranged at random. White filigree thread spiral extends from bottle base to rim, which is edged in dark blue. Stopper has same thread spiral. 2″ (5.1 cm.) diam. of base; 5½″ (13.9 cm.) overall height.

☐ Baccarat; acquired April, 1943.

566. Saint Louis. 1845–50. Colorless glass wafer tray with macédoine paperweight base containing canes, ribbons, and filigree twists assembled at random. At rim of tray is an applied red and white filigree spiral. 3⅛″ (7.9 cm.) diam. at rim of tray; 3″ (7.6 cm.) overall height.

☐ Baccarat; no date of acquisition.
(#15, p. 41, 1940 Bergstrom book; p. 42, subsequent editions.)

611. Saint Louis. 1845–50. Shot glass (used to hold buckshot or sand for cleaning quill pens) is in waisted form and is decorated with spiral of cobalt blue canes alternating with white filigree threads; exterior is finely ribbed horizontally. A double, colorless glass collar separates the shot glass and the paperweight base, which contains millefiori motif that includes a central blue-and-white cane surrounded by 5 spaced salmon-pink canes. Circle of yellow canes alter-

nating with dark blue is at periphery of base. 1¾″ (4.5 cm.) diam. of base; 3⁷⁄₁₆″ (8.7 cm.) overall height.

☐ Unrecorded.

271. Saint Louis. 1845–50. Bell-shaped shot glass with crown paperweight base. The base encloses white filigree rods alternating with red-and-green twisted ribbons (white edges) and yellow, flecked with green (white edges) twisted ribbons, all radiating from central large floret. Colorless glass collar joins base and shot glass, which is decorated with spiral of white filigree threads and pink ribbon strands. Exterior is finely ribbed horizontally. 1¾″ (4.5 cm.) diam.; 3½″ (8.9 cm.) overall height.

☐ Saint Louis; acquired Oct., 1939.
(#4, p. 41, 1940 Bergstrom book; p. 42, subsequent editions.)

314. Saint Louis. Stemless, colorless, bucket-form wineglass. Base encloses 4 concentric circles of green, brown, dark red, and white canes; outer circle is drawn to center of the underside, which is flat. 2³⁄₁₆″ (5.5 cm.) diam. at rim; 2⅜″ (6.1 cm.) height.

☐ Saint Louis; acquired April, 1940.
(#6, p. 41, 1940 Bergstrom book; p. 42, subsequent editions.)

313. Saint Louis. Stemless, colorless wineglass in bucket form. Base encloses 3 concentric circles of millefiori canes: ocher-color, opaque white with dark blue swan silhouette, and green with opaque white solid centers. Outside circle (ocher) is drawn to the center of the flat underside. 2¼″ (5.7 cm.) diam. at rim; 2⅛″ (5.4 cm.) height.

☐ Saint Louis; acquired April, 1940.

315. Saint Louis. Stemless, colorless wineglass in bucket form. Base encloses 4 concentric circles of millefiori canes, dark blue predominating, around central white floret. Outer circle is drawn to center of the flat underside. 2⅛″ (5.4 cm.) diam. at rim; 2¼″ (5.7 cm.) height.

☐ Saint Louis; acquired April, 1940.

311. Saint Louis. Stemless, colorless wineglass in bucket form. Base encloses 3 concentric circles of pale-colored millefiori canes around central cane. Outer circle (lavender) is drawn to center of the flat underside. 2¼″ (5.7 cm.) diam. at rim; 2¼″ (5.7 cm.) height.

☐ Saint Louis; acquired April, 1940.

312. Saint Louis. Stemless, colorless wineglass in bucket form. Base encloses 3 concentric circles of white, blue, and red millefiori canes around center group of varicolored canes. Blue canes in outer circle are drawn to center of the flat underside. 2⁵⁄₁₆″ (5.8 cm.) diam. at rim; 2¼″ (5.7 cm.) height.

☐ Saint Louis; acquired April, 1940.

Plate 26

519   609   307   520

566   611   271   314

313   315   311   312

Plate 27

112. Saint Louis. Dated 1848. Six concentric circles of millefiori canes surround a center silhouette cane of a dancing couple. Circle nearest center is imp or devil canes. "SL" and date "1848" appear near periphery. Canes in outer circle, flattened cobalt blue with white centers, are drawn, following contour of weight, to center of base. 3⅛" (7.9 cm.) diam.

☐ Saint Louis; acquired Feb., 1939.

(Plate III, Bergstrom book.)

136. French. Two flowers, raised, with opaque white pointed petals and thin stems, 4 green raised leaves, and a white bud make up the motif. Centers of flowers are opaque yellow spots over green. White latticinio ground; colorless base. The flower centers are similar to those of 137 in Plate 24; the petals, similar to white flower petals in the salamander weight, 230 in Plate 21. 3¼" (8.3 cm.) diam.

☐ French; acquired Aug., 1938.

(Illus. 30, Bergstrom book. Plate 29, Jokelson, *One Hundred of the Most Important Paperweights,* identifies weight as Clichy.)

425. Saint Louis. Mid-19th century. Millefiori mushroom weight. Five concentric circles of green, blue, and white millefiori canes surround a center group of small blue and green rods. Outer circle is powder-blue canes drawn down to point at base to form tuft. Torsade consists of twisted, opaque white, flat strands around which is coiled a deep blue strand. Colorless base. A small 24-pointed star is cut on the underside. 3ⁱ⁄₁₆" (7.8 cm.) diam.

☐ Baccarat; acquired Aug., 1941.

153. Saint Louis. Dated 1848. Millefiori mushroom weight with 6 concentric circles of white, blue, and green canes. Outer circle of canes with green exterior is drawn down to point at base to form tuft. "SL 1848" appears in black cane at periphery. Torsade is made of flattened, twisted, white filigree threads around which is coiled salmon-pink strand. Colorless base. A small, 16-pointed star is cut on the underside. 3ⁱ⁄₁₆" (7.8 cm.) diam.

☐ St. Louis; acquired Oct., 1938.

(Plate II, Bergstrom book.)

133. Saint Louis. Dated 1848. Millefiori mushroom weight. Four concentric circles of white, blue, green, and ocher-colored millefiori canes surround a center grouping of small, hollow, blue and white rods. In the outside circle, serrated canes with opaque white exterior are drawn to a point at base to form tuft. "SL 1848" appears in black cane at periphery. Torsade is of twisted flat white filigree threads around which is coiled a dark blue strand. Colorless base. A small, 24-pointed star is cut on the underside. 2¹⁵⁄₁₆" (7.4 cm.) diam.

☐ Saint Louis; acquired June, 1938.

134. Saint Louis. Mid-19th century. Carpet ground weight

has, as central motif, a small sulphide bust of Empress Josephine, profile to sinister, after Apsley Pellatt, set in large hollow cane lined with dark red. Concentric circles of hollow canes surround the sulphide, arranged in 3 red and 3 blue sections (alternating), with lines of white canes placed radially to separate the sections. Outer circle of canes is drawn to center of base, following contour of weight. 2¹³⁄₁₆" (7.2 cm.) diam. (See Hollister, p. 98.)

☐ Saint Louis; acquired June, 1938.

(Plate X, Bergstrom book.)

385. Saint Louis. Mid-19th century. Red and blue fuchsia flower with thin pink stem and stamens, a large red bud, 2 smaller red buds, and 4 green leaves on sturdy orange stalk are arranged against white latticinio ground over colorless base. 2⅞" (7.3 cm.) diam.

☐ French; acquired Dec., 1940.

456. Saint Louis. Dated 1848. Concentric millefiori motif. Six circles of closely packed, pastel-colored millefiori canes surround the central "imp" silhouette cane. "SL 1848" appears in a black cane near periphery. Outer circle of serrated white canes with blue centers alternating with canes with green centers is drawn to center of base, following contour of weight. 2⅝" (6.6 cm.) diam.

☐ Saint Louis; acquired Oct., 1941.

252. Origin unknown, probably French. Full-blown, lemon-yellow rose, raised, with bud, 5 green leaves, and stem is set on translucent cobalt blue ground over colorless base. High clear crown. Pinprick bubbles appear on motif and ground. Underside slightly concave. 3" (7.6 cm.) diam.

☐ Unknown, made *ca.* 1840 and possibly at Pantin factory, Saint Gobain, or Lyons; acquired Sept., 1939. (Plate XVII, Bergstrom book.) (Ex collection of the Marquis de Bailleul, Château d'Angerville.)

404. Saint Louis. Last half 19th century. Stylized flower bouquet. Floating, flat flower arrangement consists of vari-colored florets, the 11 millefiori canes drawn down into an opaque white flowerpot with handles. Colorless base. Red and white filigree spiral twist at periphery, near surface of weight, visible only from the sides. 2¹³⁄₁₆" (7.2 cm.) diam.

☐ Baccarat; acquired May, 1941.

205. Saint Louis. 1845–60. Lady's hand cooler is an egg-shaped millefiori of varicolored canes. The colorless encasing glass is thicker at one end than at the other. 2⅞" (7.3 cm.) length; 2³⁄₁₆" (5.5 cm.) diam.

☐ Saint Louis; acquired Feb., 1939.

(Illus. 22, Bergstrom book.)

296. Origin unknown; probably French. Flat spray of opaque white lily of the valley with thin stem and 2 large green leaves floats in colorless glass. 2¾" (7.0 cm.) diam.

☐ Unidentified; acquired Jan., 1940.

Plate 27

112

136

425

153

133

134

385

456

252

404

205

296

Plate 28

217. Saint Louis. Mid-19th century. Floating flat motif of 6 varicolored flowers and green leaves forms a wreath around center blue flower. Each flower has cane center. Large punty on top. Possibly this weight served as a wafer tray. Honeycomb faceting on curve. Colorless concave base. 2⅞" (7.3 cm.) diam.

☐   Saint Louis; acquired Feb., 1939.

358. Saint Louis. Mid-19th century. Upright bouquet, in colorless high-crowned weight, consists of a cobalt blue center flower and a white flower, both with bubble centers, as well as a red bud and 4 florets, all set on green leaves. Torsade at base is flat, twisted white filigree strands about which is coiled a salmon-pink strand. Colorless base. A small 24-pointed star is cut on the underside. 3¼" (8.3 cm.) diam.

☐   Saint Louis; acquired Aug., 1940.

265. Saint Louis. Mid-19th century. Millefiori mushroom motif with 4 concentric circles of varicolored canes. Center is a hollow white rod with red lining and green stamen center. Canes of outer circle (white star exterior) are drawn to amber-flashed base to form tuft. Punty on top and 6 punties on curve. 3¼" (8.3 cm.) diam.

☐   Saint Louis; acquired Sept., 1939.

214. Saint Louis. Mid-19th century. Millefiori mushroom motif. Four concentric circles of pink, blue, white, and green canes surround hollow central floret. Outer circle of serrated canes with green exterior is drawn to base to form tuft. Base is slightly concave. Underside is amber-flashed. Punty on top and 6 punties on curve. 2⅞" (7.3 cm.) diam.

☐   Saint Louis; acquired Feb., 1939.

166. Origin unknown, possibly Saint Louis. Fruit weight. Two clusters of cranberries, 3 large green leaves, and a sturdy brown stem float near the colorless base. High crown. 3⅛" (7.9 cm.) diam.

☐   Unidentified; acquired Oct., 1938.

122. Saint Louis. Mid-19th century. Millefiori mushroom motif. Three concentric circles of white, blue, and ocher canes surround a center grouping of blue and green smaller rods. Outer circle of white serrated canes is drawn to a point at base to form tuft. Tubular torsade (no core) is a spiral of white filigree and dark blue strand. Punty on top and 6 punties on curve. Colorless base. A small 24-pointed star is cut on the underside. 3" (7.6 cm.) diam.

☐   Clichy; acquired May, 1938.

477. Saint Louis. Mid-19th century. Millefiori mushroom motif. Five concentric circles of green, white, and varicolored millefiori canes surround a center grouping of smaller rods. Outer circle of serrated canes, white alter-

nating with pale chartreuse, is drawn down to a point to form tuft. Torsade is a cobalt blue strand coiled around a flat twist of opaque white strands. Colorless base. A small 24-pointed star is cut on the underside. 2¹¹⁄₁₆" (6.8 cm.) diam.

☐   Saint Louis; acquired Jan., 1942.

194. Saint Louis. Mid-19th century. Patterned millefiori motif. Five silhouette canes, including dancing girl, dog, and devil, are spaced in circle on carpet ground of white, hollow, serrated rods with pink interiors. Center cane is bundle of small rods in pink, blue, and white. Each silhouette cane and the center cane are encircled by hollow green rods. Punty on top and 5 punties on upper curve. 2⅝" (6.6 cm.) diam.

☐   Saint Louis; acquired Jan., 1939.

469. Saint Louis. Mid-19th century. Millefiori mushroom motif. Three concentric circles of red, cobalt blue, and white canes surround a large white, serrated, hollow central rod lined with cobalt blue, which encloses 4 small red-and-white florets. Outer circle of white canes with pale green centers is pulled down to a point at base to form tuft. Torsade is ocher-colored strand coiled around a flat twist of opaque white strands. Colorless base. A small 24-pointed star is cut on the underside. 2¹³⁄₁₆" (7.2 cm.) diam.

☐   Saint Louis; acquired Dec., 1941.

455. Clichy. Mid-19th century. Colorless glass encloses a single cane, not reduced in size, which rests on base. The hollow cane, dark red with wavy opaque white circle near periphery and opaque white lining, encloses a group of 7 small blue and green whorl rods. Punty on top and 4 punties on curve. 2⅛" (5.4 cm.) diam.

☐   Saint Louis; acquired Oct., 1941.

135. Saint Louis. Dated 1848. Patterned millefiori on unusual "assorted" carpet ground. Central grouping is concentric circles of small hollow green and white canes, and the typical Saint Louis cane of buff-colored cog with blue center. Four silhouette canes and 4 varicolored "bundled" canes are spaced in a circle among the closely set, serrated hollow canes of various colors. "1848" with "SL" above it appears in a black cane. 2⁹⁄₁₆" (6.5 cm.) diam.

☐   Saint Louis; acquired Aug., 1938.

182. Saint Louis. Dated 1848. Concentric millefiori. Four concentric circles of varicolored canes surround a central group of small red-and-white rods. Outer circle of chartreuse-color canes with blue centers extends, following curve of weight, to center of base. "SL 1848" appears in black cane at periphery. 2¹⁄₁₆" (5.3 cm.) diam.

☐   Saint Louis; acquired Dec., 1938.

Plate 28

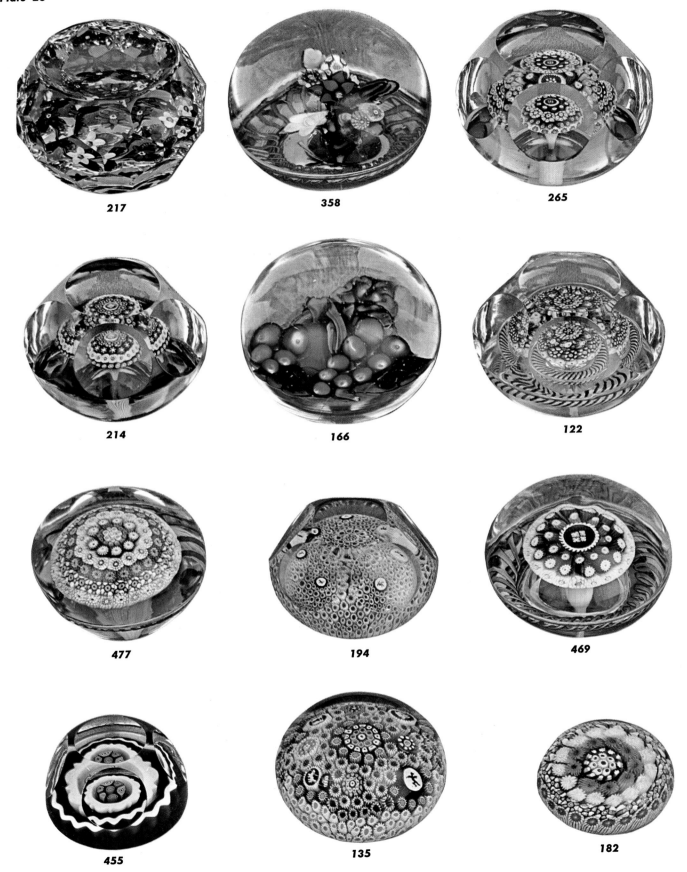

217

358

265

214

166

122

477

194

469

455

135

182

Plate 29

683. Baccarat. 1955–63. Zodiac series. Sulphide portraying "Leo" (July 24–August 23) is set on translucent cobalt blue base. Punty on top; 6 punties on curve. Baccarat insignia is etched on underside. 2¾" (7.0 cm.) diam.

Gift of Mr. and Mrs. Ralph S. Johns, 1963.

678. Baccarat. 1955–63. Zodiac series. Sulphide portraying "Pisces" (February 20–March 20). Punty on top; 6 punties on curve. Flanged base. Underside is cut in waffle-like squares and flashed with cobalt blue. The Baccarat insignia is etched on the curve near base. 2¾" (7.0 cm.) diam.

Gift of Mr. and Mrs. Ralph S. Johns, 1963.

679. Baccarat. Dated 1955. Zodiac series. Sulphide portraying "Aries" (March 21–April 20) rests on translucent cobalt blue base. Punty on top; 6 punties on curve. "Baccarat 1955" is etched on beveled edge of base. 2⅞" (7.3 cm.) diam.

Gift of Mr. and Mrs. Ralph S. Johns, 1963.

684. Baccarat. Dated 1955. Zodiac series. Sulphide portraying "Virgo" (August 24–September 23) is set on powder blue base. Punty on top; 6 punties on curve. "Baccarat 1955" is etched on beveled edge of base. 2¾" (7.0 cm.) diam.

Gift of Mr. and Mrs. Ralph S. Johns, 1963.

680. Baccarat. 1955–63. Zodiac series. Sulphide portraying "Taurus" (April 21–May 21) rests on translucent cobalt blue, flanged base. Punty on top and 6 punties on curve. Baccarat insignia is etched on underside. 2¹³⁄₁₆" (7.2 cm.) diam.

Gift of Mr. and Mrs. Ralph S. Johns, 1963.

686. Baccarat. Dated 1955. Zodiac series. Sulphide portraying "Scorpio" (October 24–November 22) is set on powder blue base. Punty on top; 6 punties on curve; horizontal miter cut between alternate punties at sides.

Flanged base. "B 1955" is etched near base. 2¾" (7.0 cm.) diam.

Gift of Mr. and Mrs. Ralph S. Johns, 1963.

677. Baccarat. 1955–63. Zodiac series. Sulphide portraying "Aquarius" (January 21–February 19) rests on translucent cobalt blue, flanged base. Punty on top, 6 punties on curve. Baccarat insignia is etched on underside. 2¾" (7.0 cm.) diam.

Gift of Mr. and Mrs. Ralph S. Johns, 1963.

682. Baccarat. Dated 1955. Zodiac series. Sulphide portraying "Cancer" (June 22–July 23) is set on powder blue, flanged base. Punty on top; 6 punties on curve. "B 1955" is etched on curve near base. 2¾" (7.0 cm.) diam.

Gift of Mr. and Mrs. Ralph S. Johns, 1963.

681. Baccarat. 1955–63. Zodiac series. Sulphide portraying "Gemini" (May 22–June 21) rests on translucent cobalt blue, flanged base. Punty on top; 6 punties on curve. Baccarat insignia is etched on underside. 2¹³⁄₁₆" (7.2 cm.) diam.

Gift of Mr. and Mrs. Ralph S. Johns, 1963.

685. Baccarat. Dated 1955. Zodiac series. Sulphide portraying "Libra" (September 24–October 23) is set on powder blue ground. Punty on top; 6 punties on curve. "Baccarat 1955" is etched on rim of base. 2¾" (7.0 cm.) diam.

Gift of Mr. and Mrs. Ralph S. Johns, 1963.

687. Baccarat. Dated 1955. Zodiac series. Sulphide portraying "Sagittarius" (November 23–December 21) is set on powder blue, flanged base. Punty on top; 6 punties on curve. "B 1955" is etched near base. 2¾" (7.0 cm.) diam.

Gift of Mr. and Mrs. Ralph S. Johns, 1963.

688. Baccarat. 1955. Zodiac series. Sulphide portraying "Capricorn" (December 22–January 20) rests on powder blue base. Punty on top; 6 punties on curve. 2⅝" (6.6 cm.) diam.

Gift of Mr. and Mrs. Ralph S. Johns, 1963.

Plate 29

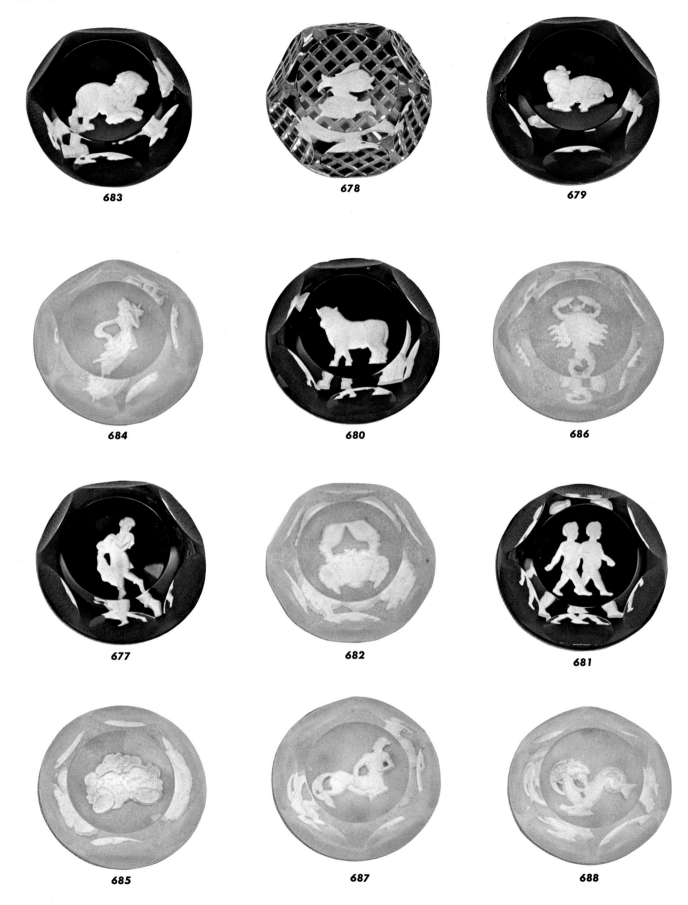

683

678

679

684

680

686

677

682

681

685

687

688

Plate 30

652. Baccarat. Dated 1955. Double overlay is royal blue over opaque white. Sulphide portrait, profile to dexter, is of Winston Churchill. "Mar 1953" appears on sulphide. Overlay is cut with punty on top and 5 punties on curve. "Baccarat 1955" is etched on beveled edge of colorless base. Underside is crosscut. 3⅛" (7.9 cm.) diam.

Gift of Mr. and Mrs. Ralph S. Johns, 1962.

663. Baccarat. Dated 1954. Sulphide bust portrait of George Washington, front view slightly to dexter. "G.P. 1953" appears on the sulphide, which rests on translucent cobalt blue base. Punty on top; 6 punties on curve. "Baccarat 1954" is etched on beveled edge of base. 2¾" (7.0 cm.) diam.

Gift of Mr. and Mrs. Ralph S. Johns, 1962.

657. Baccarat. Dated 1954. Blue over opaque white overlay. "G.P. 1953" appears on the sulphide portrait of George Washington, front view slightly to dexter. Overlay is cut with punty on top, 5 punties on curve, between which are vertical, boat-shaped cuttings. Colorless base. Underside is crosscut. "Baccarat 1954" is etched on beveled edge of base. 3⅛" (7.9 cm.) diam.

Gift of Mr. and Mrs. Ralph S. Johns, 1962.

715. Baccarat. 1963. Sulphide bust portrait, slightly to sinister, of John Fitzgerald Kennedy. "A. David 63" appears on the sulphide, which rests on translucent dark red, flanged base. Punty on top; 5 punties on curve. Baccarat insignia is etched on the underside. 2¾" (7.0 cm.) diam.

Acquired 1964.

724. Baccarat. 1964. Cobalt blue over opaque white overlay. Sulphide bust portrait is of John Fitzgerald Kennedy, slightly to sinister. "A. David 63" appears on the sulphide, which rests on translucent dark red, slightly footed base. Overlay is cut with punty on top, 5 punties on curve. Baccarat insignia is etched on underside. 3⅛" (7.9 cm.) diam.

Gift of Mr. and Mrs. Walter Gray, 1965.

667. Baccarat. Dated 1954. Sulphide portrait, profile to dexter, of Winston Churchill. "Mar 1953" appears on the sulphide, which rests on a colorless base. The underside is cut in waffle-like squares and flashed with ruby glass. Punty on top; 6 punties on curve. "B 1954" is etched near base. 2¾" (7.0 cm.) diam.

Gift of Mr. and Mrs. Ralph S. Johns, 1962.

595. Baccarat. 1953. "G. Poillerat" appears on sulphide double portrait of Queen Elizabeth II and Prince Philip, profiles to dexter. Punty on top, 5 punties on curve. Colorless base. Underside is diamond cut. 2⅝" (6.6 cm.) diam.

☐ Unrecorded.

592. Baccarat. Dated 1953. "G. Poillerat" appears on the sulphide double portrait of Queen Elizabeth II and Prince Philip, profiles to dexter, which is enclosed in colorless glass. Double overlay is blue over opaque white, cut with punty on top, 5 punties on curve, and narrow oval cuttings between the punties. "Baccarat 1953" is etched on beveled edge of the colorless base. Underside is diamond cut. 3⅛" (7.9 cm.) diam.

☐ Unrecorded.

603. Baccarat. Dated 1953. Sulphide double portrait, profiles to dexter, of Queen Elizabeth II and Prince Philip. "G. Poillerat" appears on the sulphide, which rests on translucent cobalt blue base. Punty on top, 6 punties on curve. "Baccarat 1953" is etched on rim of flat base. 2⅝" (6.6 cm.) diam.

☐ Unrecorded.

656. Baccarat. Dated 1954. Double overlay is blue over opaque white. Sulphide bust portrait, front view slightly to sinister, is of Abraham Lincoln. "G.P. 1953" appears on the sulphide. Overlay is cut with large punty on top, 5 punties on curve, between which are narrow, vertical boat-shaped facets. "Baccarat 1954" is etched on the beveled edge of the colorless base. Underside is crosscut. 3⅛" (7.9 cm.) diam.

Gift of Mr. and Mrs. Ralph S. Johns, 1962.

662. Baccarat. Dated 1954. Sulphide bust portrait of Abraham Lincoln, front view slightly to sinister. "G.P. 1953" appears on the sulphide, which rests on translucent amethyst base with a cloudy appearance. Punty on top, 6 punties on curve. "Baccarat 1954" is etched on rim of base. 2⅝" (6.6 cm.) diam.

Gift of Mr. and Mrs. Ralph S. Johns, 1962.

Plate 30

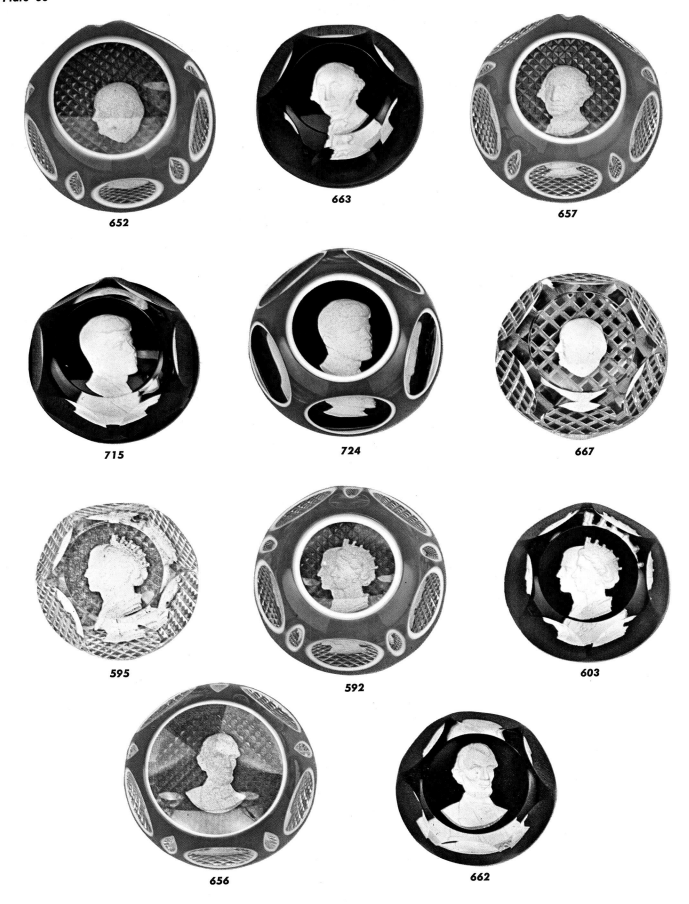

652

663

657

715

724

667

595

592

603

656

662

Plate 31

602. Baccarat. Dated 1953. Sulphide portrait of Dwight Eisenhower, profile to dexter, rests on translucent cobalt base. "547" appears on the sulphide. Punty on top, 5 punties on curve. "Baccarat 1953" is etched on the beveled edge of base. 2¾" (7.0 cm.) diam.

☐ Unrecorded.

650. Baccarat. 1953–59. Double overlay, rose over opaque white. Sulphide portrait, profile to dexter, is of Dwight Eisenhower. Overlay is cut with punty on top, 5 punties on curve, narrow oval cuttings between punties. Colorless base. Underside is crosscut. 3⅛" (7.9 cm.) diam.

Gift of Mr. and Mrs. Ralph S. Johns, 1962.

661. Baccarat. Dated 1958. Sulphide bust portrait of Martin Luther, front view, slightly to sinister. "Luther 1483–1546 G.P. 1955" appears on the sulphide. Punty on top, 6 punties on curve. "Baccarat 1958" is etched on beveled edge of colorless base. Underside has waffle-like cut and is flashed with red. 2¾" (7.0 cm.) diam.

Gift of Mr. and Mrs. Ralph S. Johns, 1962.

658. Baccarat. Dated 1954. Double overlay is rose over opaque white. "G.P. 1953" appears on the sulphide portrait, profile to sinister, of Thomas Jefferson. Overlay is cut with large punty on top; 5 punties on curve with vertical boat-shaped cuttings between. "Baccarat 1954" is etched on the beveled edge of the colorless base. Underside is crosscut. 3⅛" (7.9 cm.) diam.

Gift of Mr. and Mrs. Ralph S. Johns, 1962.

664. Baccarat. Dated 1954. Sulphide portrait of Thomas Jefferson, profile to sinister (marked "G.P. 1953") rests on translucent cranberry base. Punty on top, 6 punties on curve. "Baccarat 1954" is etched on the beveled edge of the base. 2¹¹⁄₁₆" (6.8 cm.) diam.

Gift of Mr. and Mrs. Ralph S. Johns, 1962.

651. Baccarat. Dated 1957. Double overlay, green over opaque white. Sulphide bust portrait of Martin Luther, front view slightly to sinister, has "Martin Luther 1483–1546 G.P. 1955" imprinted on it. Overlay is cut with punty on top, 5 punties on curve. "Baccarat 1957" is etched on beveled edge of the colorless base. Underside is crosscut. 3⅛" (7.9 cm.) diam.

Gift of Mr. and Mrs. Ralph S. Johns, 1962.

666. Baccarat. 1955–59. Sulphide bust portrait of Lafayette, slightly to dexter (marked "B G.P. 1955"), rests on red and white jasper ground over colorless base. Punty on top, 6 punties on curve. 2¹¹⁄₁₆" (6.8 cm.) diam.

Gift of Mr. and Mrs. Ralph S. Johns, 1962.

653. Baccarat. 1955–59. Double overlay, pale blue over opaque white. Sulphide bust portrait of Lafayette, slightly to dexter (marked "B G.P. 1955"), rests on a colorless base. Overlay is cut with punty on top, 5 punties on curve. Underside is crosscut. 3⅛" (7.9 cm.) diam.

Gift of Mr. and Mrs. Ralph S. Johns, 1962.

668. Baccarat. Dated 1954. Sulphide portrait, profile to dexter, of Robert E. Lee (marked "B Mar 1954") rests on a colorless base with "Baccarat 1954" etched on the beveled edge. Punty on top, 6 punties on curve. The underside is crosscut. 2¾" (7.0 cm.) diam.

Gift of Mr. and Mrs. Ralph S. Johns, 1962.

655. Baccarat. 1960. Opaque white single overlay has punties outlined in gilt. Sulphide bust portrait is of Pope Pius XII, profile to dexter, and shows his hands. "A. David 1959" appears on the sulphide. The base, which protrudes about ¼" (.6 cm.), is slightly smaller in diameter than the weight. Underside is cut with a 32-pointed star and is flashed with ruby glass at edge. 3⅛" (7.9 cm.) diam.

Gift of Mr. and Mrs. Ralph S. Johns, 1962.

669. Baccarat. 1960. Sulphide bust portrait of Pope Pius XII, profile to dexter, showing his hands. "A. David 1959" appears on the sulphide, which rests on a colorless base. The underside, star cut and slightly concave, is flashed with ruby glass. One punty on top, 6 punties on curve. Baccarat insignia is etched on base. 2¹³⁄₁₆" (7.2 cm.) diam.

Acquired 1960.

659. Baccarat. Dated 1955. Double overlay, pale gray over opaque white. "B Mar 1954" appears on the sulphide portrait of Robert E. Lee, profile to dexter. Overlay is cut with punty on top, 5 punties on curve with vertical boat-shaped cuttings between. "Baccarat 1955" is etched on the beveled edge of the colorless base. Underside is crosscut. 3⅛" (7.9 cm.) diam.

Gift of Mr. and Mrs. Ralph S. Johns, 1962.

Plate 31

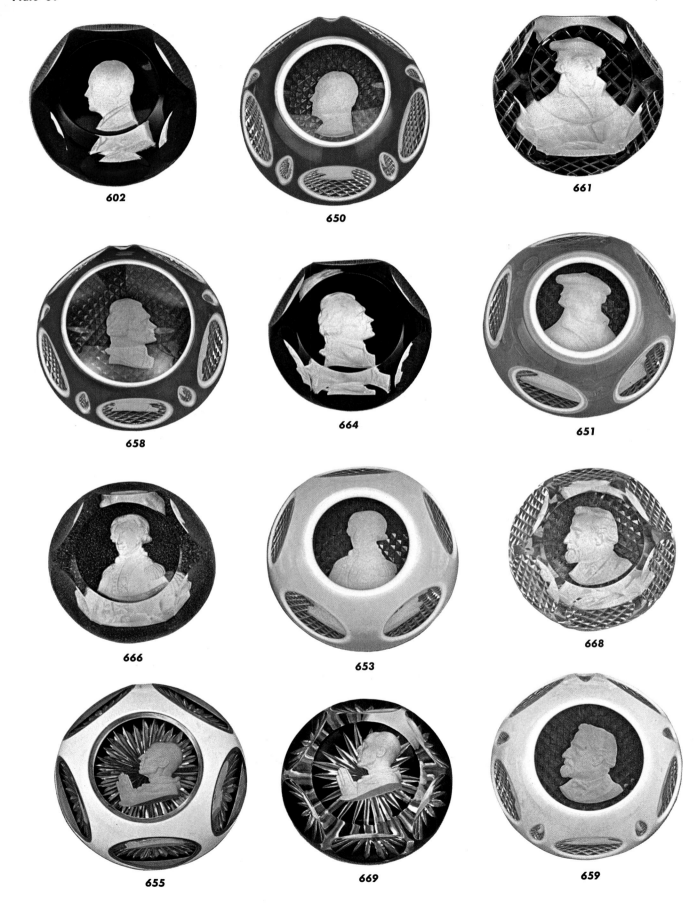

602

650

661

658

664

651

666

653

668

655

669

659

Plate 32

711. Saint Louis. Dated 1953. Double overlay is dark green over opaque white. Millefiori tuft consists of vari-colored canes, many hollow with star centers. "SL 1953" appears in a red cane. Overlay is cut with punty on top, 5 punties on curve. A small 24-pointed star is cut on the underside. 3⅛" (7.9 cm.) diam.

Gift of Mr. and Mrs. Ralph S. Johns, 1963.

710. Baccarat. 1958–63. Close millefiori, the canes of paler shades than in antique weights. The number 8 appears in one cane. High, clear crown. 2⅞" (7.3 cm.) diam.

Gift of Mr. and Mrs. Ralph S. Johns, 1963.

742. Baccarat. 1966–67. Yellow and white double overlay. Sulphide bust portrait of Pope John XXIII, profile to dexter, shows his right hand raised. "A. David Paris 1964" appears on the sulphide, which rests on transparent ruby red base slightly smaller than the weight; base protrudes about ¼" (.6 cm.). Top is faceted in 6-petaled rosette pattern; curve near base has 6 olive cuts. Baccarat insignia is etched on underside. 3⅛" (7.9 cm.) diam.

Acquired 1967.

725. Baccarat. 1966. Sulphide bust portrait of Pope John XXIII, profile to dexter, shows his right hand raised. "A. David Paris 1964" appears on the sulphide, which rests on translucent amber flanged base. Punty on top, 5 punties on curve. Baccarat insignia is etched on underside. 2¹³⁄₁₆" (7.2 cm.) diam.

Acquired 1966.

654. Baccarat. 1954–59. Opaque white single overlay has gold tracery. Sulphide portrait of Queen Elizabeth II, profile to dexter, is by Gilbert Poillerat, the initials "G.P." being barely visible. Punty on top, 5 punties on curve. Colorless base. Underside is crosscut. 3⅛" (7.9 cm.) diam.

Gift of Mr. and Mrs. Ralph S. Johns, 1962.

594. Saint Louis. 1953. Sulphide portrait of Queen Elizabeth II, profile to dexter, rests on opaque turquoise base. Circle of rose and green canes at periphery. Punty on top, 5 punties on curve. "Couronnement 2–6–53 Saint Louis—

France" is etched on underside in a circle. 2¾" (7.0 cm.) diam.

☐ Unrecorded

590. Baccarat. Dated 1953. Low-crowned, sulphide double portrait of Queen Elizabeth II and Prince Philip, profiles to dexter. "G. Poillerat" appears on the sulphide. Colorless base has "Baccarat 1953" etched on the beveled edge. Underside is fan cut. 2⅝" (6.6 cm.) diam.

☐ Unrecorded

593. Saint Louis. 1953. Sulphide portrait of Queen Elizabeth II, profile to dexter, rests on translucent ruby base. Circle of rose and white canes at periphery. Punty on top, 5 punties on curve. "Couronnement 2–6–53 Saint Louis—France" is etched on the underside in a circle. 2¾" (7.0 cm.) diam.

☐ Unrecorded.

665. Baccarat. Dated 1955. Sulphide bust portrait of Benjamin Franklin, profile to dexter, rests on a translucent cobalt blue, flanged base. "G.P. 1954" appears on the sulphide. Punty on top, 6 punties on curve. "B 1955" is etched near base. 2¹³⁄₁₆" (7.2 cm.) diam.

Gift of Mr. and Mrs. Ralph S. Johns, 1962.

660. Baccarat. Dated 1956. Transparent red single overlay. Sulphide bust portrait of Benjamin Franklin, profile to dexter. "G.P. 1954" appears on the sulphide. Overlay is cut with punty on top, 4 punties on curve. Between curve punties are 3 star cuts, one above the other. "Baccarat 1956" is etched on the beveled edge of the colorless base. Underside is cut with a 32-pointed star. 3⅛" (7.9 cm.) diam.

Gift of Mr. and Mrs. Ralph S. Johns, 1962.

733. Cristalleries d'Albret. 1966. Sulphide bust portrait of Christopher Columbus, front view slightly to dexter, after a sculpture by Georges Simon, rests on translucent cobalt blue ground. "Columbus G. S. 1966" is inscribed on the sulphide. Punty on top, 6 oval cuts on curve. 2¾" (7.0 cm.) diam.

Gift of Mr. Paul Jokelson, 1967.

Plate 32

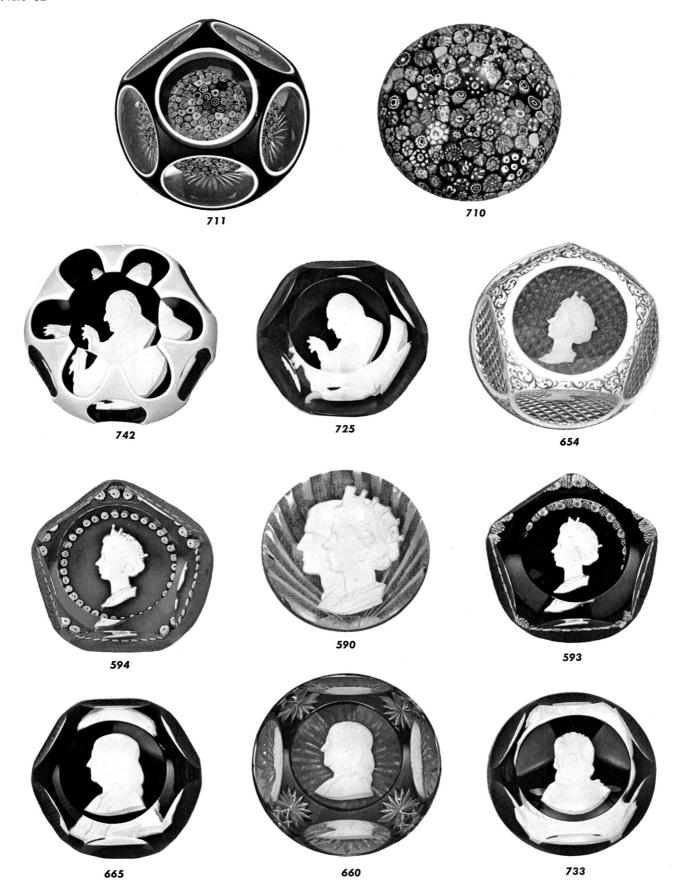

711

710

742

725

654

594

590

593

665

660

733

2

BRITISH AND EUROPEAN WEIGHTS

[France excepted]

When the paperweight researcher leaves France, problems of historical attribution, identification, and cataloguing become more complex. For example, it has already been mentioned that millefiori paperweights were exhibited in Vienna in 1845, made by the Venetian Pietro Bigaglia, but in spite of this early impetus Venice did not excel in the art of paperweight making in the antique period.

England more than the continental countries responded to reverberations of the paperweight explosion in France from 1845 to 1850, and the repeal of the glass excise duty in England in 1845 further stimulated both experimentation in paperweight techniques and an increase in the number of weights manufactured, for the release from this tax burden enabled British glassmakers to compete favorably with European production. Furthermore, many French-trained artisans found their way to Britain, bringing with them not only their craft but also examples of their work, and these examples—plus direct importation of finished weights from established French factories—inspired English craftsmen to perfect their art. The result was an output of paperweights in England rivaling the French artistry and quality. In particular, the work of the factory of George Bacchus and Sons in Birmingham is comparable to creations of the "big three" in France. As an example of how additional information clarifies problems of attribution, Mrs. Bergstrom did not know about this factory when she wrote her book, and two of the weights identified by her as Saint Louis and Clichy are now attributed to Bacchus.

Another prominent factory was the early Whitefriars glasshouse in London (it became Whitefriars Glass, Ltd., Wealdstone, Middlesex, in 1922), which in 1848 produced paperweights of predominantly millefiori technique in concentric design. Their work does not have the fineness of Bacchus products in construction or color, and so seems crude in comparison. Mrs. Bergstrom also attributed weights to Bristol, Nailsea, and Stourbridge, but it is not certain that any paperweights were made in these factories, though all are famous for their glassware.

As early as the 1830's green bottle-glass paperweights appeared in England, made by J. Kilner of Wakefield in Yorkshire; they could have been the first of all paperweights. Subsequently, they were produced by many bottle factories, especially in the north of England. Green bottle-glass weights are distinguished by airy flower patterns growing from pots, which were often enclosed in bullet-shaped or ovoid forms, and by crude enclosures of sulphide figures. Weight 46 in Plate 33 shows a sulphide of the "Prince of Wales" feather. The examples of green bottle-glass weights in the Bergstrom collection are considered to be of late-nineteenth-century origin and from Castleford, Yorkshire.

The famous Belgian factory, Val St. Lambert, was founded in 1825. Throughout the nineteenth century, it ranked equally with the leading French factories in the quality of fine glassware produced. However, their paperweight production is conspicuous by its scarcity. (There is one example in the Bergstrom collection, 249, Plate 39.) Why were so few weights produced by Val St. Lambert in the decade between 1845 and 1855 when Baccarat, Clichy, and Saint Louis were producing them by the thousands? A satisfactory explanation was suggested to me recently during a visit to Val St. Lambert. In 1825, François Kemlin and Auguste LeLievre, originally associated with Monsieur d'Artigues in the Vonèche Glass Co. (Belgium), severed relations with their associate and became owners of the newly founded Val St. Lambert. Simultaneously, d'Artigues purchased what was later to become Baccarat, and ultimately an agreement evolved between the two manufacturing concerns that Val St. Lambert would not use the millefiori technique in their production. This no doubt accounts for the small number of Val St. Lambert weights and, also, for the scarcity of canes used in those we do recognize. The weights with enclosures were undoubtedly made as presentation items and never as commercial production pieces.

Recent discoveries have changed our thinking about another area of production. Careful research by Paul Hollister, Jr. (*The Encyclopedia of Glass Paperweights,* 1969), has enabled us to assign certain weights to Bohemian-Silesian origin. Specifically, millefiori weights with the signature "J 1848" have been baffling students for years; they were considered by some to be Venetian, by others French. Now,

Mr. Hollister's exciting breakthrough contributes convincing evidence that Bohemia-Silesia is the origin, and thus adds a bit more luster to the influence of Bohemian glass and craftsmanship, which has always been strong in many branches of art glass manufacture, and particularly important to French, English, and American paperweight production. Many of the decorative techniques of enameling, intricate faceting in overlays, and exquisite engraving can be traced directly to Bohemian influence. The Bergstrom cobalt blue overlay weight (75, Plate 58) exemplifies the high degree of technique attained.

One of the few paperweight makers living today whose work is comparable to the antique French is Paul Ysart of Caithness, Scotland. The multinationality of his background perhaps illustrates the complex nature of influences, for his family is of Czech origin, and he was born in Spain in 1904 and later moved to Scotland, where his production of weights has been carried on. Mrs. Bergstrom knew him only as "P Y" and believed his work was of the 1850 era. She learned of her mistake after her book had gone to press, and removed the illustrations of the two "P Y" weights from subsequent printings. She also removed these two weights from her collection, but later acquired another (412, Plate 40).

At the present time, students and collectors of paperweights are becoming aware of a new influx from various European sources such as West Germany, Czechoslovakia, the Low Countries, and Scandinavia; and are also aware of improvement in the quality of Italian production. Paperweight connoisseurs are reticent about making direct comparisons between these new arrivals and the older established weights, but whatever the attitude taken, one cannot deny that the presence in the market of contemporary weights has stimulated active overall interest in paperweight collecting.

*The numbers used to identify the illustrations and their captions are the Bergstrom acquisition numbers. The infor-
mation that follows the □ device in a caption is Mrs. Bergstrom's attribution of that item and other data about it from
her records. Her spellings are retained.*

Plate 33

266 and **267.**   Attributed to Bristol (England). 19th century. Pair of mantel ornaments. Colorless spheres enclose
lily-like flower motif of yellow glass with varicolored
spatter. Large bubble appears in center, surrounded by 3
lilies each with a smaller center bubble. Colorless glass
standards, not attached, have a waisted center section of
transparent green glass, with collar above and below. Circular flat foot. 4⅛″ (10.5 cm.) diam. of ornament; 9½″
(24.1 cm.) overall height.

□ Bristol; acquired Sept., 1939.
(#3, p. 41, 1940 Bergstrom book; p. 42, later editions.)

465.   North of England. Late-19th century. Ovoid doorstop with flat base. Green bottle glass encloses sulphide
figure of a child sitting sidewise on an elephant. The animal
stands on a rocklike mound rising from the base. Pontil
mark on underside. 3⅝″ (9.2 cm.) diam.; 4⁹⁄₁₆″ (11.6 cm.)
height.   □ Unidentified; acquired Oct., 1941.

30.   Castleford, Yorkshire (England). Late-19th century.
Ovoid weight with flat base. Green bottle glass encloses
translucent motif consisting of upright flowerpot with two
flowers, each with 5 petals, growing from it, one above the
other. Pontil mark on underside. 3″ (7.6 cm.) diam.; 3⅞″
(9.9 cm.) height.

□ Nailsea; also Castleford; acquired June, 1937.
(Illus. 46, 1940 Bergstrom book; Illus. 44, subsequent
editions.)

256.   Castleford, Yorkshire (England). Late-19th century.
Sphere-shaped weight of darker green bottle glass than the
usual, and heavier. Enclosed is a large center elongated
bubble above which is an umbrella-shaped, translucent glass
motif covered with tiny bubbles. Spaced bubbles of varying
sizes are scattered in crown and sides of base. Circular ridge
of last gather of encasing glass appears on the flat underside; also pontil mark. 4¼″ (10.8 cm.) diam.

□ Castleford; acquired Sept., 1939.

46.   North of England. Late-19th century. Ovoid weight
with flat base. Green bottle glass encloses sulphide motif
of "Prince of Wales Feather," which rests on mound of
translucent glass at base. Pontil mark on concave underside.
2¹⁵⁄₁₆″ (7.4 cm.) diam.; 3⁹⁄₁₆″ (9.1 cm.) height.

□ Castlebar; acquired Aug., 1937.

124.   Attributed to Bristol area (England). *Ca.* 1850–60.
Transparent blown glass sphere has flattened base and
mottled coloring in yellow, red, and blue. Sapphire blue
glass hen, free formed, is applied to top of weight. Pontil

mark on underside. 3¾″ (9.6 cm.) diam. (The hen is
similar to the swan in 50, Plate 45.)

□ Nailsea; also Bristol; acquired May, 1938.
(Illus. 44, 1940 Bergstrom book; Illus. 42, subsequent
editions.)

726.   Origin unknown. Small, flat scent bottle with no
stopper is of colorless glass with dark ruby and milk-white
stripes from base to neck. 3½″ (8.9 cm.) height.

□ Unrecorded.

255.   Castleford, Yorkshire (England). Late-19th century.
Green bottle glass in bullet shape encloses motif of a 12-
petaled silvery flower near crown, with narrow stem extending to translucent flowerpot. Four small silvery blossoms
appear at rim of pot. Rough pontil mark on the flat underside. 2¼″ (5.7 cm.) diam.; 4⅛″ (10.5 cm.) height.

□ Castleford; acquired Sept., 1939.

408.   Origin unknown; possibly Paul Ysart (Scotland).
Crown weight, dome-shaped. Colorless glass encloses alternating white filigree tubular rods and white filigree rods
with a core of red and green strands. Radiating from a
center bubble, the rods are swirled to form a pinwheel design over a translucent blue ground and converge at a point
near base. Pontil mark on underside. 3⁵⁄₁₆″ (8.4 cm.) diam.
(Similar to weight 494.)

□ Unidentified; acquired May, 1941.

319.   Attributed to Paul Ysart (Scotland). *Ca.* 1935–40.
Patterned millefiori on opaque cobalt blue ground. Butterfly in center has wings of ocher-colored canes; body and
tips of feelers are opaque orange. Encircling the butterfly is
a garland—a chain of 6 links, 3 of which are soft green
canes and 3 a soft pink. Underside is slightly concave.
3¾″ (9.6 cm.) diam.   □ Bristol; acquired April, 1940.
(Illus. 43, 1940 Bergstrom book; Illus. 41, subsequent editions.)

494.   Origin unknown; possibly Paul Ysart (Scotland).
Crown-type weight. Pale green spirals of filigree threads
alternating first with opaque white ribbon twists striped
with red and blue, and then with opaque red ribbon twists
about which are coiled white filigree threads, all radiate
from a central bubble and converge at point at the base.
The twists and spirals are set on a transparent blue-green
sphere, the whole being encased in colorless glass. Pontil
mark on underside. 3¼″ (8.3 cm.) diam. (Similar to 408.)

□ Unidentified; acquired May, 1942.

Plate 33

266

465

267

46

30

256

124

726

255

408

319

494

Plate 34

607. English. *Ca.* 1746–66. Jacobite wineglass has conical bowl with engraved motto ("Audentior Ibo") above portrait (front view) of Charles Edward Stuart. On the reverse are engraved a rose with one bud and leaves and a thistle with two leaves. Double-knopped stem with air twists. Conical foot. 6¾₁₆″ (15.7 cm.) height. ☐ Unrecorded.

169. Attributed to Whitefriars, London. Mid-19th century. Large, heavy weight has high clear crown. Enclosed at base are 4 concentric circles of blue-and-white, and red-and-green canes; outside circle of ocher-colored hollow canes with red interiors extends to base following curve of weight. Center is large, opaque white pastry-mold cane. Circular groove on exterior between colorless base and crown. Underside of weight is flat with slight concavity at center. 4⅛″ (10.5 cm.) diam. (Canes are similar to the "1848" dated Whitefriars concentrics.)

☐ Bristol; acquired Nov., 1938.

608. English. *Ca.* 1746–66. Jacobite wineglass has conical bowl with "Fiat" engraved above an engraved star. Rose with two buds and leaves is engraved on reverse. Double-knopped stem with air twists. Conical foot; pontil mark on underside. 6⁵₁₆″ (16.0 cm.) height. ☐ Unrecorded.

391. Bacchus, Birmingham (England). Mid-19th century. Colorless glass weight with large top concave punty, which might have served as a wafer tray. Concentric millefiori mushroom motif is made up of 4 circles of purple-hued canes surrounding a central star-shaped hollow cane. Outer circle is drawn down to form tuft. Flute cuttings appear between the 8 olive cuts on curve. Flat base, slightly concave. 3½″ (8.9 cm.) diam. (Hollister, *The Encyclopedia of Glass Paperweights,* p. 160 and Col. Fig. 80.)

☐ Saint Louis; acquired March, 1941.

114. Bacchus, Birmingham (England). Mid-19th century. Concentric millefiori design consists of 6 circles of large, tubular canes, predominantly white. One circle is opaque white lined with red; another is lined with blue. The center is a bundle of smaller, hollow pastel-colored rods. The outside circle is hollow serrated white canes lined with pink and drawn to center of base following the curve. Weight is smooth, slightly concave on underside. 3⅝″ (9.2 cm.) diam.

☐ Stourbridge; acquired Feb., 1938.
(Illus. 48, 1940 Bergstrom book; Illus. 46, later editions.)

203. Bacchus, Birmingham (England). Mid-19th century. Millefiori tuft has 5 concentric circles of deep blue, green, white, and pink star-shaped hollow canes, all with white exterior. Red center cane is hollow and star-shaped. Outer circle shows pink through the white, and the canes are drawn to a point at base to form tuft. Torsade is twisted strands of white filigree threads around which is coiled a dark blue strand. Base is smooth and slightly concave. 3⁷₁₆″ (8.7 cm.) diam. ☐ Clichy; acquired Feb., 1939.

165. Attributed to James Powell & Sons of Whitefriars, London. *Ca.* 1850. Blown mercury weight. The inside of the sphere is silvered; the outside is ruby-flashed with faceting in a "cross" design and half-circular cuttings. Enclosed in underside of base is a metal disk on which "Patent Hale Thomson's, London" is imprinted. Very light in weight. 2¹³₁₆″ (7.2 cm.) diam.

☐ Unidentified; acquired Oct., 1938.

419. Bacchus, Birmingham (England). Mid-19th century. Concentric millefiori weight. Center silhouette cane with woman's profile, to dexter, in dark blue is surrounded by concentric circles of millefiori canes, some hollow and serrated, in pink, blue, and white. Outer circle, of serrated white canes lined with blue, extends, following curve of weight, to a point at center of base. The silhouette and circles of canes are visible in miniature on underside of weight. Center silhouette cane of a woman's profile is same as in weight 141, Plate 45. 2⅞″ (7.3 cm.) diam.

☐ Saint Louis; acquired June, 1941.

318. English. *Ca.* 1850–73. Marbrie weight. The colorless casing of the hollow, opaque white, globular glass interior is decorated with blue and dark red loops of festoons, in 6 sections simulating a 6-pointed star. 3⅜″ (8.6 cm.) diam. ☐ Nailsea; acquired April, 1940.

248. Origin unknown; possibly English. Blown weight. The hollow, cobalt blue sphere has, on top, a pressed, colorless glass motif portraying the coat of arms of the King of England with the motto of the House of Windsor (Dieu et Mon Droit). On the curve is a pressed, colorless glass circle of strands that extend in points to the center of the underside. The decorated sphere is entirely encased in colorless glass. Underside is flat and smooth. 3⅛″ (7.9 cm.) diam. Similar in construction to weight 43, Plate 49.

☐ Unidentified; acquired July, 1939.

446. English. Gourd-shaped weight with smooth, flattened base encloses strands of white filigree and opaque ribbons of various colors drawn from base to top of weight. 3¼″ (8.3 cm.) diam. ☐ Nailsea; acquired Sept., 1941.

572. Origin unknown. Colorless, sparkling glass encloses a thin, opaque white glass disk, floating midway in weight, on which is portrayed in colored powdered glass the figure of a man with tall hat (resembles a Charles Dickens character), standing in a path, reading a newspaper, holding an umbrella between his knees. Tree and shrubbery beneath blue sky make up the background. Tiny bubbles appear all over the surface of the disk. Circular depression on exterior about ½″ (1.2 cm.) above smooth, flat base. 2¹³₁₆″ (7.2 cm.) diam. (Mr. Lloyd J. Graham commented, regarding this weight, on its similarity to his "mystery" weight illustrated in the 1959 *Bulletin of the Paperweight Collectors' Association.*) ☐ Unrecorded.

Plate 34

607

169

608

391

114

203

165

419

318

248

446

572

Plate 35

1. Whitefriars, London. Dated 1848. Ink bottle has 5 concentric circles of purple, white, and pink canes resting on its flat base. The serrated canes are large and crude. In one circle the date "1848" appears in crude numerals. Stopper contains 4 concentric circles of canes in shades of lavender. Pontil mark on underside of bottle. 4⅝" (11.7 cm.) diam. of base; 6" (15.3 cm.) overall height.

☐ White Friars—London; acquired March, 1935.
(#5, p. 41, 1940 Bergstrom book; p. 42, subsequent editions; Illus. 49, 1940 edition; Illus. 47, subsequent editions.)

635. Attributed to Whitefriars Glass, Ltd., Wealdstone, Middlesex (England). *Ca.* 1922–40. Table lamp base, colorless glass. Between the tapered, hollow, 6-sided stem and the thick, flat, circular base is a dome-shaped weight with 5 concentric circles of red, white, and blue canes, the outer circle being of hollow opaque white rods lined with red. At center is a large blue cane with opaque white, 6-petaled design. A 32-pointed star is cut on the underside, the rays extending to periphery. 9½" (24.1 cm.) height to brass mounting; 3⅜" (8.6 cm.) diam. of paperweight; 6" (15.3 cm.) diam. of base.

☐ Unrecorded.

513. Attributed to Whitefriars Glass, Ltd., Wealdstone, Middlesex (England). *Ca.* 1930. Colorless glass tumbler with 5 concentric circles of rose-colored, blue, and white millefiori canes in the base. Outer circle of rose canes is drawn to center of base. Flat underside has trace of pontil mark. 2" (5.1 cm.) diam. at base; 4¾" (12.1 cm.) height.

☐ Baccarat; acquired Nov., 1942.

238. Attributed to Bristol (England). Colorless wine goblet of round funnel form. Vintage decoration is engraved on bowl. A coarse ribbon spiral of red, white, and blue is enclosed in the straight stem. Low conical, circular foot has pontil mark on underside. 4⅝" (11.7 cm.) diam. at rim of bowl; 10⅛" (25.8 cm.) height.

☐ Bristol; acquired June, 1939.
(#11, p. 41, 1940 Bergstrom book; p. 42, later editions.)

88. Attributed to Whitefriars, London. Dated 1848. Ink bottle has 6 concentric circles of serrated canes in red, white, and blue resting on the base. Canes are more refined than in weight #1. The date "1848" in crudely made numerals appears in one circle. Five concentric circles of canes in the stopper surround a center green-and-white cane. Colorless base, approximately ¼" (.6 cm.) deep, is smaller in diameter than the bottom of the bottle. Underside has slight concavity. 4¹³⁄₁₆" (10.6 cm.) diam. at base; 5¾" (14.6 cm.) overall height.

☐ Bristol; acquired Nov., 1937.

542. Attributed to Baccarat (French). Large, heavy weight. Colorless glass encloses floating motif, near base, of varicolored single, deeply cupped flowers and green leaves. Centers of some flowers are opaque yellow or white dots; others appear to have filmy, pale yellow cane centers. Unusually high crown. Lower half of weight is deeply cut on outside in diamond-shaped facets diminishing in size toward base. Underside is flat and smooth. 3¾" (9.6 cm.) diam.; 3⅜" (8.6 cm.) height. (Similar to 541.)

☐ Unrecorded.

280. English. Mid-19th century. Inkwell of colorless glass, inverted cone shape, with 4 concentric circles of serrated canes at base. Outer 3 circles are hollow white rods with green, red, and blue interiors. Large center cane (white, plaited, with red interior) is encircled by red canes with opaque solid white interiors. Outer circle is drawn to center of base, following curve of weight. On flat underside near periphery is a circular ridge. Slight concavity at center. 3¹¹⁄₁₆" (9.4 cm.) diam. at base.

☐ Stourbridge; acquired Nov., 1939.
(Illus. 47, 1940 Bergstrom book; Illus. 45, subsequent editions.)

541. Attributed to Baccarat (French). Large, heavy weight. Colorless glass encloses a floating motif, near base, of 3 pansies, 9 green leaves, and a purple bud on green stem. The pansies have 3 yellow over opaque white lower petals, and 2 velvet-textured purple upper petals. Unusually high crown; exterior of lower half of weight is deeply cut in diamond-shaped facets diminishing in size toward base. Flat underside. 3⅞" (9.9 cm.) diam.; 3⁷⁄₁₆" (8.7 cm.) height. (Similar to 542.)

☐ Unrecorded.

23. Whitefriars, London. Dated 1848. Shallow millefiori weight. Colorless glass encloses 5 concentric circles of yellow, pink, blue, and white canes. The date "1848" appears in crudely formed numerals in canes next to outer circle. Underside is concave. 3¼" (8.3 cm.) diam.

☐ White Friars and Bristol; acquired June, 1937.
(Illus. 50, 1940 Bergstrom book; Illus. 48, later editions.)

162. Attributed to Saint Louis (French). Octagon-shaped ruler of colorless glass. White filigree strands are coiled around spiral twists of red and blue strands. 10" (25.5 cm.) long; ½" (1.2 cm.) diam.

☐ Unidentified; acquired Oct., 1938.

24. Whitefriars, London. Dated 1848. Shallow millefiori weight. Colorless glass encloses 6 concentric circles of red, white, and blue canes. The date "1848" appears in crudely formed numerals in canes next to outer circle. Underside has slight concavity. 3⅛" (7.9 cm.) diam.

☐ White Friars; acquired June, 1937.

Plate 35

1

513

635

238

88

542

280

541

23

162

24

Plate 36

324.   English. Early-19th century. Hollow witch ball. Colorless glass encases mottled red, blue, and green glass over opaque white. The ball is lined with plaster and has a hole in center of base. 5¼″ (13.3 cm.) diam.

☐   Nailsea; acquired April, 1940.

(#17, p. 41, 1940 Bergstrom book; p. 42, subsequent editions.)

351.   English. Early-19th century. Hollow witch ball of transparent deep blue glass rests in bowl-shaped standard of matching glass. Sides and foot of standard are slightly ribbed. 4½″ (11.4 cm.) diam. (Hollow blue balls were also made in American factories in the late-18th and early-19th centuries.)

☐   Nailsea; acquired May, 1940.

(#2, p. 41, 1940 Bergstrom book; p. 42, subsequent editions.)

325.   Attributed to Bristol (England). *Ca.* 1850–60. Colorless glass cylindrical inkwell has translucent cobalt blue interior in the shape of a wineglass. Basal ring; pontil mark appears on underside. 2⁵⁄₁₆″ (5.8 cm.) diam.; 4⁵⁄₁₆″ (10.9 cm.) height.

☐   Bristol; acquired May, 1940.

376 and **377.**   Attributed to Bristol (England). A pair of steeple-shaped mantel ornaments. Colorless glass encloses design of opaque pastel-colored glass drawn upward into peaks and spikes. Applied colorless circular foot with bladed knopped stem. 11″ (27.9 cm.) overall height.

☐   Bristol; acquired Dec., 1940.

330.   Attributed to Bristol (England). Colorless glass, cylindrical inkwell has opaque yellow, cup-shaped interior above a varicolored and opaque white glass design drawn up to peaks or spikes. Flat, colorless flange at base. 2¼″ (5.7 cm.) diam.; 4″ (10.2 cm.) height.

☐   Bristol; acquired May, 1940.

364A.   Origin unknown. 19th century. Flask of transparent mauve-colored glass has opaque white loop design. Narrow neck. Flat sides are rounded at base. 6⅝″ (16.8 cm.) height.

☐   Unrecorded.

364.   English. Mid-19th century. Opaque white glass flask with decoration of pink loops. Narrow neck; flat sides taper toward base. 7½″ (19.1 cm.) height.

☐   Nailsea; acquired Aug., 1940.

19.   Dupont-Baccarat (French). *Ca.* 1930. Shallow weight contains a floating motif of 6 concentric circles of canes surrounding opaque white, rectangular center cane with date "1851" in black. Colors range from deep blue and brick red to pastel hues. Flat base. 2½″ (6.3 cm.) diam. (Hollister, *The Encyclopedia of Glass Paperweights,* pp. 174 and 270.)

☐   Bristol; acquired June, 1937.

(Illus. 45, 1940 Bergstrom book; Illus. 43, subsequent editions.)

287.   Czechoslovakian. *Ca.* 1918–38. Five morning glory flowers have varicolored stripes over opaque white, with narrow stems extending into cushion made of tiny particles of opaque white glass with spots of green and blue. Flat punty on top and 4 on the curve, each punty encircled by small radial miter cuts and "framing" one of the flowers. Vertical leaf design cuttings appear between the side punties. 3⁵⁄₁₆″ (8.4 cm.) diam.

☐   Bristol; acquired Nov., 1939.

(Illus. 42, 1940 Bergstrom book; Illus. 40, subsequent editions.)

20.   Dupont-Baccarat (French). *Ca.* 1930. Shallow weight. Colorless glass with a gray tinge encloses a floating motif consisting of a garland of brick-red and ocher-colored canes; a circlet in the center surrounds an opaque white rectangular cane with the date "1848" in red. Between loops of the garland are separate canes with butterfly centers. Flat base. 2¹³⁄₁₆″ (7.2 cm.) diam. (Hollister, *The Encyclopedia of Glass Paperweights,* pp. 174 and 270.)

☐   Bristol; acquired June, 1937.

Plate 36

324

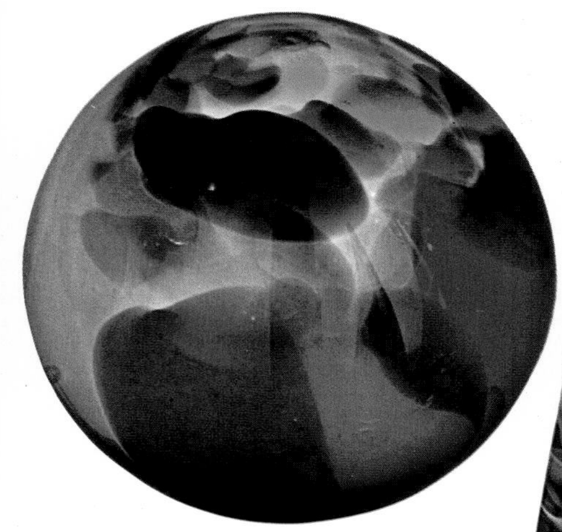

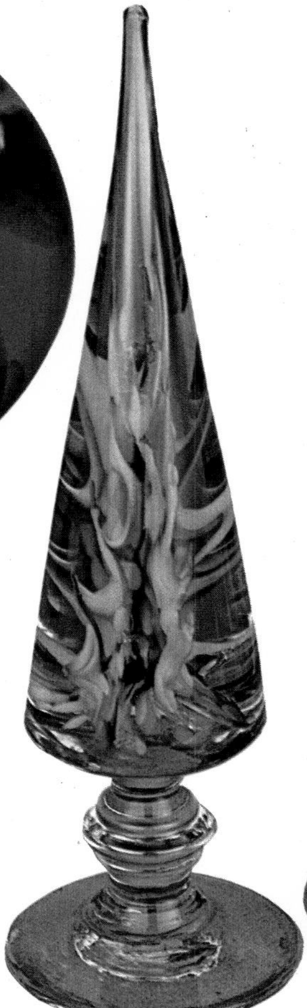

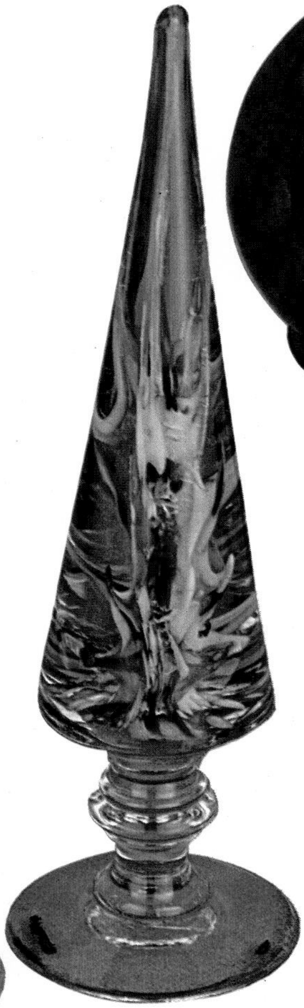

351

325

376

377

330

364A

364

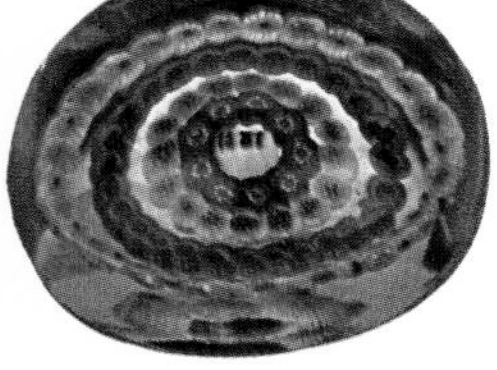

19

287

20

Plate 37

363. Unknown origin; possibly English. Gemel flask (2 necks, 2 compartments). The colorless glass is decorated with loops of opaque white across which are bands of transparent pink. Applied lip on each neck is cobalt blue. 10″ (25.4 cm.) height.

☐ Unidentified; acquired Aug., 1940.

645. Origin unknown; probably American.

a. Colorless glass rod with twist at each end encloses red, white, and blue threads spiraled around opaque white core. 6″ (15.3 cm.) length.

b. Two opaque white glass pens with red stripes are pointed at one end and twisted at the other end. 6″ (15.3 cm.) length.

☐ Unrecorded.

610. Saint Louis (French). *Ca.* 1840–50. Colorless glass cylindrical scent bottle with stopper tapers toward neck. Delicate spirals of cobalt blue cane lined with opaque white alternate with strands of white filigree threads, from the footed base to the neck. The narrow neck has a flange lip. Matching spiral appears in ball-shaped stopper. 1½″ (3.8 cm.) diam. at base; 4½″ (11.4 cm.) overall height.

☐ Unrecorded.

644. English. Four glass canes or walking sticks:

a. Translucent emerald green; 33½″ (85.2 cm.) length.

b. Transparent pale green glass, twisted, with spirals (not encased) of white, brown, yellow, and blue threads coiled from end to handle; 42⅝″ (103.2 cm.) length. (A similar cane, pictured in Plate 28 in Hugh Wakefield's *19th Century British Glass,* is said to have been made in Warrington, at the Orford Lane glassworks, about 1840.)

c. Transparent, hollow, pale green glass walking stick is filled with what appears to be powdered chalk in sections of white, blue, and brown. End is open, with cork insert. 37⅝″ (95.5 cm.) length.

d. Translucent, pale green glass cane, twisted, with brown thread spiral (not encased), tapers toward handle. 42 (106.7 cm.) length. (Note under cane **b.** applies to this cane also.)

☐ Unrecorded. (Each cane has paper sticker "Made in England.")

730. Attributed to Bristol area (England). Mid-19th century. Opaque white glass flask encased in colorless glass with decoration of blue loopings. Narrow neck; flat sides, tapering toward base. 8¾″ (22.2 cm.) height.

☐ Unrecorded.

91. L. L. Paris, France. *Ca.* 1889. Snow weight (liquid has evaporated). Thin sphere of colorless glass encloses replica of the Eiffel Tower, probably in a ceramic material. Dried "flakes" surround the base of tower. Sphere is mounted on square ceramic base with "L. L. Paris MADE IN FRANCE" impressed on underside. 2 9/16″ (6.5 cm.) diam.; 1¾″ × 1¾″ × ⅞″ (4.5 cm. × 4.5 cm. × 2.2 cm.) base.

☐ Unidentified; acquired Nov., 1937.

649. Origin unknown; possibly Sandwich, Mass. (American.) Wineglass has cup-shaped bowl of ruby craquelle with gilt band at rim. Six-sided straight stem of colorless glass encloses red strand and fine white filigree threads spiraled around a pink and white ribbon twist. Foot is colorless glass craquelle on upper side, flashed with ruby on underside. Gilt bands on collars joining bowl to stem, and stem to foot. 3 3/16″ (8.1 cm.) diam. of bowl; 6⅛″ (15.6 cm.) height.

☐ Unrecorded.

(This type of ruby craquelle is pictured on p. 67 in Albert Christian Revi's *Nineteenth Century Glass,* and identified as Clichy, France, *Ca.* 1850.)

Plate 37

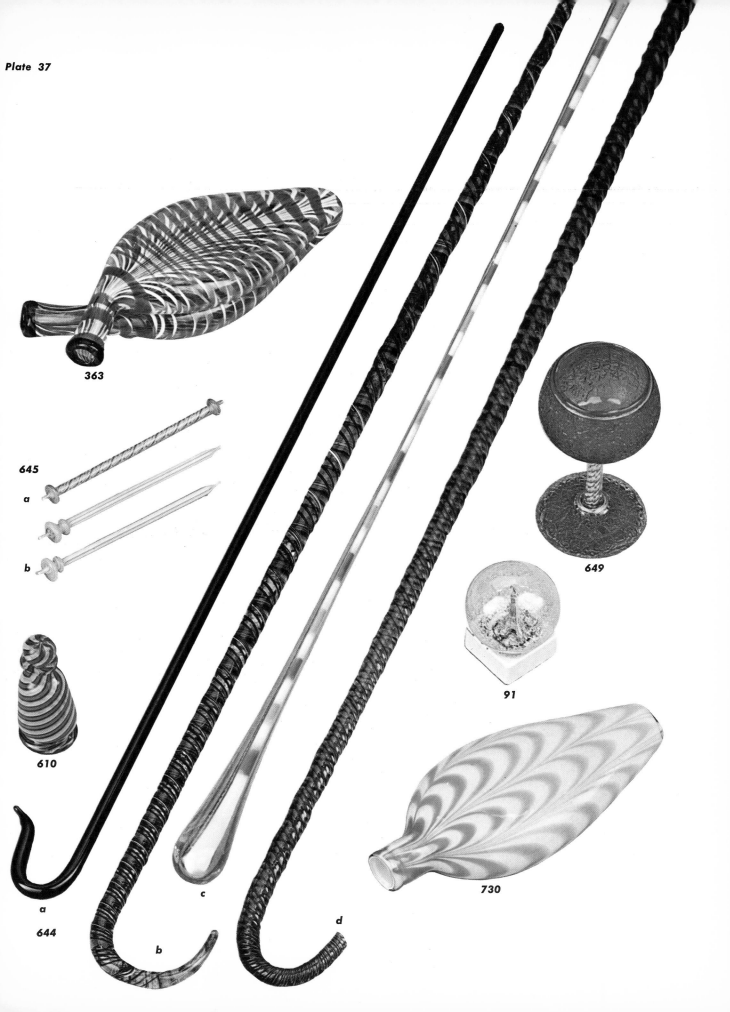

363

645
a
b

610

649

91

730

644
a
b
c
d

Plate 38

454. Origin unknown; possibly Venetian. Colorless glass weight in the form of an apple, with applied leaf at top. Interior is translucent ruby-red sphere with spaced bubbles and flecks of goldstone. Pontil mark on underside. 3¼″ (8.3 cm.) diam. (Weights of this form have also been made in American factories during the 20th century.)

☐ Unidentified; acquired Oct., 1941.

337. Bohemian-Silesian. Dated 1848. Small, cylindrical, opaque white overlay vase (cut with round facets) is supported by a spaced millefiori paperweight base; colorless glass collar between the two. The paperweight base encloses multiple-colored millefiori canes spaced on muslin ground. "J 1848" appears in one cane. Two canes resemble Clichy roses. 2½″ (6.3 cm.) diam. of base; 4″ (10.2 cm.) overall height.

☐ Unidentified; acquired May, 1940.

732. Origin unknown; possibly Nicholas Lutz, Sandwich, Mass. (American.) (Shows Venetian influence.) *Ca.* 1870. Cup and saucer of very thin "striped" glass. Flattened white filigree twists alternate with yellow filigree coils around goldstone core, and white filigree with center of pink spiral strand. The cup is footed with same striping. Colorless stem and handle both applied. 2⅞″ (7.3 cm.) diam. of cup; 4¾″ (12.1 cm.) diam. of saucer.   ☐ Unrecorded.

(A similar item is illustrated in R. W. Lee's *19th Century Art Glass,* Plate 29.)

559A. Italian, probably Murano. *Ca.* 1930. Crown weight, dome-shaped, of colorless glass with tubular white filigree rods alternating with opaque pink ribbon twists, edged with goldstone, radiating from a point at top of crown and converging at base. Underside is flat. 3⅛″ (7.9 cm.) diam.

☐ Unrecorded.

553. Origin unknown. Small, flat-sided, colorless glass flask is decorated with blue-lined-with-opaque-white canes; bands of goldstone alternate with the canes and spiral from base of flask to lip of narrow neck. Very light. 3 1/16″ (7.8 cm.) width; 6½″ (16.5 cm.) height.   ☐ Unrecorded.

251. Venetian. Possibly mid-19th century. Crown weight, hollow. Twists of white filigree threads and goldstone alternate with blue strands and goldstone twists over opaque white ground. Twists radiate from central bubble and converge on underside. Pontil mark on base. 2 15/16″ (7.4 cm.) diam.

☐ Venetian; acquired Sept., 1939.
(Illus. 51, 1940 Bergstrom book; Illus. 49, subsequent editions.) (Ex Collection of the Marquis de Bailleul, Château d'Angerville.)

535. Venetian; attributed to Pietro Bigaglia. Dated 1847. Macédoine weight. Motif, which extends to encasing glass, consists of a variety of millefiori canes, white filigree twists,

and goldstone. The date "1847," the initial "R," a bird, a checkerboard, a lyre, and an Italian inscription reading "IX Congreso degli Scienziati in Venezia 47" appear in individual canes. Slightly frosted base. Pontil mark on underside. 2⅞″ (7.3 cm.) diam.

☐ Italian; acquired May, 1944.

432. Origin unknown; probably American. Seal of colorless glass with diamond-faceted handle that encloses coarse thread spirals of dark blue and white. Monogram "EB" is engraved on seal. 3¼″ (8.3 cm.) length.

☐ Unidentified; acquired Aug., 1941.

617. Origin unknown; probably French. Letter seal has colorless glass handle enclosing spiral band of translucent amethyst glass around core of white filigree threads. 3¼″ (8.3 cm.) length. (Brass seal end is similar to 616.)

☐ Unrecorded.

616. Origin unknown; probably French. Letter opener and seal. Each has colorless glass handle enclosing red and white, fine filigree thread spirals. Steel blade of letter opener has gilt design. (Brass mountings; seal mounting is similar to that on 617.) 3 5/16″ (8.4 cm.) length of seal; 5⅛″ (13.1 cm.) length of letter opener.   ☐ Unrecorded.

399. Venetian. Dated 1846. Rectangular weight is framed in silver and mounted on rectangular colorless glass base with beveled edges. Seven separate millefiori canes are spaced among segments of varicolored opaque canes and goldstone. In center is silhouette cane with a gondola and blue waves on opaque white, encircled by tiny white stars. Two canes show on the underside; the date "1846" appears in one and the initials "GBF" in the other. (Presumably these stand for Giambatista Franchini.) 1¼″ × 1⅞″ (3.2 cm. × 4.8 cm.) dimensions of millefiori plaque; 2¾″ × 4 7/16″ (7.0 cm. × 11.1 cm.) dimensions of base.

☐ Venetian; acquired March, 1941.

381. Italian. *Ca.* 1860's. Macédoine weight. The motif, which extends to encasing glass, consists of segments of filigree twists, ribbons, opaque colored rods, a male bust portrait cane (possibly of Garibaldi), and two pansy florets. Light in weight. Pontil mark. 2 7/16″ (6.2 cm.) diam.

☐ Italian; acquired Nov., 1940.

552. Venetian; attributed to Giambatista and Jacopo Franchini. 1840–70. Four millefiori canes: One is a portrait, presumably of Count di Cavour, Italian statesman (1810–61); two are portraits of either Victor Emmanuel II or Garibaldi; the fourth shows a gondola on white ground encircled by dark glass with tiny white stars. The canes are about ⅛″ (.3 cm.) to ¼″ (.6 cm.) diam.   ☐ Unrecorded.

640. Italian. *Ca.* 1930's. Sixty-two glass beads of graduated sizes made of millefiori canes ground to oval shape are strung on a gold chain.   ☐ Unrecorded.

Plate 38

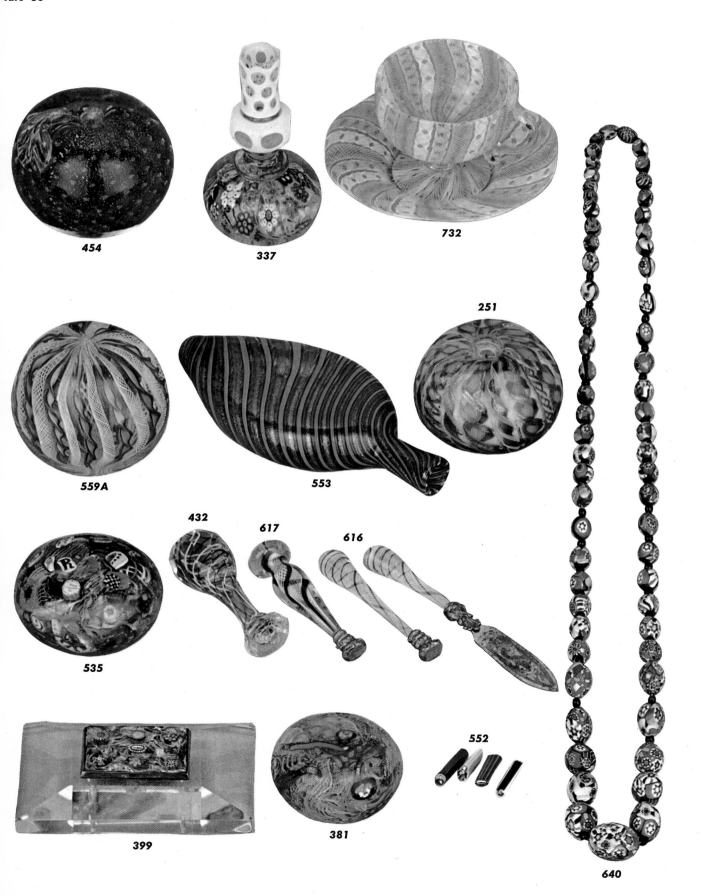

454

337

732

251

559A

553

432

617

616

535

399

381

552

640

Plate 39

673. Swedish. Kosta Glass Works. 1962. Colorless glass, solid, hexagonal weight, tapering toward base, has engraved portrait of Dag Hammarskjöld, profile to dexter, by Vicke Lindstrand, on underside. "Dag Hammarskjöld Kosta Lindstrand No. 54" is inscribed on side near top. 3½" (8.9 cm.) diam. of top side; 1⁹⁄₁₆" (3.9 cm.) high.

Gift of Mr. Paul Jokelson, 1962.

714. Swedish. Kosta Glass Works. 1963. Colorless glass, solid, triangular weight with engraved portrait head, slightly to sinister, of Albert Einstein, by Vicke Lindstrand, on underside. "Albert Einstein Kosta Lindstrand No. 54" is inscribed on sides, which are cut in varying angles. 4" (10.2 cm.) base of triangle.

Gift of Mr. Paul Jokelson, 1963.

676. Swedish. Kosta Glass Works. 1963. Colorless glass, solid, rectangular weight with engraved portrait head, almost full front view, of Alexander Graham Bell by Vicke Lindstrand, on underside. "Alexander Graham Bell Kosta Lindstrand No. 51" is inscribed on sides near top of weight. 3⁹⁄₁₆" × 3" × 1½" (9.1 cm. × 7.6 cm. × 3.8 cm.).

Gift of Mr. Paul Jokelson, 1963.

249. Belgian. Val St. Lambert. *Ca.* 1920's. Transparent cobalt blue, single overlay weight. The motif consists of 4 loops of white filigree strands with a central floret and spaced bubbles, around which is a rope twist (red, white, blue, and yellow strands, with core of opaque white). Motif is on a center cushion-mound of rose over opaque white, which rests on colorless flat base. Overlay is elaborately cut: radial notches frame the 4 oval flat facets on curve and circular flat facet on the top; between facets, star-shaped and spray design. 3⅝" (9.2 cm.) diam.

☐   Val St. Lambert; acquired Aug., 1939.

(Plate XIV, Bergstrom book.)

672. Swedish. Kosta Glass Works. 1962. Colorless glass, solid, hexagonal weight, tapering toward base, has engraved portrait, profile to dexter, of Albert Schweitzer by Vicke Lindstrand, on underside. "Albert Schweitzer Kosta Lindstrand No. 114" is inscribed on side near top of weight. 3⁹⁄₁₆" (9.1 cm.) diam. of top side; 1¾" (4.5 cm.) high.

Gift of Mr. Paul Jokelson, 1962.

752. Scottish. Strathearn, Ltd. 1967. Dome-shaped weight. Colorless glass encloses red lily flower with 5 smooth, pointed petals, bubble center, red stem, and 3 narrow, bright green leaves, all rising from a deep cushion with black top and sides of varicolored spatter. One ocher cane bearing "S" signature is visible in spatter near base. Weight

is flat and smooth on underside. 2¼" (5.7 cm.) diam. 3½" (8.9 cm.) high.

Gift of Mr. Arthur Gorham, 1967.

483. Probably Bohemian; possibly French. Mid-19th century. Colorless glass has portrait (bust) of Empress Eugénie etched on underside of amber-flashed base, which is slightly concave. The inscription "Eugénie Imper ce" appears below portrait. The solid crown is faceted; punty on top and 6 punties on curve. (A pair with 482.) 3¼" (8.3 cm.) diam. (Similar to 369, Plate 13, attributed to French manufacture.)

☐   Bohemian; acquired Feb., 1942.

250. Attributed to Bohemia. Sulphide bust portrait, to sinister, of Charles X of France, on translucent cranberry base. The crown of the weight is cut away, leaving a raised, slightly concave top, which is encircled by white enamel dots with gilt trim. Band of leaf design in gilt appears on curve. Exterior has a circular in-cut between base and crown (not a foot). On underside are 48 radial miter cuts extending to periphery. 3½" (8.9 cm.) diam.

☐   Bohemian; made in 1820; acquired Sept., 1939.

(Illus. 35, 1940 Bergstrom book; Illus. 33, subsequent editions. Similar sulphide identified as Louis Philippe, in Jokelson's *Sulphides*, p. 83, Fig. 78.) (Ex collection of the Marquis de Bailleul, Château d'Angerville.)

482. Probably Bohemian; possibly French. Mid-19th century. Colorless glass with portrait bust of Napoleon III etched on underside of amber-flashed base, which is slightly concave. "Napoleon III" appears beneath the portrait. Solid crown is faceted; punty on top and 6 punties on curve. (A pair with 483.) 3¹⁄₁₆" (7.8 cm.) diam.

☐   Bohemian; acquired Feb., 1942.

734. Scottish. Vasart Glass. 1960's. Patterned millefiori motif is set on an opaque pale blue ground. The spaced pastry-mold and serrated hollow canes are in pastel shades. Segments of gray and white filigree twists, laid radially, divide the pattern into eight sections. Center cane is made up of many tiny varicolored rods. Base is flattened and smooth. 2¾" (7.0 cm.) diam.

Gift of Mr. Paul Jokelson, 1967.

625. Origin unknown. Circular incised marble or soapstone mold, probably the type used in making sulphides, portraying bust profile of Angelus Politianus, Italian poet (1454–94). The name "Angelus Politianus" (in reverse) encircles the portrait, near periphery. 1¾" (4.5 cm.) diam.

☐   Unrecorded.

Plate 39

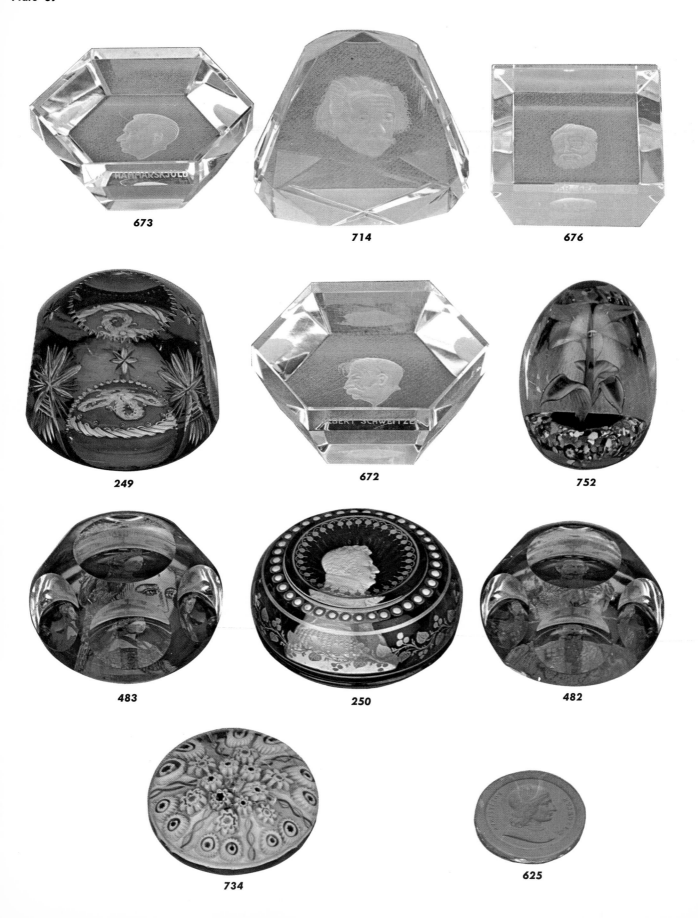

673

714

676

249

672

752

483

250

482

734

625

Plate 40

525. Attributed to Czechoslovakia. *Ca.* 1918–38. Dome-shaped, colorless glass encloses 5 opaque varicolored flowers with round petals and bubble centers. Central flower is at top of crown; 4 surrounding flowers are near surface at periphery. Stems extend to two-layered varicolored pebble ground. A circle of contiguous concave cuttings borders the flat top; 4 olive punties are on the sides of the weight. Colorless flat base. 3⁹⁄₁₆″ (9.1 cm.) diam.

☐ Unrecorded.

83. Danish. 1880–1920. Heavy weight. Colorless glass encloses, near top of crown, a layer of coarse, varicolored (predominantly blue) pebble ground through which 5 elongated bubbles extend down to a second, smaller layer of pebble ground. Entire motif floats an inch above the flat base of the weight. Pontil mark on underside. 3¹¹⁄₁₆″ (9.4 cm.) diam.

☐ Danish; acquired Oct., 1937.

291. Swedish. Early-20th century. Heavy weight. Glass of pale, creamy hue encloses two layers of coarse spatter glass, predominantly orange, into which a large central bubble and 4 smaller elongated bubbles (at periphery) extend downward. Flat base. 3⁷⁄₁₆″ (8.7 cm.) diam.

☐ Modern Swedish; no record of acquisition.

131. Czechoslovakian. *Ca.* 1918–38. Colorless glass encloses three flowers—opaque red, yellow-green, and purple—each with 8 petals and a bubble center; the stems grow from a pot of varicolored pebble. Five thin bubbles project from sides of the pot. Weight is faceted to a point at the top and has 5- and 6-sided facets at curve. Flat base. 3″ (7.6 cm.) diam.

☐ Unidentified; acquired June, 1938.

574. Unknown origin. Probably *Ca.* 1920. Large, heavy weight. Colorless glass encloses central elongated bubble and 4 smaller elongated bubbles extending down through a coarse varicolored pebble layer, below which is a spatter of opaque white simulating a basket. Flat base. 3⁷⁄₁₆″ (8.7 cm.) diam.

☐ Unrecorded.

38. Czechoslovakian. *Ca.* 1918–38. Colorless glass encloses 5 opaque white flowers with colored stripes on petals and small bubble centers. Stems of flowers grow out of translucent green mound at base. Weight is faceted to a point at top; 5- and 6-sided facets on curve. Flat base. 2¹³⁄₁₆″ (7.2 cm.) diam.

☐ Modern; acquired June, 1937.

689. Paul Ysart (Scotland). Mid-20th century. Doorknob with high crown. Sparkling colorless glass encloses patterned millefiori impressed into opaque powder-blue ground. In center is a circular grouping of purple, white, and green canes. At periphery is a circle of blue canes alternating with green serrated canes, with segments of tubular white filigree laid radially between the canes. 3″ (7.6 cm.) diam.

Gift of Mr. and Mrs. Ralph S. Johns, 1963.

89. Attributed to Czechoslovakia. *Ca.* 1918–38. Colorless glass encloses a single red nasturtium-type flower with 6 petals and a bubble center, above a varicolored pebble mound. Near surface of weight are rows of graduated, opaque pink loops; these begin at the base and proceed regularly upward as far as the outer part of the crown; the top loops form an 8-pointed "frame" above the motif. Flat base. 2⅞″ (7.3 cm.) diam.

☐ Unidentified; acquired Nov., 1937.

708. Paul Ysart (Scotland). 1963. Colorless glass encloses single pink flower with five grooved, pointed petals and orange pastry-mold center cane. Five green leaves surround the flower; three green leaves are on stem. Signature cane "PY" appears between stem and one leaf. At periphery is a circle of red and pink canes. All on translucent olive-green ground. Flat base. "Caithness 1963" is scratched on the underside. 3″ (7.6 cm.) diam. (The flower is similar to that in 706.)

Gift of Mr. and Mrs. Ralph S. Johns, 1963.

707. Paul Ysart (Scotland). 1963. Red-eyed dragonfly has yellow spots on goldstone body and 4 mottled green wings. Circle of serrated green and white canes at periphery includes a "PY" signature cane. Translucent olive-green ground. "Caithness 1963" is scratched on flat base. 3″ (7.6 cm.) diam.

Gift of Mr. and Mrs. Ralph S. Johns, 1963.

706. Paul Ysart (Scotland). 1963. Sparkling colorless glass encloses floating pink flower with 5 grooved, pointed petals and an orange pastry-mold center cane. Five green leaves surround the flower; 3 leaves are on stem. Signature cane "PY" appears between stem and one leaf. At periphery is a circle of tubular white filigree rods pulled to base in cuplike formation. Flat base. Trace of pontil mark on underside. 2¹⁵⁄₁₆″ (7.4 cm.) diam. (Flower is similar to that in 708.)

Gift of Mr. and Mrs. Ralph S. Johns, 1963.

412. Paul Ysart (Scotland). *Ca.* 1940. Colorless glass with gray tinge encloses floating patterned millefiori design. In center is cluster of varicolored canes, one of which bears the "PY" signature. Circle of alternating blue and ocher canes is at periphery. "Made in England" appears on paper sticker fastened to the flat base. 3″ (7.6 cm.) diam.

☐ Unidentified; acquired May, 1941.

Plate 40

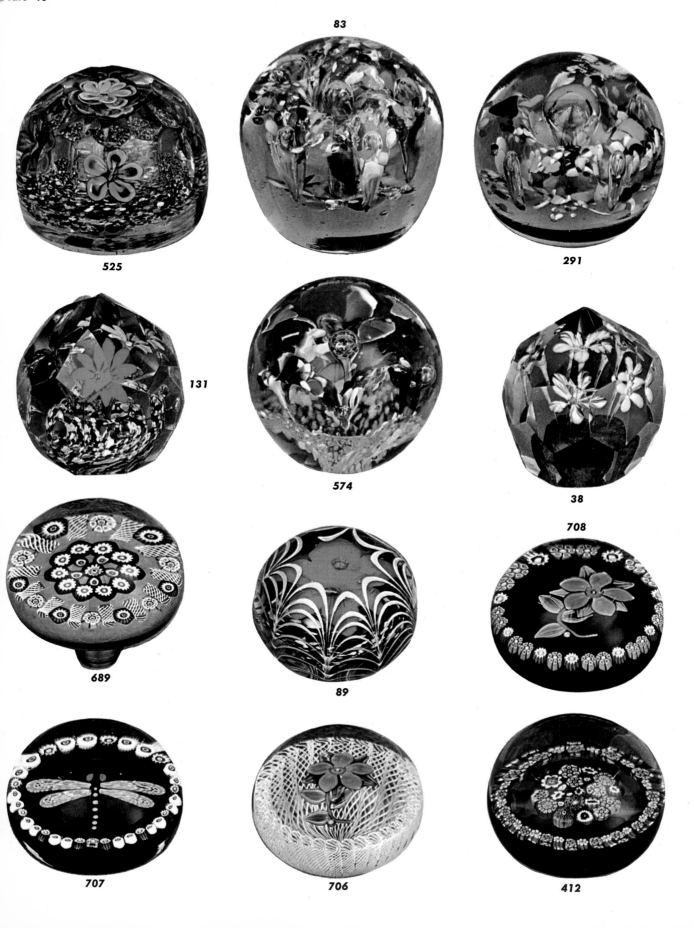

83

525

291

131

574

38

708

689

89

707

706

412

3

AMERICAN WEIGHTS

There is a tendency among paperweight connoisseurs to believe that if a weight is inferior, it must be American. Though it is probably true that we have been exposed to more poor American examples than poor European examples, there is no doubt that some weights comparable to the finest French production were made in American factories, and even that some of the fine weights attributed to France were actually made in America. Such mistakes in identification can be explained quite logically. Skilled glassmakers immigrated to the United States, and produced in American factories in the 1850's and 1860's the same types of weights they had been trained to make in Europe and England. And we suspect, also, that many arrived carrying with them canes and color formulas used in their native glasshouses.

There is little definite data on which to base positive identifications of early American weights, and few examples from any of the early factories have been incontrovertibly authenticated. Students have been dependent, necessarily, on affidavits or the word of descendants of glassmakers. One aid to the identification of weights in general is the use of the ultraviolet light, sometimes referred to as the "black light." J. P. Boore of Hemet, California, who has done extensive research on this subject, agrees that it is an aid to identification, but "It is far from an exact science," he says. "It should never be used to examine a weight without using a check weight of known origin for comparison. Even then, the comparisons may not be absolute because of the various batches." Consistencies in the content of glass cannot be held from one batch to another, to say nothing about consistency held over a period of years.

It is difficult to distinguish the work of one factory from that of another because designs were freely interchanged and there was traffic between companies in the canes themselves. And, too, the same personnel sometimes headed more than one factory. Deming Jarves, one of the foremost promoters of glass manufacturing of the early American era, had a hand in forming three Massachusetts glass companies between 1817 and 1837, all of which were subsequently important in paperweight manufacture. However, probably the most influential factor in contributing to the confusion was the restlessness of the workmen, who often moved from one factory to another. A prime example was Nicholas Lutz, one of the great weight makers of the nineteenth century. Born in Alsace, and trained in the Saint Louis factory, Lutz began his American career at the Dorflinger Glass Works at Greenpoint, Long Island (1860 to 1863), and White Mills, Pennsylvania (1863 to 1867), and then went on to four Massachusetts factories: the New England Glass Company (1867 to 1869), the Boston & Sandwich Glass Company (1869 to 1888), the Mt. Washington Glass Works in New Bedford until 1895, and finally the Union Glass Company at Somerville. (He died in 1904.) Because of this constant moving about by the craftsmen, today we inevitably find similar canes, motifs, cuttings, and so on in the weights of different factories, and thus have increased difficulty in designating correct attributions.

The Boston & Sandwich Glass Company in Sandwich on Cape Cod, founded by the aforementioned Deming Jarves, was in existence from 1825 to 1888. It enjoyed great success in making an enormous quantity of many types of glassware. Around 1850, paperweights became one of the company specialties. The earliest were probably the macédoine type, sometimes called "end of day," and often enclosed the date "1825" among the canes. Mrs. Bergstrom believed the 2 and the 5 were probably reversed. Segments of various canes arranged at random made up the motif of these weights; usually the enclosing glass was sparkling clear. Flower and fruit weights were also popular, the finest of them being attributed to Nicholas Lutz. Another Sandwich workman trained abroad was an Austrian who took the name of Timothy Collins. It was to him Mrs. Bergstrom attributed the two strawberry weights in her collection (170 and 501, Plate 41).

Of even more importance in paperweight history is the New England Glass Company of East Cambridge, Massachusetts; its career paralleled that of Sandwich in many aspects. Deming Jarves was among its several founders about 1818, and it too continued operation until 1888. According to some authorities, it led all New England glasshouses in the production of high-quality glassware. The paperweights produced here bear a marked resemblance to, and are often confused with, those of Sandwich. Their wide range included millefiori, vegetables and fruit in latticinio baskets, crown weights, sulphides, and blown fruit weights, the latter being perhaps the best known, at least the most recognizable. A pressed weight portraying Victoria and Albert and dated 1851 and a millefiori dated 1854 seem to be the earliest known NEGC weights, but the period from 1860 to 1875 was the height of paperweight popularity at East Cambridge. In 1888, Edward D. Libbey moved the business to Toledo, Ohio, where it was continued under the name of the Libbey Glass Company.

The Mt. Washington factory was moved from South Boston, Massachusetts, in 1869 when William L. Libbey purchased the New Bedford Glass Works (New Bedford, Massachusetts) and took it over as the new home of the Mt. Washington Glass Works. It operated under this name until 1876, when it was reorganized and became the Mt. Washington Glass Company; in 1894 it, in turn, was absorbed by the Pairpoint Manufacturing Company. The most famous of its paperweights were made in the 1869 to 1876 period and are known as "Mt. Washington roses" (375 and 244, Plate 42). These are large weights, their distinction lying in superb workmanship rather than artistic design. Similar in size are the famous strawberry weights previously mentioned, thought by Mrs. Bergstrom to be of Sandwich origin and now identified as Mt. Washington.

The factory of John L. Gilliland and Company of Brooklyn, New York, also known as the Brooklyn Flint Glass Works, was important from the 1820's through the 1860's for its superior quality of cut and engraved glassware. Gilliland was the recipient of awards at various exhibitions in the United States, and also won the prize for the best flint glass at the London Crystal Palace Exposition in 1851. Some of the finest of American paperweights have been attributed to Gilliland by Mrs. Bergstrom and other experts. However, the basis for these attributions is not known. Kenneth Wilson of the Corning Museum of Glass, in his lecture at the 1967 Bergstrom Paperweight Symposium, stated that Gilliland attributions needed further study. More recently, Paul Hollister, Jr. (*Antiques,* October, 1968, page 562), gave the results of his research on this subject, saying that to credit paperweights to Gilliland has been a "fanciful assumption." He believes these weights are more likely to be the products of the New England Glass Company. We do know that Gilliland was with NEGC before setting up business for himself, so once again the moving about of a craftsman has contributed to difficulties of identification. Until such a time as definite data is discovered regarding Gilliland and paperweights, we have chosen to attribute the examples in question to the New England Glass Company.

Our information concerning William T. Gillinder (whose name no doubt has often been confused with Gilliland) and his role in the paperweight field is more specific. Through correspondence between Mrs. Bergstrom and his grandson, James Gillinder, we know that William T. Gillinder was born in England and made paperweights in the Birmingham area before 1854, at which time he came to the United States to work at the New England Glass Company. In 1861, he established his own factory in Philadelphia, and there he manufactured a great many different kinds of paperweights. Among the workmen he employed was Charles Challinor, whose work was exceptional and who, according to his son, Frank Challinor (*Bulletin of the Paperweight Collectors' Association,* 1959 and 1960), made some paperweights. As evidenced by weight 141, Plate 45, the work of the Gillinder factory in a weight of this type quite logically shows resemblance to that of Bacchus in Birmingham, England. Such weights are among the finest of those made in America.

The Millville, New Jersey, area plays an important role in the annals of American paperweights. "Millville roses" were made in the early 1900's, many at Whitall, Tatum & Company in Millville. Ralph Barber seems to have been foremost in perfecting the rose weights (328, Plate 45); Michael Kane, John Rhulander, Marcus Kuntz, Emil Stanger, and Emil Larson were other craftsmen in the Millville area whose work in paperweights is considered outstanding.

Midwestern glass factories were established following the discovery of natural gas, which provided a constant fuel source. Paperweights have been attributed to the Pittsburgh area, to many factories in Ohio (Ravenna and Zanesville are among the better known), and to Indiana.

Jean S. Melvin's book, *American Glass Paperweights and Their Makers* (1967), has covered so completely the contemporary work in America that little need be added. It should be particularly mentioned that the superb work of Charles Kaziun is unequaled. Other craftsmen such as Harold Hacker, F. D. Whittemore, and Ronald Hansen are displaying increasing excellence in technique and artistry. A departure from traditional motifs and forms is appearing in the work of some of the present-day glass craftsmen. The weights of Dominick Labino of Grand Rapids, Ohio (760, Plate 55), and of Harvey T. Littleton of Madison, Wisconsin (709, Plate 55), offer examples of this trend.

The numbers used to identify the illustrations and their captions are the Bergstrom acquisition numbers. The information that follows the □ device in a caption is Mrs. Bergstrom's attribution of that item and other data about it from her records. Her spellings are retained.

Plate 41

170. Mt. Washington Glass Works, New Bedford, Mass. *Ca.* 1869–94. Large weight. Colorless glass encloses 5 strawberries and 4 white blossoms, each centered in pale green leaves. Flat, smooth base. 4³/₁₆″ (10.6 cm.) diam.

□ Sandwich; "Only 5 of these weights ever made"; acquired Nov., 1958.
(Illus. 54, 1940 Bergstrom book; Illus. 52, subsequent editions. Plate 95, Jokelson, *One Hundred of the Most Important Paperweights.*)

126. New England Glass Co., East Cambridge, Mass. *Ca.* 1852–88. Motif is three-dimensional flower spray with fruit, on white latticinio ground. Bouquet consists of a red flower, white flower, blue flower, and lavender flower, each with a cane center; green leaves, a yellow bud, 2 red berries, and 2 fruit pieces. Concave base. 3¹³/₁₆″ (9.7 cm.) diam.

□ Sandwich; acquired May, 1938.
(Plate XVI, Bergstrom book.)

501. Mt. Washington Glass Works, New Bedford, Mass. *Ca.* 1869–94. Large weight. Colorless glass encloses 5 strawberries and 4 opaque white blossoms, each set in a cluster of dark green leaves. Flat, smooth base. 4″ (10.2 cm.) diam. (Similar to 170.) □ Sandwich; acquired July, 1942.

338. Saint Louis (French). Mid-19th century. Sparkling colorless glass encloses single pink camomile flower with 3 green leaves, pink bud, and green stem. Motif rests on white latticinio ground. Slightly concave base. 3⁵/₁₆″ (8.4 cm.) diam. □ Sandwich; acquired June, 1940.
(Illus. 53, 1940 Bergstrom book; Illus. 51, later editions.)

105. Boston & Sandwich Glass Co., Sandwich, Mass., *ca.* 1855–88; or New England Glass Co., East Cambridge, Mass. Colorless glass encloses cluster of 7 pieces of varicolored fruit, 7 green leaves, and pointed stem. Occasional bubbles near fruit. Concave base. 3³/₁₆″ (8.1 cm.) diam.

□ Sandwich; acquired Dec., 1937.
(Illus. 55, Bergstrom book; Illus. 53, subsequent editions.)

515. Boston & Sandwich Glass Co., Sandwich, Mass. *Ca.* 1855–88. Sparkling clear glass encloses 2 full-blown pink roses, a bud, 2 green leaves, and stem. Motif rests on white latticinio ground. Concave base. 2⅞″ (7.3 cm.) diam.

□ Sandwich; acquired April, 1943.
(Plate 81, Jokelson, *One Hundred of the Most Important Paperweights,* lists as "Origin Unknown.")

51. Boston & Sandwich Glass Co., Sandwich, Mass. *Ca.* 1869–88. Single pink flower with 10 opaque smooth petals has center white cane; dewdrop bubbles appear on petals and leaves. Motif also includes 3 green leaves and stem and a detached second stem with red bud. White latticinio

ground over colorless concave base. 3¹/₁₆″ (7.8 cm.) diam.

□ Sandwich, acquired Aug., 1937.
(Illus. 2, Bergstrom book.)

534. Boston & Sandwich Glass Co., Sandwich, Mass., *ca.* 1870; or New England Glass Co., East Cambridge, Mass., *ca.* 1852–88. Double overlay, geranium-red over white. Colorless glass encloses upright bouquet consisting of opaque white center flower, 4 millefiori canes, and 6 green leaves, all resting on opaque white cushion. Overlay is cut (Bohemian influence in style of cutting) with circular facet on top, round and oblong cuttings on curve. A grooved cutting encircles weight above the level of the motif. Diagonal thumbprint cuts near the colorless base. Underside is flat and smooth. 2⁷/₁₆″ (6.2 cm.) diam.

□ Sandwich, attributed to Nicholas Lutz; acq. Nov., 1943.

22. Boston & Sandwich Glass Co., Sandwich, Mass. *Ca.* 1870–88. Attributed to Nicholas Lutz. Pink flower with 12 smooth pointed petals has center cane similar to a white-and-green Clichy rose. Five emerald-green leaves surround the flower; pointed green stem. Bubbles appear between and on petals. Slightly concave colorless base. 2⅞″ (7.3 cm.) diam.

□ Unidentified; acquired June, 1937.

422. Saint Louis (French). Mid-19th century. Sparkling colorless glass encloses white flower with yellow stamen center, 2 pink strawberries, one darker than the other, 4 green leaves, and stem. White latticinio ground. Base bears trace of pontil mark. 2¹³/₁₆″ (7.2 cm.) diam.

□ Sandwich; acquired Aug., 1941.

423. Boston & Sandwich Glass Co., Sandwich, Mass., *ca.* 1870; or New England Glass Co., East Cambridge, Mass., *ca.* 1852–88. Colorless glass encloses, in white latticinio basket, an upright bouquet consisting of center dark blue flower with cane center, blue, white, and translucent pink flowers, and 3 canes, all surrounded by 6 dark green leaves. Concave colorless base. 2⁹/₁₆″ (6.5 cm.) diam.

□ Baccarat; acquired Aug., 1941.

310. Boston & Sandwich Glass Co., Sandwich, Mass. *Ca.* 1852–88. Hollow, crown weight. Red and green (white edged) ribbon twists alternate with white filigree thread spirals and pink-lined-with-white ribbon spirals, all radiating from a central blue and white pastry-mold cane that bears the date 1825. Under the date are 2 dots, which magnification reveals to be rabbit silhouettes. Encasing glass is cut in spirals; circular cuttings on curve. Concave, colorless base. 2⅜″ (6.1 cm.) diam.

□ Sandwich; acquired April, 1940.
(Illus. 59, 1940 Bergstrom book; Illus. 57, later editions.)

Plate 41

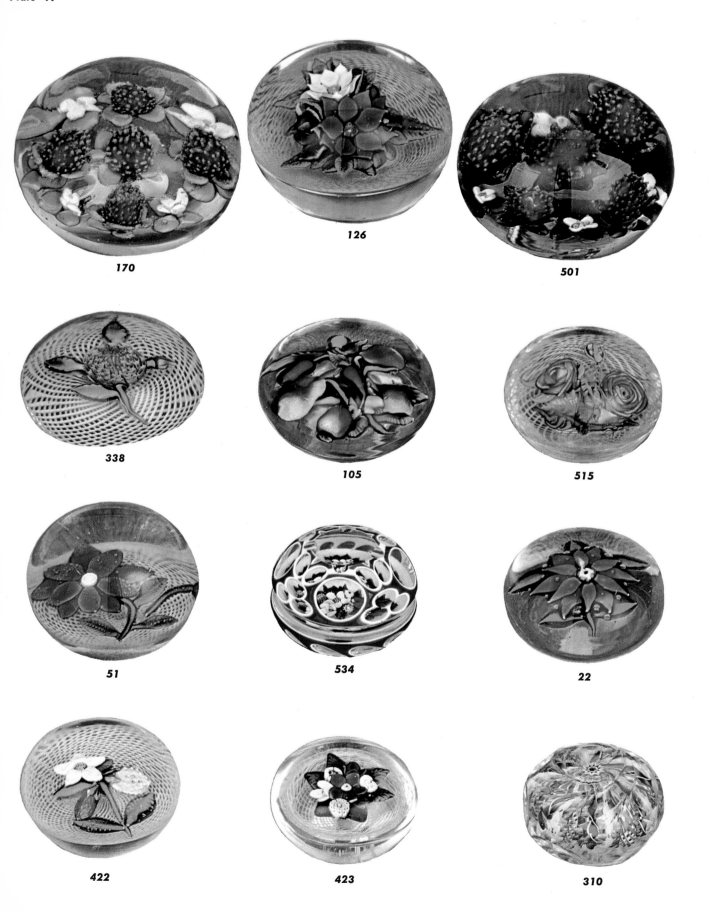

170

126

501

338

105

515

51

534

22

422

423

310

Plate **42**

375. Mt. Washington Glass Works, New Bedford, Mass. *Ca.* 1869–94. Large, heavy weight. Colorless glass encloses three-dimensional motif of white-and-lavender full-blown rose, pink bud, blue bud, 4 red berries, 4 yellow berries, 4 pale green leaves, and darker green stem, all resting on base. Multicolored butterfly at top of rose. 4⁵⁄₁₆″ (10.9 cm.) diam.

☐ Mt. Washington; acquired Nov., 1940.

591. Mt. Washington Glass Works, New Bedford, Mass. *Ca.* 1869–94. Rectangular weight with beveled edges. Colorless glass encloses a 3-dimensional floating spray made up of 4 pink and 3 purple flowers (each with smooth pointed petals and stamen centers), 2 buds, and pale green leaves. Pink and white striped ribbon crosses the stems. Coarse grid cutting on base. 5³⁄₁₆″ × 3½″ × 1¼″ (13.2 cm. × 8.9 cm. × 3.2 cm.).   ☐ Unrecorded.

244. Mt. Washington Glass Works, New Bedford, Mass. *Ca.* 1869–94. Large, heavy weight. Colorless glass encloses 3-dimensional motif consisting of a frilly pink and yellow full-blown rose with goldstone center, 2 buds, 2 fruit pieces, 4 pale green leaves near flower, and smaller green leaves near buds. Sturdy stem is held by woman's hand. Near top of flower are 2 butterflies. 4¼″ (10.8 cm.) diam.

☐ Mt. Washington, New Bedford, Mass.; acq. June, 1939. (Illus. 64, 1940 Bergstrom book; Illus. 62, subsequent editions. Plate #83, Jokelson, *One Hundred of the Most Important Paperweights.*)

262. Pairpoint Corp., New Bedford, Mass. *Ca.* early 1900's. Ovoid, footed weight. Colorless glass encloses red and white strands swirling from base to crown. Flower and leaf engraving appears on top of crown. Underside of circular flat foot is engraved with 3 leaf designs and cross-cuts. 2¾″ (7.0 cm.) diam.

☐ Pairpoint Glass Co.; acquired Sept., 1939. (Illus. 65, 1940 Bergstrom book; Illus. 63, later editions.)

516. Mt. Washington Glass Works, New Bedford, Mass. *Ca.* 1869–94. Motif is made up of a red flower with 12 veined, pointed petals and center of yellow, blue, and white upright petals simulating stamens, 7 dark green leaves surrounding the flower, and a green pointed stem. High, clear crown. 3⁵⁄₁₆″ (8.4 cm.) diam.

☐ Mt. Washington; acquired April, 1943. (Plate #85, Jokelson, *One Hundred of the Most Important Paperweights.*)

440. Attributed to Pairpoint Corp., New Bedford, Mass. *Ca.* 1920–40. Dome-shaped, hollow weight. Colorless glass encloses translucent red cone on which bubbles are spaced in swirl formation. 3¹³⁄₁₆″ (8.1 cm.) diam.

☐ Unidentified; acquired Sept., 1941.

441. New England Glass Co., East Cambridge, Mass. *Ca.* 1852–68. Double overlay weight. Patterned millefiori motif, floating near top of crown, is made up of light pink, blue, and white canes on a white latticinio cushion. The dark red over opaque white overlay is cut with concave hexafoil design on top and punties and leaflike cuts on curve. 2⅞″ (7.3 cm.) diam.   ☐ Sandwich; acquired Sept., 1941.

168. New England Glass Co., East Cambridge, Mass. *Ca.* 1851–68. Single overlay weight. Colorless glass encloses opaque white column, the upper part and top of which are decorated with circles of deep green and pastel-colored canes. The bluish white overlay is cut in a concave quatrefoil at top, 2 circles of round and oval cuts on the curve, and 2 circles of diagonal oval cuts near base. 3¼″ (8.3 cm.) diam.   ☐ Gillerland; acquired Nov., 1938.

(Illus. 78, 1940 Bergstrom book; Illus. 76, later editions.)

195. New England Glass Co., East Cambridge, Mass. *Ca.* 1855. Small bouquet (flat spray), consisting of 3 florets centered among 4 pointed green leaves, floats above a millefiori basket with a rim formed of pink-white-and-blue canes. The canes are drawn downward to form the basket. Allover honeycomb faceting. 3″ (7.6 cm.) diam. (Similar to 478.)

☐ Unidentified; acquired Jan., 1939.

478. New England Glass Co., East Cambridge, Mass. *Ca.* 1855. Small, flat spray consisting of 3 white florets centered among 4 pointed deep green leaves floats above a millefiori basket. Two circles of canes (one blue, one pink) are drawn downward and swirled to form basket. 3¹⁄₁₆″ (7.8 cm.) diam. (Similar to 195.)

☐ Saint Louis (French); acquired Jan., 1942.

120. New England Glass Co., East Cambridge, Mass. *Ca.* 1852–68. Motif, rosette of pastel canes in a circle of 7 spaced white canes with dark centers portraying butterflies or bees, floats above white latticinio ground. 2¹⁵⁄₁₆″ (7.4 cm.) diam.   ☐ Unidentified; acquired May, 1938.

333. New England Glass Co., East Cambridge, Mass. *Ca.* 1852–68. Colorless glass encloses dark purple flower with velvet texture, opaque yellow center, and scattered bubbles, 5 dark green leaves, the stems of which end in a point, and a white latticinio ground. Weight is faceted in a concave quatrefoil on top with flutes between the lobes; two sizes of punties on curve. 2½″ (6.3 cm.) diam.

☐ Gilliland; acquired May, 1940.

294. New England Glass Co., East Cambridge, Mass. *Ca.* 1852–68. Flat spray motif consists of 3 white canes (stylized flower) set on 4 green leaves, and stem, floating above white latticinio ground. Two circles of canes surround the flower, the outer one of ocher alternating with dark blue, and the inner of pastel colors. Faceted on top in concave quatrefoil with flute cuts between the lobes; punties of two sizes on curve. 2⅝″ (6.6 cm.) diam.

☐ South Ferry Glass Co., Gillerland; acq. Nov., 1939. (Illus. 79, 1940 Bergstrom book; Illus. 77, later editions.)

Plate 42

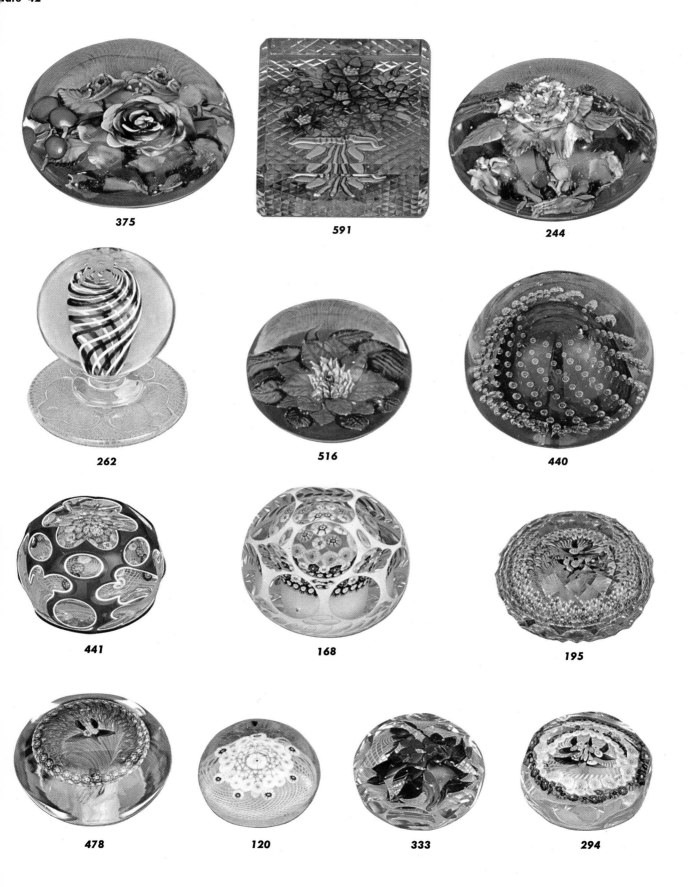

375

591

244

262

516

440

441

168

195

478

120

333

294

Plate 43

121. New England Glass Co., East Cambridge, Mass. *Ca.* 1860. Blown pear weight, brown shading to yellow, has applied colorless glass circular base. Stem touches base; black blossom. 2″ (5.1 cm.) diam. of pear; 3³⁄₁₆″ diam. of base.

☐ Cambridge; acquired May, 1938.
(Illus. 62, 1940 Bergstrom book; Illus. 60, later editions.)

491. New England Glass Co., East Cambridge, Mass. *Ca.* 1860. Blown quince weight, orange shading to yellow, on applied colorless square base. Translucent yellow stem; black blossom. 2¹³⁄₁₆″ (7.2 cm.) diam. of quince. 3⅝″ × 3⅝″ (9.2 cm. × 9.2 cm.) base.

☐ New England Glass Co., acquired April, 1942.

471. New England Glass Co., East Cambridge, Mass. *Ca.* 1860. Blown pear weight, amber shading to green-yellow, on applied circular base. Black blossom and stem. 2⅜″ (6.1 cm.) diam. of pear; 2¹⁵⁄₁₆″ (7.4 cm.) diam. of base.

☐ New England Glass Co.; acquired Dec., 1941.

283. Attributed to Dorflinger Glass Works, White Mills, Pa. 1863–1915. Pair of doorknobs. Brilliant colorless glass encloses floating design of spaced canes in pink, cobalt blue, green, and ocher. Serrated canes enclosing 5-pointed stars predominate and are of finest quality. 1¹³⁄₁₆″ (4.6 cm.) diam. (Canes are similar to those in weights 71, Plate 2; 445, Plate 44; and 254, Plate 62.)

☐ Cambridge; acquired Nov., 1939.

498. Attributed to New England Glass Co., East Cambridge, Mass. *Ca.* 1880. Also resembles work of Nicholas Lutz at Sandwich. Marbrie-type weight. Interior is a sphere of colorless glass that is decorated with red and white loopings, on the center-top of which is set a single red flower with 10 smooth petals and an opaque red and green center with goldstone; pale green stem and 2 leaves. Colorless encasing glass is faceted all over in diamond-shaped cuts. Underside is flat and smooth. 3⅜″ (8.6 cm.) diam.

☐ Libbey Glass Works, Cambridge, Mass.; acquired June, 1942.
(This weight was included in the NEGC exhibit, Toledo Museum of Art, 1963, Cat. No. 250.)

139. New England Glass Co., East Cambridge, Mass. *Ca.* 1860. Fruit weight. Colorless glass encloses a cluster of stemless fruit (5 yellow and red pears, each with bubble at blossom end, and 4 red berries) and 8 dark green leaves all in coarse, white latticinio basket. Trace of pontil mark on top of weight. 2⁷⁄₁₆″ (6.2 cm.) diam.

☐ New England Glass Works; acquired Sept., 1938.
(Illus. 3, Bergstrom book.)

563. Attributed to New England Glass Co., East Cambridge, Mass. *Ca.* 1886. Free-blown pear of opaque white glass shading to rose toward top is encased in transparent amber glass. Stem is amber. Small hole in flattened under-side. 2⅝″ (6.6 cm.) diam. ☐ Unrecorded.

36. Gillinder & Sons, Philadelphia, Pa. *Ca.* 1876. Pressed, round, flat weight has profile bust, to sinister, of Abraham Lincoln on underside in intaglio and frosted. Edge is grooved with 2 rings and frosted. 3¼″ (8.3 cm.) diam.; 1″ (2.6 cm.) deep.

☐ Unidentified; noted "Thompson, N.Y."; acquired April, 1937.

185. Attributed to New England Glass Co., East Cambridge, Mass. *Ca.* 1850–55. Colorless glass with gray tinge encloses floating sulphide, near top of weight, portraying double profile bust portraits, to dexter, of Victoria and Albert. Underside is smooth. 2¹¹⁄₁₆″ (6.8 cm.) diam.

☐ New England Glass Co., Cambridge; acquired Dec., 1938.
(Illus. 63, 1940 Bergstrom book; Illus. 61, subsequent editions. This weight included in NEGC exhibit, Toledo Museum of Art, 1963, Cat. No. 239. Fig. XXVI and Fig. XXVIII, Jokelson, *Sulphides,* show similar sulphides, both identified as Clichy weights.)

97. New England Glass Co., East Cambridge, Mass. *Ca.* 1860. Blown apple weight in translucent amber shades, with applied colorless circular base. Very light in weight. Underside is concave. Apple stem is pressed into base; blossom end shows pontil mark. 2⁵⁄₁₆″ (5.8 cm.) diam. of apple; approx. 2½″ (6.3 cm.) diam. of base.

☐ New England Glass Works, Cambridge; acquired Nov., 1937.
(Illus. 61, 1940 Bergstrom book; Illus. 59, later editions.)

57. American, possibly New England Glass Co., East Cambridge, Mass. *Ca.* 1865. Colorless glass encloses sulphide bust portrait, profile to sinister, of Robert E. Lee on cushion of opaque red, white, and blue strands in pinwheel form. Flat and smooth on underside. 2⁵⁄₁₆″ (5.8 cm.) diam.

☐ Pairpoint; acquired Aug., 1937.
(Illus. 66, 1940 Bergstrom book; Illus. 64, later editions.)

53. American. *Ca.* 1865. Colorless glass encloses sulphide bust portrait, profile to dexter, of Robert E. Lee floating above mica-flaked, colorless cushion. 2¼″ (5.7 cm.) diam.

☐ Unidentified; acquired Aug., 1937.

292. New England Glass Co., East Cambridge, Mass., and probably made as a souvenir weight for the Providence, R.I., Inkstand Co. 1876–88. Pressed, colorless glass reproduction of Plymouth Rock, showing the crack in the rock and the date 1620. A poem and an explanation of the crack are imprinted on edge of base. "Pilgrim Rock Trademark, Providence Inkstand Co., 1876" appears on underside of rim edge. 4⅛″ (10.5 cm.) length.

☐ Inkstand Co., Providence, R.I., 1876; acquired Dec., 1939.
(Illus. 82, 1940 Bergstrom book; Illus. 80, later editions.)

Plate 43

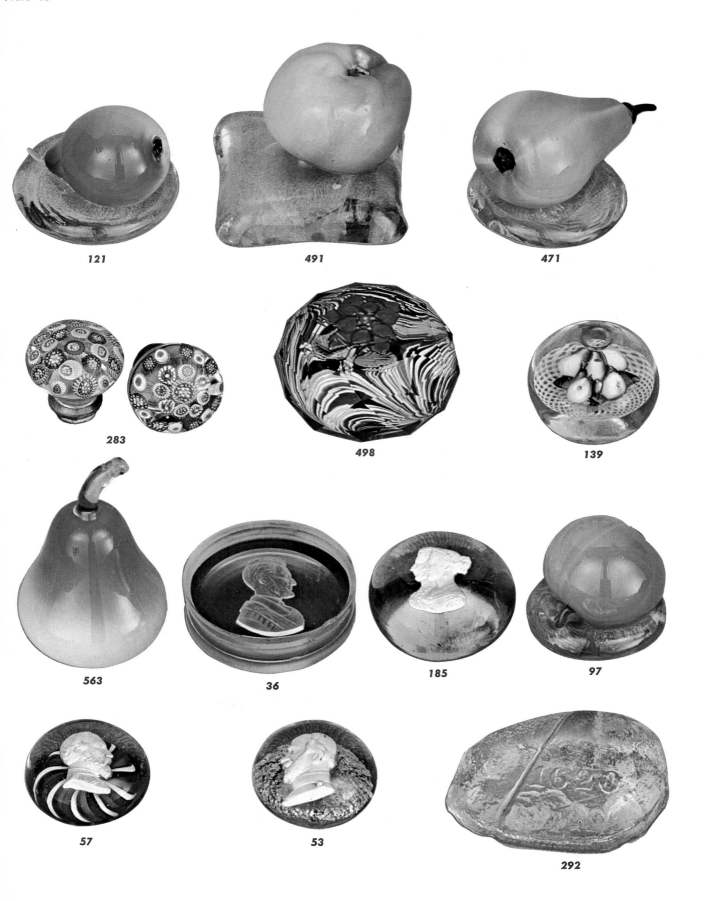

121

491

471

283

498

139

563

36

185

97

57

53

292

Plate 44

529. Tiffany Studios, Corona, Long Island, N.Y. *Ca.* 1900. Doorstop. Pale green glass encloses "under sea" motif near top, with long tentacles in blue-green color extending toward base. "L. C. Tiffany Favrile 3914 D" is signed on the concave underside. 4^{15}/$_{16}$" (12.5 cm.) diam. 4 lbs. weight.

☐ Tiffany Glass; acquired Nov., 1943.

548. Nicholas Lutz, Boston & Sandwich Glass Co., Sandwich, Mass., *ca.* 1875; or Saint Louis (French), *ca.* 1852. Small, flat-sided, striped, glass flask. Colorless glass encloses twists of yellow and blue ribbon, and of red and green ribbon, each alternating with twists of white filigree strands. At neck, the twists are drawn into strands. Circular facet is cut on each flat side; swirl cuttings on ends. 3" (7.6 cm.) width; 3^{15}/$_{16}$" (10.1 cm.) height. ☐ Unrecorded.
(V. Van Tassel, in *American Glass,* p. 118, illustrates similar flask identified as Nicholas Lutz, Boston & Sandwich Glass Co., *ca.* 1875, Metropolitan Museum of Art. Some time after the publication of Van Tassel's book, Victor Lutz told George S. McKearin that his father [Nicholas Lutz] made these flasks at the Saint Louis factory and brought them to America. If that is true, the date of manufacture would be about 1852.)

320. Tiffany Studios, Corona, Long Island, N.Y. *Ca.* 1900. Doorstop. Aquamarine glass encloses "under sea" motif of rocks and sea urchins. Canes appear in the design, and green strands of glass near the surface. Underside is concave and unsigned. 5^{5}/$_{16}$" (13.4 cm.) diam. 6 lbs. weight.

☐ Tiffany; acquired April, 1940.
(Illus. 68, 1940 Bergstrom book; Illus. 66, subsequent editions.)

329. Philip Bunamo, Union Glass Co., Somerville, Mass. *Ca.* 1910. Large, heavy weight with high clear crown. The motif includes 3 opaque white pigs looking into central green basket, all set on a sparse multiple-colored pebble ground. Underside is smooth and flat. 3^{7}/$_{8}$" (9.9 cm.) diam.

☐ Phillip Bonano, Somerville, Mass., *ca.* 1864; acquired May, 1940.
(Illus. 67, 1940 Bergstrom book; Illus. 65, subsequent editions.)

718. Attributed to Fostoria Glass Co., Fostoria, Ohio. *Ca.* 1880–1900. Motif is a 4-petaled lily of red and pink mottled glass over opaque white, with an elongated central bubble. The petals bend downward, extending to base, each with an elongated bubble near tip. Underside is flat; frosted around pontil mark. 3^{11}/$_{16}$" (9.4 cm.) diam.

☐ Unrecorded.

453. Union Glass Co., Somerville, Mass. Probably made by Philip Bunamo, *ca.* 1910. Large heavy weight with high clear crown. Motif includes 2 opaque white doves with pink wings looking into a central green nest with 2 eggs. Surrounding nest are 2 pink and blue flowers with pale green leaves. Bubbles on birds and flowers. Underside is smooth and flat. 3^{7}/$_{8}$" (9.9 cm.) diam.   ☐ Unrecorded.

321. Probably Boston & Sandwich Glass Co., Sandwich, Mass.; possibly New England Glass Co., East Cambridge, Mass. *Ca.* 1853–60. Pair of mercury glass doorknobs. One is flashed with green, the other with cobalt blue. Intricate, decorative faceting extending onto curve simulates a 6-pointed star. 2^{11}/$_{16}$" (6.8 cm.) diam. of blue knob; 2^{13}/$_{16}$" (7.2 cm.) diam. of green knob. (Mercury knobs were also made at Union Glass Co., Somerville, Mass., 1862.)

☐ Sandwich; acquired April, 1940.
(Illus. 58, 1940 Bergstrom book; Illus. 56, subsequent editions.)

445. American; possibly Dorflinger, White Mills, Pa. Heavy sparkling glass encloses upright 4-petaled motif, each petal with single large cane at tip. Petals are opaque white overlaid with red, cobalt blue, and green, and rest on multiple-colored ground. Elongated bubble floats in center. The canes are of superior quality, serrated, enclosing 5-pointed stars in various designs. 3^{1}/$_{4}$" (8.3 cm.) diam. (The 4 canes are similar to those in 71, Plate 2; 283, Plate 43; and 254, Plate 62.)

☐ Saint Louis (French); acquired Sept., 1941.

421. New England Glass Co., East Cambridge, Mass. *Ca.* 1855. Blown mercury glass weight has floral spray engraving on top surface. On underside of weight, beneath the casing glass, is a hole about ½" diam. (no disk). (Similar weights are known with disk marked NEGC.) 3^{3}/$_{16}$" (8.1 cm.) diam.

☐ Sandwich; acquired Aug., 1941.

12. Boston & Sandwich Glass Co., Sandwich, Mass. 1851–88. Cobalt blue clematis with 10 pointed petals and cane center, green stem, and 3 green leaves rests on red and white jasper ground. Underside is concave. 2^{5}/$_{8}$" (6.6 cm.) diam. ☐ Sandwich; acquired May, 1936.

172. Boston & Sandwich Glass Co., Sandwich, Mass. *Ca.* 1880. Blown weight. Decalcomania transfers of Victorian mottoes, flowers, birds, and so on, on an opaque white blown sphere are encased in transparent pale green glass. Circular opening on underside is filled with ceramic clay. 2^{7}/$_{8}$" (7.3 cm.) diam. ☐ Sandwich; acquired Nov., 1938.
(Illus. 60, 1940 Bergstrom book; Illus. 58, subsequent editions.)

281. Boston & Sandwich Glass Co., Sandwich, Mass. 1851–88. Single flower motif. Flower has 5 opaque white petals (peripheral edges turn up) on which a white star is centered. Star has pink-white-and-yellow center. Motif also includes a bud on a stem and 5 green leaves. Ground is red and white jasper above a colorless base. Underside is concave. 2^{7}/$_{8}$" (7.3 cm.) diam.

☐ Sandwich; acquired Nov., 1939.

Plate 44

529

548

320

329

718

453

321

445

421

12

172

281

Plate 45

466. Attributed to Ravenna Glass Company, Ravenna, Ohio. Late-19th century. Colorless glass encloses opaque white lily with 5 narrow petals. Central bubble and stem of lily extend to base. Five "trumpet" flowers with center bubbles in yellow, green, light blue, dark blue, and white appear at periphery at base. Underside is flat and frosted and has pontil mark. (This design was patented by Henry Miller, Pittsburgh, Pa., 1890.) 3½″ (8.9 cm.) diam.

☐ Ravenna Glass Co.; acquired Oct., 1941.

328. Ralph Barber, Whitall Tatum & Co., Millville, N.J. 1905–12. Colorless glass with gray tinge encloses pink rose with 12 petals shading to lighter pink; green stem supports 2 branches, one with 5 green leaves and a red bud, the other with 4 green leaves. Globular weight is mounted on colorless standard with waisted stem rising from a circular foot with pontil mark. Rose faces the side of the weight. (An affidavit in the Bergstrom files, signed by Lewis I. Hudson, reads: "This weight was made by Ralph Barber at Whitall Tatum and given to Mr. Franklin Pierce, his superintendent, who had it in his possession until his death in 1913. His widow, Mrs. Phoebe Pierce, gave it to Mr. Hudson and it was in his possession until April, 1940, when he sold it to Mrs. Bergstrom." *Note:* Mr. Hudson was employed by Whitall Tatum at the time Mr. Barber made this and other weights, and had seen him making rose weights.) 3½″ (8.9 cm.) diam.; 6″ (15.2 cm.) overall height.

☐ Ralph Barber, Millville, N.J.; acquired April, 1940. (Plate XVIII, Bergstrom book.)

3. Boston & Sandwich Glass Co., Sandwich, Mass. *Ca.* 1852–88. "End of Day" weight. Sparkling glass encloses a variety of millefiori canes, opaque ribbon twists, and segments of white filigree, assembled at random; small bubbles are spaced throughout. Underside is concave. 2⅞″ (7.3 cm.) diam.

☐ Unidentified; acquired June, 1936.

63. Boston & Sandwich Glass Co., Sandwich, Mass. *Ca.* 1852–88. Macédoine weight. Sparkling glass encloses two layers of a variety of millefiori canes, segments of opaque rods, and bits of goldstone, assembled at random. Central bubble appears near top of crown, and spaced smaller

bubbles at periphery. Underside is flat and smooth. 2⁹⁄₁₆″ (6.8 cm.) diam.

☐ Unidentified; acquired Sept., 1939.

141. Gillinder & Sons, Philadelphia, Pa. *Ca.* 1861–71. Probably Wm. T. Gillinder; possibly Charles Challinor (after 1867). Tuft motif consists of concentric circles of hollow ruffled canes in pale yellow, white, and, at the periphery, pink-lined canes. At center is an opaque white cane with a woman's profile silhouetted in black. Punty on top, and 6 vertical oval cuts on curve. Flat smooth underside. (Similar silhouette center cane in weight 419, Plate 34.) 3³⁄₁₆″ (8.1 cm.) diam.

☐ Saint Louis; acquired Oct., 1938.
(Ex collection of Oscar Wilde.)

675. Midwest, American. Late-19th–early-20th century. Brilliant, colorless glass encloses a central red lily with 5 narrow petals and bubble center, close to top of crown, the red stem extending to varicolored mottled and opaque white ground, which is pulled down in 5 sections. Bubble between each 2 sections, at periphery. Underside is flat and frosted. 2¹³⁄₁₆″ (7.2 cm.) diam.

Acquired 1963.

50. Origin unknown. Free-formed figure of a swan in sapphire blue glass. Pontil mark on swan's back. "Guaranteed old" appears on a paper sticker. 3¼″ (8.3 cm.) wing to wing; 3¾″ (9.6 cm.) height. (Similar to hen that is top part of weight 124, Plate 33.)

☐ Stiegel glass (notation: Lockport, N.Y.); acquired Aug., 1937.

418. Attributed to Millville, N.J., area. *Ca.* 1910. A group of ten collar buttons or shirt studs; colorless glass encloses tiny millefiori canes. (Winfield Rutter, Millville, N.J., is known to have made collar buttons and studs about 1940.)

☐ Unrecorded.

461. Zanesville Glass Works, Zanesville, Ohio. Mid-19th century. Dark brown, free-formed glass turkey or rooster on cylindrical stem rising from smooth, flat, circular foot. 2¹³⁄₁₆″ (7.2 cm.) diam. of foot.

☐ Zanesville Glass Works, Zanesville, Ohio; acquired Oct., 1941.

Plate 45

466

328

3

63

141

675

50

418

461

Plate 46

225. Millville, N.J. 1905–12. Amber rose shading to pink has 12 petals and 3 translucent green leaves. Three punties on curve. Circular colorless foot. 3¼″ (8.3 cm.) diam.

☐ Millville; acquired Feb., 1939.

393. Millville, N.J. 1905–12. Colorless glass encloses yellow rose with yellow stamen and 15 petals and 3 pointed green leaves with lighter green edges. Circular foot has pontil mark. 3⅝″ (9.2 cm.) diam.

☐ Millville; acquired March, 1941.

395. Millville, N.J. 1905–12. Dark red rose shading to pink has 16 petals and 3 green leaves. Circular foot bears pontil mark. 3¾″ (9.6 cm.) diam.

☐ Millville, New Jersey; acquired March, 1941.

236. Millville, N.J. 1905–12. Pink rose shading to lighter pink has 12 petals; 3 pale green leaves extend to top of rose. Motif floats above base. Underside of foot is concave. 3¹¹⁄₁₆″ (9.4 cm.) diam.

☐ Millville; acquired June, 1939.
(Illus. 69, 1940 Bergstrom book; Illus. 67, subsequent editions.)

323. Vineland, N.J., attributed to Emil Larson. 1934–35. Red rose shading to lighter tones has 12 petals, one stamen, and 3 dark green leaves. Enclosing glass has gray tinge. Pontil mark on underside of foot. 3⅝″ (9.2 cm.) diam.

☐ Jersey; acquired April, 1940.

394. Millville, N.J. 1905–12. Pink rose with 16 petals and 3 dark green leaves floats near top of crown. Circular foot bears pontil mark on underside. 3⅝″ (9.2 cm.) diam.

☐ Millville; acquired March, 1941.

237. Millville, N.J. Early 1900's. Pink water lily with 14 tuberous petals and yellow stamen is surrounded by alternating opaque white and opaque green, pointed, upright leaves. Motif fills the globular colorless glass encasement. Circular foot is smooth on underside with concave center. 3⅜″ (8.6 cm.) diam.

☐ Millville; acquired June, 1939.
(Plate XIX, Bergstrom book.)

200. Millville, N.J., attributed to Ralph Barber. 1905–12. Floating above base is a pink rose with 11 thick petals with paler pink tips; 3 very dark green leaves extend above flower. Thin, narrow foot is frosted on underside. 3⅝″ (9.2 cm.) diam.

☐ Millville; acquired Jan., 1939.

272. Millville, N.J., attributed to Ralph Barber. 1905–12. Floating above the base is a pink, shading to lighter pink, rose with 11 thin petals, somewhat translucent, and 2 green stems that cross at base of rose. Each stem supports small green leaves, which extend upward to top of flower. Circular colorless foot is concave on underside. 3⅝″ (9.2 cm.) diam.

☐ Millville; acquired Nov., 1939.

171. Millville, N.J. 1905–12. Pale yellow rose has 12 petals shading to white at tips and 3 very dark green leaves, which extend upward around the flower. Motif floats above colorless flat base. Not footed. 3⁷⁄₁₆″ (8.7 cm.) diam.

☐ Millville; acquired Nov., 1938.

270. Millville, N.J., attributed to Michael Kane. *Ca.* 1900. Colorless glass encloses floating motif made of finely ground colored glass and portraying a hunter in blue coat shooting at wildfowl, with brown and white dog pointing. A fallen log lies in foreground. Allover geometric faceting, the facets larger near the flat, smooth base. 3¾″ (9.6 cm.) diam.

☐ Millville; acquired Oct., 1939.
(Illus. 77, 1940 Bergstrom book; Illus. 75, subsequent editions.)

398. Millville, N.J. 1905–12. Motif consisting of red rose shading to light pink at tips of the 13 petals, and 3 green leaves, rests on base with high clear crown above. Smooth underside is not footed. Trace of pontil mark at top of crown. 3½″ (8.9 cm.) diam.

☐ Millville; acquired Feb., 1941.

Plate 46

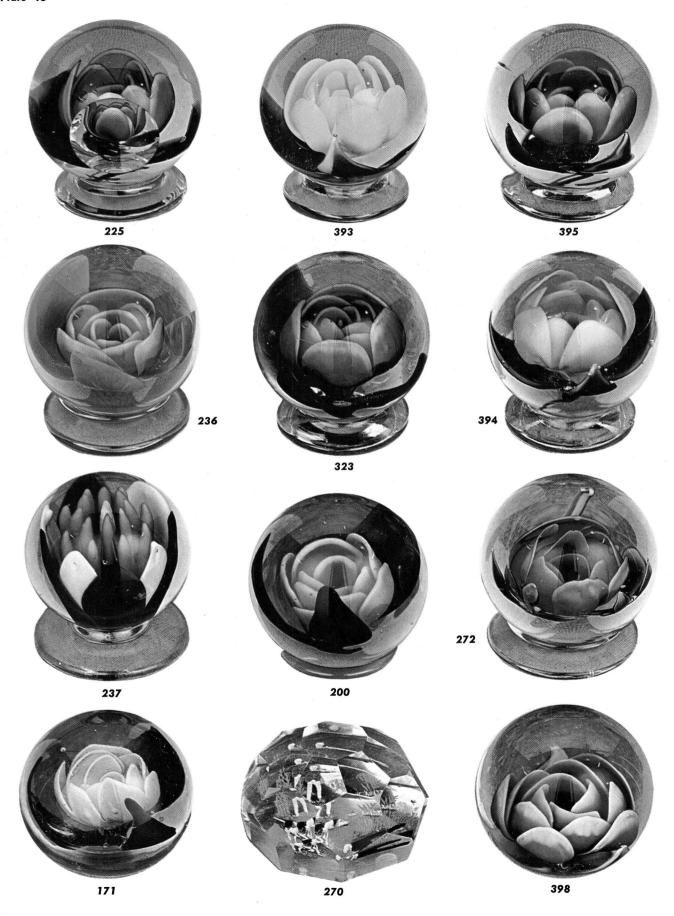

225

393

395

236

323

394

237

200

272

171

270

398

Plate 47

349. Millville, N.J., probably the work of Emil Stanger or Marcus Kuntz. *Ca.* 1900. Opaque white lily design (umbrella form) with spatter of yellow, red, brown, and blue glass. Stem of lily is drawn to a point at base. The stemmed, circular, flat foot has pontil mark. 3⅛″ (7.9 cm.) diam; 4⅝″ (11.7 cm.) overall height.

☐ John Rhulander, Millville, New Jersey; acquired July, 1940.

380. Millville, N.J. 1880–1910. Colorless glass ink bottle with stopper. The spherical base encloses "devil's fire" design—mottled red, light blue, dark blue, and opaque white glass drawn upward into peaks and slightly swirled. Pointed stopper encloses red, white, and blue spiral strands. Trace of pontil mark remains on the slightly concave underside. 3½″ (8.9 cm.) diam.; 7″ (17.8 cm.) overall height.

☐ Millville; acquired Nov., 1940.

34. Millville, N.J., attributed to Emil Stanger. *Ca.* 1900. Tall inkstand with large stopper. In both bottle and stopper is an opaque white lily (umbrella form and center bubble) that is decorated with coarse spatter of yellow, red, and blue glass. Lily stems are drawn downward to base. Circular foot with collar has pontil mark on underside. 3⅜″ (8.6 cm.) diam. of bottle; 2¾″ (7.0 cm.) diam. of stopper; 10¼″ (26.0 cm.) overall height.

☐ Millville, South Jersey; acquired June, 1937.
(Illus. 75, 1940 Bergstrom book; Illus. 73, later editions.)

350. John Rhulander, Millville, N.J. Early-20th century. Large, opaque white lily set high in the crown has a tapered stem extending to base. Lily has bubble center, and there are smaller bubbles between the 8 sections of the flower. The globe of encasing glass has a gray tinge. Underside of circular foot is slightly concave. 3⅜″ (8.6 cm.) diam.

☐ John Rhulander, Millville; acquired July, 1940.

138. Millville, N.J., attributed to Michael Kane. *Ca.* 1900. Thin, flat motif in opaque white glass portrays a dog flushing a covey of quail, with the word "Faithful" overhead; motif and word are placed vertically within the globe of glass, which has gray tinge. Circular colorless foot has pontil mark on underside. 3⁷⁄₁₆″ (8.7 cm.) diam.

☐ Millville; acquired Sept., 1938.
(Illus. 74, 1940 Bergstrom book; Illus. 72, later editions.)

84. Millville, N.J., probably the work of Emil Stanger or Marcus Kuntz. *Ca.* 1900. Colorless glass encloses opaque white lily design (umbrella form) with coarse spatter of yellow, red, green, and blue glass. Stem is drawn to a point at base. Small bubble appears at center near flat circular cutting on top of weight. Circular foot has trace of pontil mark. 3½″ (8.9 cm.) diam.

☐ Millville; acquired Oct., 1937.
(Illus. 73, 1940 Bergstrom book; Illus. 71, subsequent editions.)

492. Millville, N.J., attributed to Michael Kane. 1880–1910. Thin, flat motif of finely ground, opaque white glass portraying a ship with red flag and a blue sea is placed vertically within the globe of glass, which has gray tinge. Three punties are cut on the curve. Circular foot bears pontil mark. 3¾″ (9.6 cm.) diam.

☐ Millville; acquired April, 1942.
(Similar to Illus. 76, 1940 Bergstrom book; Illus. 74, subsequent editions.)

370. Millville, N.J., attributed to Michael Kane. 1880–1910. Thin, flat motif of finely ground, opaque white glass includes a log cabin, fence, double path to door, tree, and "Home Sweet Home" in a half-circle above the cabin. Motif is set vertically in center of a globe of colorless glass. One punty is cut on top of weight, and two on the curve, framing the motif on each side. Circular foot is smooth on underside and slightly concave. 3½″ (8.9 cm.) diam.

☐ Millville; acquired Oct., 1940.

285. Millville, N.J. 1880–1910. Dome-shaped weight with flat base encloses a wreath design in thin opaque white glass, with the motto "Remember Me" and leaves encircling a central spray of rosebud, stem, and 4 leaves. This flat motif floats above a layer of multiple-colored pebble ground over a colorless base. Punty on top of weight. Underside is smooth and has concavity at center. 3⁵⁄₁₆″ (8.4 cm.) diam.

☐ Millville; acquired Nov., 1939.
(Illus. 70, 1940 Bergstrom book; Illus. 68, subsequent editions.)

629. Millville, N.J., probably Whitall Tatum & Co. Early-20th century. Wrought-iron crimper with wooden handle, used in making the Millville-type rose weights. 2⅛″ (5.4 cm.) diam.

☐ Unrecorded.
(Illus. 72, 1940 Bergstrom book; Illus. 70, subsequent editions.)

285A. Millville, N.J. 1880–1910. Circular steel plate with incised cut of "Remember Me" (in reverse) in wreath motif on one side (used in making weight 285), and, on the other side, incised cut of "Friendship" (in reverse), 2 hearts with arrow, and branch of leaves. 2½″ (6.3 cm.) diam.

☐ Unrecorded.
(Illus. 71, 1940 Bergstrom book; Illus. 69, subsequent editions.)

18. Millville, N.J., attributed to Marcus Kuntz. 1880–1910. Colorless glass with gray tinge encloses "devil's fire" motif. Strands of deep blue and red glass are drawn and swirled toward top of weight from a ground of mottled glass. Pontil mark on underside. 3⁹⁄₁₆″ (9.1 cm.) diam.

☐ Unidentified; acquired May, 1936.

Plate 47

349

380

34

350

138

84

492

370

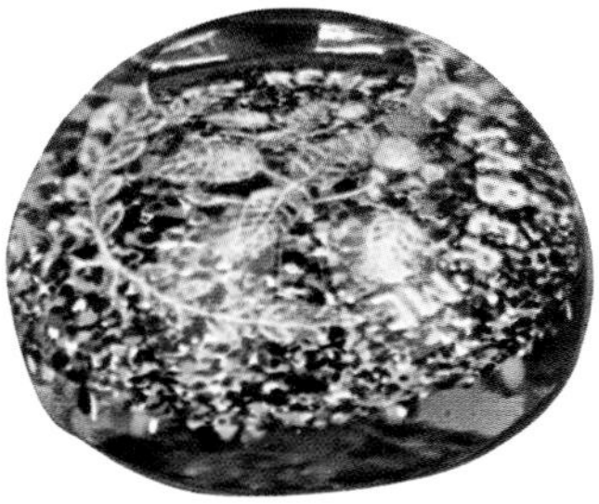

285

629

285A

18

Plate 48

109. Origin unknown; probably American. Spherical-shaped ink bottle of colorless glass with ball-shaped stopper. Base of bottle encloses two layers of varicolored glass in waves, with 4 elongated bubbles. Pontil mark on underside. Neck of bottle has thick, flat lip. 3¼″ (8.3 cm.) diam.; 4½″ (11.4 cm.) overall height.

☐ Unidentified; acquired Dec., 1937.

411. Millville, N.J. *Ca.* 1905. Opaque white rose with 11 petals is suspended in a sparkling sphere of colorless glass. Tips of some petals are black with slight red tinge. No leaves. The foot is not applied, but formed from the same gather that encloses the rose. Pontil mark on underside. 3″ (7.6 cm.) diam.; 4¼″ (10.8 cm.) overall height.

☐ Jersey rose; acquired May, 1941.

371. Millville, N.J., attributed to Marcus Kuntz. 1880–1910. Conical-shaped ink bottle with "devil's fire" decoration. Mottled colored glass in base of bottle is drawn up into peaks. Both the bottle and stopper are faceted in geometric cuts, the cutting being attributed to a Mr. Clunn. Underside of bottle is concave. 3⅛″ (7.9 cm.) diam.; 5½″ (13.9 cm.) overall height.

☐ Millville; acquired Oct., 1940.

192. Whitall Tatum & Co., Millville, N.J. 1905–12. Very heavy globe of colorless glass encloses opaque white rose with 19 petals (no leaves) drawn to a point at base. Circular foot has pontil mark on underside. (The form of this rose is similar to that of roses attributed to Ralph Barber.) 3⁹⁄₁₆″ (9.1 cm.) diam.

☐ Millville; acquired Jan., 1939.

518. Millville, N.J. *Ca.* 1900. Globe of colorless glass encloses opaque white calla lily bud with red stamen. The bud rests on base of weight. Flat, circular foot has pontil mark on underside. 3½″ (8.9 cm.) diam.

☐ Millville; acquired April, 1943.

235. Millville, N.J. 1905–12. Opaque white rose with 12 petals, no leaves, is suspended in a globe of colorless glass. Circular foot has pontil mark on underside. (The petals of this rose are similar to tulip petals.) 3⅝″ (9.2 cm.) diam.

☐ Millville; acquired June, 1939.

511. Origin unknown; American. Globular weight. Dark green glass encloses rose with 11 pink and white striped petals; small bubble in center. Circular foot has pontil mark on underside. 2¹⁵⁄₁₆″ (7.4 cm.) diam.

☐ Unidentified; acquired Nov., 1942.

527. Millville, N.J. *Ca.* 1900. Sparkling colorless glass encloses opaque white crocus with 5 petals and a yellow-tipped stamen; no leaves. Low conical, circular foot has pontil mark on underside. 2⅞″ (7.3 cm.) diam.

☐ Unrecorded.

77. Attributed to Millville, N.J. Early-20th century. Globe of colorless glass encloses pink rose shading to lighter pink, with the 11 thick petals drawn to a point on translucent green dish-shaped ground (no leaves) over clear base. Underside of weight is flat and smooth. 3³⁄₁₆″ (8.1 cm.) diam.

☐ Millville; acquired Sept., 1937.

554. Attributed to Millville, N.J. 1880–1905. Dome-shaped weight. Colorless glass encloses floating flat design in opaque white portraying a cross on a mound, foliage, and ground, with "Rock of Ages" above the cross. Six red dots appear on the cross. Flat base shows pontil mark. (Similar in construction to 537.) 3¼″ (8.3 cm.) diam.

☐ Unrecorded.

537. Attributed to Millville, N.J. 1880–1905. Dome-shaped weight. Colorless glass encloses opaque white, flat design of sailboat with flag, birds in flight, a lighthouse, and waves, placed on translucent dark amber ground. The amber ground is approximately ½-inch thick. Flat base has circular frosted concavity at center. 3⁵⁄₁₆″ (8.4 cm.) diam. (Similar in construction to 554.)

☐ Unrecorded.

82. Attributed to Millville, N.J. *Ca.* 1900. Colorless glass with yellow tinge encloses floating, flat, opaque white motto "Home Sweet Home to Mother" over pink, yellow, and white spatter ground, which is drawn down into 6 sections. Below ground is translucent pink glass simulating a "dish" or basket form. Pontil mark on underside. 3⅜″ (8.6 cm.) diam.

☐ Unidentified; acquired Oct., 1937.

Plate 48

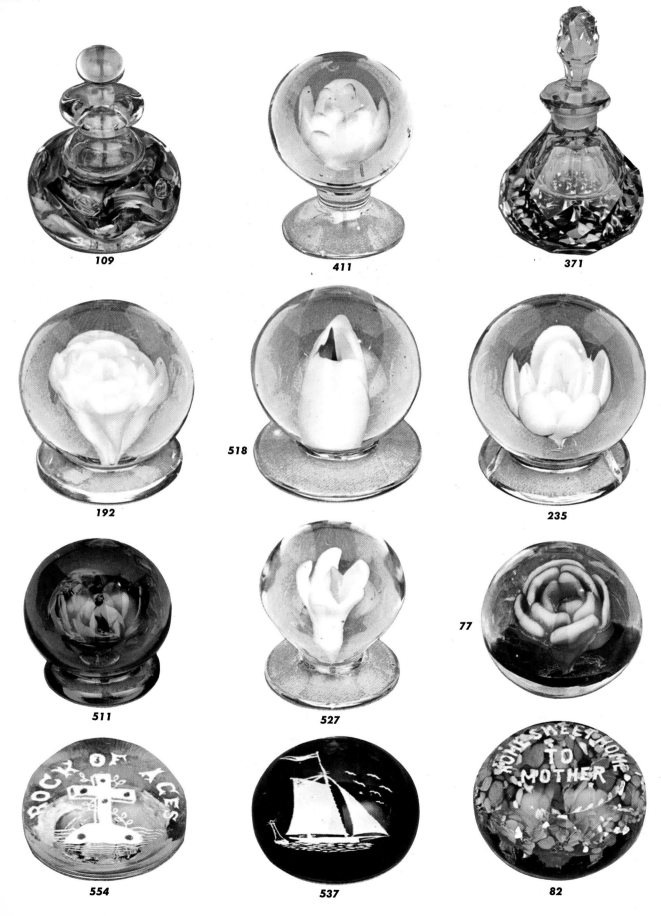

109

411

371

192

518

235

511

527

77

554

537

82

Plate 49

356. Ravenna Glass Works, Ravenna, Ohio. Pair of globular mantel ornaments with standards (separate pieces). Glass ball encloses varicolored pebble glass layer depressed by 4 elongated bubbles, which extend to base, and a large center bubble. Applied colorless glass threads encircle the stems of the pale green glass standards, which enclose colored strands. Conical foot has trace of pontil mark on underside. 3⅜″ (8.6 cm.) diam. of ball; 7¾″ (19.7 cm.) overall height.

☐ Ravenna; acquired Aug., 1940.

741. American, Ohio or Indiana. *Ca.* 1920–30. Doorstop. Colorless glass encloses large, dark red center flower near crown with 5 velvet-textured petals and center bubble; stem of flower extends to base. Surrounding the stem is band of opaque white glass with lacelike appearance, drawn to base at 4 intervals with 4 elongated bubbles. Red spatter ground matches the flower. Pontil mark on underside. 5⅞″ (14.9 cm.) diam.; 9 lbs. weight.

☐ Unrecorded.

460. Attributed to Pittsburgh, Pa. Six-sided colorless glass inkwell has ruby glass inside in the shape of a wineglass. The six edges are faceted in notches. Stopper is hexagonal with tapered, hollow finial; its edges are also notched. Flat, smooth base. 6¾″ (17.2 cm.) overall height.

☐ Hendrix Works, Findley, Ohio; acquired Oct., 1941. (McKearin, *American Glass,* Plate 57A #6, attributed similar item to Pittsburgh. This type also made at Tiffin Glass Co., Tiffin, Ohio.)

719. John St. Clair, Elwood, Ind. *Ca.* 1930. Doorstop. Aquamarine glass encloses blue and white spatter glass design in 2 layers simulating lily-type pattern, with 6 elongated bubbles and a large central bubble. Coarse pebble ground is blue and white glass. Pontil mark on underside. 8¹⁄₁₆″ (20.4 cm.) diam.; 11½ lbs. weight.

Gift of Mr. Joseph St. Clair, 1964.

43. Origin unknown. Colorless glass weight. Encased, blown-molded sphere has allover top design of closely spaced indentations; the underside motif is radial strands of glass, ending in points at center. The indentations, when encased, trapped pockets of air, giving the appearance of silvered glass. 3⅝″ (9.2 cm.) diam. (Similar construction to 248, Plate 34. Similarly constructed balls with red or blue interior, probably used for newel posts, have been seen in France; they are said to be of *ancien* French manufacture.)

☐ Unidentified; acquired June, 1937.

16. Benjamin F. Leach, Fowlerton, Ind. 1896–98. Heavy, elongated spherical weight. Colorless glass encloses arches of small bits of opaque yellow glass with air bubbles—a large center bubble and 4 bubbles between arches—giving a sparkling, mossy appearance. Translucent brown ground. Underside is flat and frosted. 3⅜″ (8.6 cm.) diam.

☐ Fowlerton; acquired March, 1935.
(Illus. 83, 1940 Bergstrom book; Illus. 81, subsequent editions.)

586. Edward Rithner, Wellsburg, W. Va. 1930–50. Inside the weight is a layer of gold ruby spatter over opaque white, through which 4 elongated bubbles extend to the colorless base. "Bergstrom" in white powdered glass floats near the crown. 3⁷⁄₁₆″ (8.7 cm.) diam.

☐ Unrecorded.

596. American. Ovoid-shaped weight. Colorless glass encloses circlets of spaced bubbles near surface. Smooth, frosted underside. Paper sticker reads "Handmade, made in U.S.A. American Cut Crystal Corp." 2⁹⁄₁₆″ (6.5 cm.) diam.

☐ Unrecorded.

31. American. *Ca.* 1900. Dome-shaped colorless glass weight. Floating above a varicolored, coarse, pebble ground, with scattered bubbles, is a chain of glass made up of 3 large links. One link is green and yellow, one is red, white, and blue, and the third is red and white. Pontil mark on underside. 3⁵⁄₁₆″ (8.4 cm.) diam.

☐ Unidentified; titled this weight "The Atlantic Cable"; acquired June, 1937.

432. Origin unknown; probably American. Seal of colorless glass has diamond-faceted handle enclosing coarse thread spirals of dark blue and white. Monogram "EB" is engraved on the flat end. 3¼″ (8.3 cm.) length.

☐ Unidentified; acquired Aug., 1941.

728. American; probably Ohio or Indiana. 1920–50. Darner. Sparkling glass encloses red 5-petaled lily-type flower. The petals have a lacy appearance. Bubble center, green stem, and opaque white strands with 5 elongated bubbles all extend to end of handle. 5¼″ (13.3 cm.) length.

☐ Unrecorded.

Plate 49

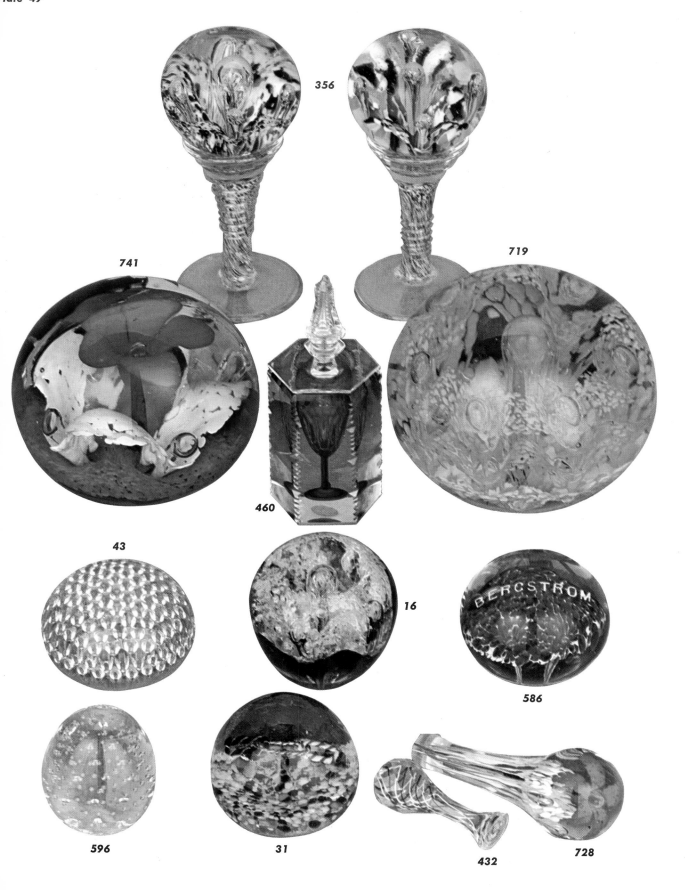

356

741

719

460

43

16

586

596

31

432

728

Plate 50

620. Attributed to Boston & Sandwich Glass Co., Sandwich, Mass. *Ca.* 1880. Six paperweight buttons are made from millefiori cane with dog in center, 2 tiny roses at periphery, green leaves, and goldstone, on a latticinio ground over amethyst base. Each button is approximately ½″ (1.3 cm.) diam.

☐ Unrecorded.

374. Attributed to Crystal Art Glass Co., Cambridge, Ohio, *Ca.* 1930's. Probably the work of Charles or John Degenhart. Gear shift knob. Colorless glass encloses opaque white plaque outlined in blue, on which the name "R. Barber" appears in black letters. Plaque rests on varicolored spatter cushion. At corners of plaque are 4 small lily-type flowers, 2 yellow and 2 pink, each with bubble center. Knob has flat top and geometric facets on curve. 2″ (5.1 cm.) diam. (The dealer who sold this knob identified it as the work of Ralph Barber, Millville, N.J., in the early 1900's.)

☐ Unidentified, acquired Nov., 1940.

642. Origin unknown; probably 19th century (rare). Paperweight button. Vaseline-colored glass encloses sulphide portrait head, profile to dexter, on translucent cranberry ground. 11⁄16″ (1.7 cm.) diam.

☐ Unrecorded.

636. Attributed to Charles Kaziun, Brockton, Mass. *Ca.* 1940. Paperweight tie pin. Colorless glass encloses fine white and blue filigree threads with red dot in center.

☐ Unrecorded.

65. Origin unknown; possibly Sandwich, Mass. Colorless glass encloses "pincushion" motif in salmon pink shading to amber, over opaque white; large center bubble and small bubbles are spaced in the diamond quilt pattern of the cushion. High clear crown. Underside of weight is flat and smooth. (Also appears in green.) 2 15⁄16″ (7.4 cm.) diam.

☐ Bristol; acquired Sept., 1937.

612A. Origin unknown. Colorless glass bead has vari colored millefiori canes near surface. The colors resembl those seen in Chinese weights. ¾″ (1.9 cm.) diam.

☐ Unrecorded.

638. Charles Kaziun, Brockton, Mass. *Ca.* 1944. Paper weight buttons of varying sizes with roses, filigree threads and goldstone. (The button in this group resembling morning glory is probably the work of Thure Erickson Brockton, Mass. *Ca.* 1945.)

☐ Unrecorded.

639. Origin unknown. Three paperweight buttons (n shanks), each an individual millefiori cane encased in color less glass. One is a pink Clichy rose with green, another a pastry-mold cane. 5⁄16″ (.7 cm.) diam. each.

☐ Unrecorded.

619. Attributed to Frank X. Weinman, Boston, Mass. *Ca* 1940. A pair of translucent amethyst cuff links with gold stone enclosed at knob ends. Also a paperweight butto with goldstone on amber base and spaced bubbles. 11⁄16 (1.7 cm.) diam. Smaller paperweight button with gold stone on amethyst base.

☐ Unrecorded.

42. Wilfred Smith & Co., 150 Nassau St., N.Y.C. *Ca* 1900. Rectangular colorless pressed-glass souvenir weigh with photograph of the First Presbyterian Church, Neenah Wis. (taken at the time of its dedication 1900–1901 inserted in the underside. The oval inset is of the Reveren John E. Chapin, D.D., minister of the church from 187 to 1903. On paper covering back the words "Manufacture by Wilfred Smith & Co., 150 Nassau St., New York" ar printed. 2 11⁄16″ × 4⅛″ × ⅞″ (6.8 cm. × 10.5 cm. × 2. cm.).

☐ Unidentified; acquired June, 1937.

Plate 50

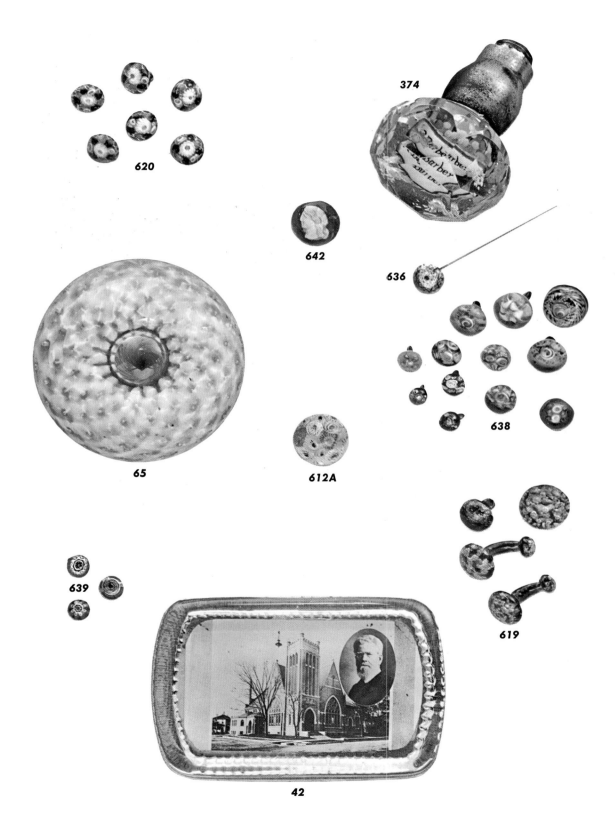

620

374

642

636

65

638

612A

639

619

42

Plate 51

290. Ernst von Dohlin, Dorflinger Glass Works, White Mills, Pa. Early 1900's. Heavy sparkling weight. Colorless glass encloses blue lily motif, the 4 large upright petals being blue inside and opaque white outside. Elongated bubble in center extends to base. Small bubble between petals. Pontil mark on underside. (Similar to weight 173.) 3⅞₆″ (8.7 cm.) diam.

☐ Ralph Barber, Millville, N.J.; acquired Nov., 1939.

583. Corning, N.Y. 1941. Sparkling, colorless glass weight. Near top of crown are 3 petunia flowers: opaque white; red over opaque white; and blue over opaque white —each with bubble center. Motif floats over coarse white latticinio ground flecked with blue. "Steuben Nov. 1941" is inscribed on underside. 3½″ (8.9 cm.) diam.

☐ Unrecorded.

173. Ernst von Dohlin, Dorflinger Glass Works, White Mills, Pa. Early 1900's. Heavy, sparkling weight. Colorless glass encloses green lily motif, the 4 large upright petals being green inside and opaque white outside. Elongated bubble in center and smaller ones between petals. (Similar to 290.) 3⅞₆″ (8.7 cm.) diam.

☐ Unidentified; acquired Nov., 1938.

415. American, probably Dorflinger, White Mills, Pa. Early 1900's. Heavy, sparkling weight. Colorless glass encloses red, white, and blue upright lily flower consisting of 4 double-layer petals, the colored glass being laid over opaque white: red on top side of upper layer and blue on underside of lower layer. Large elongated bubble in center and smaller ones between petals. 3⅛″ (7.9 cm.) diam.

☐ Unidentified; acquired May, 1941.

585. Corning, N.Y. 1941. Large blue and pink lily-type flower with silver flecks and bubble center. The 5 petals are bordered with opaque white. Flower stem extends into green over opaque white ground. "Steuben, Nov. 1941" is inscribed on the flat underside.* 3¹¹⁄₁₆″ (9.4 cm.) diam.

☐ Unrecorded.

576. Corning, N.Y. 1941. Large lily-type flower has 5 pink pointed petals bordered with blue and a central bubble; flower stem extends into green over opaque white base. "Steuben 1941" is inscribed on the flat underside. 3³⁄₁₆″ (8.1 cm.) diam.

☐ Unrecorded.

129. Corning, N.Y. Large magnolia flower with bubble center has 4 translucent deep blue petals bordered with pink and opaque white. Opaque blue-white stem extends to the colorless flat base. 3½″ (8.9 cm.) diam.

☐ Corning, New York, "Made about 1870"; acquired June, 1938.

587. Corning, N.Y. 1934. Sparkling glass encloses large lily-type flower consisting of 4 red, white, and blue striped petals, the colors laid over opaque white glass; large center bubble. Flower stem extends into blue over opaque white cushion. "Steuben 1934" is inscribed on the underside. 3⁵⁄₁₆″ (8.4 cm.) diam.

☐ Unrecorded.

---

* Although this and other weights here are signed "Steuben," they are not—correctly speaking—products of the Steuben factory. No colored glass has been produced there since 1933. These weights are sometimes referred to as "offhand Steuben paperweights," and were doubtless made by Steuben workers during off-hours.

Plate 51

290

583

173

415

585

576

129

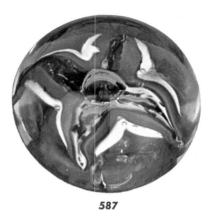

587

Plate 52

579. Peter Gentile, G—F Glass Co., Morgantown, W. Va.* *Ca.* 1947. Heavy spherical weight. Colorless glass encloses purple and white butterfly with cane body, the feelers being attached to a silver flower. Motif floats near top of crown above spaced bubbles. This type of weight was patented by John G. Funfrock, 1948. 3⁵⁄₁₆″ (8.4 cm.) diam.

☐ Unrecorded.

589. Peter Gentile, G—F Glass Co., Morgantown, W. Va.* *Ca.* 1947. Heavy spherical weight. Colorless glass encloses opaque white flying goose with orange head and yellow bill. Motif is near top of crown over spaced bubbles. This type of weight was patented by John G. Funfrock, 1948. 3⁷⁄₁₆″ (8.7 cm.) diam.

☐ Unrecorded.

581. Peter Gentile, G—F Glass Co., Morgantown, W. Va.* *Ca.* 1947. Heavy spherical weight. Colorless glass encloses opaque white and yellow butterfly with blue cane body and an opaque red and white flower with stem, all floating near top of crown over spaced bubbles. Flat base is slightly concave. This type of weight was patented by John G. Funfrock, 1948. 3⁵⁄₁₆″ (8.4 cm.) diam.

☐ Unrecorded.

588. G—F Glass Co., Morgantown, W. Va.* *Ca.* 1946. Ovoid weight. Colorless glass encloses 3 deep pink and white spatter calla lilies with bubble centers, the stems extending to base of the exterior of a deep cushion of thin, opaque white glass with spaced bubbles. Colorless flat base.

* G—F Glass Co., Morgantown, W. Va. (Gentile-Funfrock), became the Gentile Glass Co., Star City, W. Va., in 1948.

"Funfrock, April 11, 1946" appears on paper sticker on underside. 3⁷⁄₁₆″ (8.7 cm.) diam. (Similar to 584.)

☐ Unrecorded.

717. Joseph St. Clair, St. Clair Glass Co., Elwood, Ind. 1964. Heavy spherical weight. Colorless glass encloses pink and white ceramic pig with black eyes and tail. Pig stands on emerald green spatter ground over colorless base. Pontil mark on underside. 3⁹⁄₁₆″ (9.1 cm.) diam.

Gift of Mr. Joseph St. Clair, 1964.

584. G—F Glass Co., Morgantown, W. Va.* *Ca.* 1947. Ovoid of colorless glass encloses 3 opaque white spatter calla lilies with bubble centers, the green stems extending to base between sections of a mound of transparent blue glass with spaced bubbles. "Funfrock April 14, 1947" appears on paper sticker on base. 3⁵⁄₁₆″ (8.4 cm.) diam. (Similar to 588.)

☐ Unrecorded.

80. Attributed to Charles Degenhart (1882–1958), Cambridge, Ohio. *Ca.* 1930. Colorless glass encloses translucent cobalt blue snake with raised head and green eyes, resting on a layer of varicolored spatter ground over colorless base. Pontil mark on underside. 2¹⁵⁄₁₆″ (7.4 cm.) diam.

☐ Unidentified; acquired Sept., 1937.

743. John Degenhart (1884–1964), Cambridge, Ohio. *Ca.* 1950. Gold-ruby and white rose is set deep in base of colorless glass sphere, which has a gray tinge. Circular foot has concave center on flat underside. 2¹¹⁄₁₆″ (6.8 cm.) diam.

Gift of Mrs. John Degenhart in memory of her husband, 1967.

Plate 52

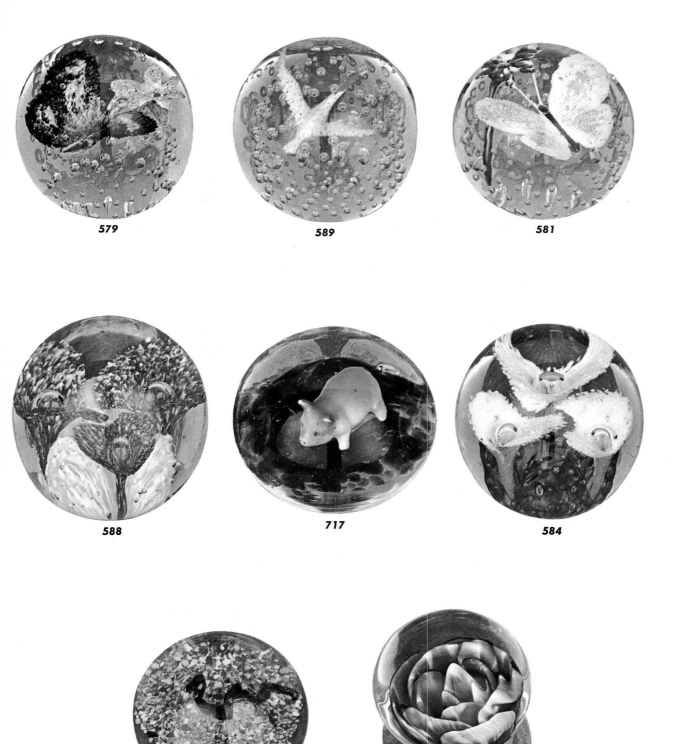

579

589

581

588

717

584

80

743

Plate 53

692. Charles Kaziun, Brockton, Mass. Early 1960's. Perfume bottle in spherical form has enclosed, in both stopper and base, an upright full-blown rose (pink shading to darker pink) surrounded by 4 green leaves. "K" cane with hearts appears at joining of leaves. 2″ (5.1 cm.) diam.; $3^{11}\!/_{16}$″ (9.4 cm.) overall height.

Gift of Mr. and Mrs. Ralph S. Johns, 1963.

693. Charles Kaziun, Brockton, Mass. Early 1960's. Perfume bottle in spherical form has enclosed, in both stopper and base, an upright full-blown rose (red shading to darker red) surrounded by 4 green leaves. "K" cane with red hearts appears at joining of leaves. $1\frac{7}{8}$″ (4.8 cm.) diam.; $3\frac{5}{8}$″ (9.2 cm.) overall height.

Gift of Mr. and Mrs. Ralph S. Johns, 1963.

691. Charles Kaziun, Brockton, Mass. Early 1960's. Double overlay weight. An upright pink rose is centered on 4 green leaves. The opaque yellow over opaque white overlay is cut with punty on top, 5 punties on curve. "K" cane with red hearts appears at joining of leaves and is visible from underside. A 16-pointed star is cut on the underside of flat, colorless base. $2\frac{1}{4}$″ (5.7 cm.) diam.

Gift of Mr. and Mrs. Ralph S. Johns, 1963.

713. Charles Kaziun, Brockton, Mass. Early 1960's. Ovoid perfume bottle has an opaque white, full-blown rose with 4 green leaves enclosed in the base. The steeple stopper also encloses an upright opaque white rose with elongated petals and 4 green leaves. The "K" signature cane with red hearts appears at joining of leaves. Slightly concave colorless base. $2^{1}\!/_{16}$″ (5.3 cm.) diam.; $6\frac{1}{2}$″ (16.5 cm.) overall height.

Gift of Mr. and Mrs. Ralph S. Johns, 1963.

696. Charles Kaziun, Brockton, Mass. Early 1960's. Nineteen spaced pastry-mold canes, predominantly white, are arranged on a transparent cobalt blue base. "K" signature cane with red hearts appears in center. Base is concave. $2\frac{3}{8}$″ (6.1 cm.) diam.

Gift of Mr. and Mrs. Ralph S. Johns, 1963.

703. Charles Kaziun, Brockton, Mass. 1950's. Miniature weight. An opaque pink rose with tiny gold-leaf butterfly is surrounded by 3 pointed green leaves interspersed with 3 pastry-mold green-and-white canes—the whole against a white muslin over translucent cobalt blue ground. Gold-

leaf "K" enclosed and visible on underside of blue ground. The weight is tilted and attached to a colorless foot. $1^{7}\!/_{16}$″ (3.7 cm.) diam.

Gift of Mr. and Mrs. Ralph S. Johns, 1963.

637. Charles Kaziun, Brockton, Mass. 1940–45. Paper weight buttons, including a rose-colored double overlay an a cobalt blue single overlay, both with concentric millefior canes and "K" cane in center. (The rose double overlay wa inspired by the frontispiece, Plate I, of Mrs. Bergstrom' book, *Old Glass Paperweights*.)

☐ Unrecorded.

705. Charles Kaziun, Brockton, Mass. Early 1960's. Spher of colorless glass encloses opaque yellow snake with re stripes, black head, and green eyes on white muslin ove transparent amethyst ground. The snake lies in double-formation. "K" cane with red hearts is enclosed and visibl on underside of ground. Concave colorless base. $2\frac{3}{8}$″ (6. cm.) diam.

Gift of Mr. and Mrs. Ralph S. Johns, 1963.

699. Charles Kaziun, Brockton, Mass. Early 1960's. Sub miniature weight. Colorless glass encloses upright yellow lily with 4 narrow green leaves, on gold-flecked aqua ove opaque white ground. Gold leaf "K" enclosed and visibl on underside of ground. The weight, cut with punties, i tilted and attached to a colorless foot. $1^{5}\!/_{16}$″ (2.4 cm. diam.; $1\frac{1}{4}$″ (3.2 cm.) overall height.

Gift of Mr. and Mrs. Ralph S. Johns, 1963.

539. Charles Kaziun, Brockton, Mass. Early 1940's. Minia ture weight, one of Kaziun's earliest weights. Colorless glas encloses opaque pink and white rose surrounded by 4 gree leaves, goldstone, and one blue cane on translucent cobal blue ground. Base is concave. $1\frac{3}{4}$″ (4.5 cm.) diam.

☐ Unrecorded.

698. Charles Kaziun, Brockton, Mass. Early 1960's. Sub miniature weight. Colorless glass encloses upright whit lily lined with red, with 4 narrow green leaves, on gold flecked cobalt blue over opaque white ground. Gold "K is enclosed and visible on underside of ground. The weigh cut with punties, is tilted and attached to a colorless foo 1″ (2.6 cm.) diam.; $1\frac{1}{4}$″ (3.2 cm.) overall height.

Gift of Mrs. and Mrs. Ralph S. Johns, 1963.

Plate 53

692

713

693

691

696

703

637

705

699

539

698

Plate 54

694. Charles Kaziun, Brockton, Mass. Early 1960's. Globe of colorless glass encloses an upright, floating chrysanthemum of lavender shading to white, and 4 green leaves. "K" signature cane with red hearts appears on underside of motif at joining of leaves. The weight is mounted on stemmed, flat, circular foot. 2¼" (5.7 cm.) diam.

Gift of Mr. and Mrs. Ralph S. Johns, 1963.

695. Charles Kaziun, Brockton, Mass. Early 1960's. Miniature weight. Colorless glass encloses a stylized red and white flower at center made up of 6 cane petals (opaque white canes with red edges and red arrows) around a yellow stamen center, 3 pointed green leaves, and a twisted short green stem. Six pale chartreuse canes with red centers are spaced at periphery. Motif is set on opaque white ground above a colorless base. A gold-leaf "K" appears on underside of ground. The weight is tilted and mounted on a stemmed, flat, circular foot. 1⁷⁄₁₆" (6.2 cm.) diam.

Gift of Mr. and Mrs. Ralph S. Johns, 1963.

697. Charles Kaziun, Brockton, Mass. Early 1960's. Upright rose in pink shading to white is surrounded by 4 green leaves, the whole enclosed in glass sphere. "K" cane with red hearts appears at joining of leaves. Weight is mounted upright on stemmed, flat, circular foot. 2¹⁄₁₆" (5.3 cm.) diam.

Gift of Mr. and Mrs. Ralph S. Johns, 1963.

690. Charles Kaziun, Brockton, Mass. 1950–60. Spaced millefiori design is set on opaque pale pink (moonglow) ground. Six separate pastry-mold canes with opaque centers surround a center green cane with red hearts encircling a blue-on-white "K" (his signature cane). Base is colorless. Weight is mounted on short-stemmed, flat, circular foot. 2¹⁄₁₆" (5.3 cm.) diam.

Gift of Mr. and Mrs. Ralph S. Johns, 1963.

704. Charles Kaziun, Brockton, Mass. 1950–60. Miniature weight. Colorless glass encloses a central grouping of pastel-colored canes (one of which is a blue "K" cane) on a white muslin over transparent amethyst ground. A gold-leaf "K" appears on underside of ground. The weight is tilted and attached to a stemmed, flat, circular foot. 1⅛" (2.8 cm.) diam.

Gift of Mr. and Mrs. Ralph S. Johns, 1963.

720. Charles Kaziun, Brockton, Mass. 1964–65. Colorless glass encloses blue and white striped convolvulus flower, blue bud, 3 green leaves, and green stem on transparent amethyst ground. Gold "K" appears on underside of ground above colorless, slightly concave base. 2" (5.1 cm.) diam.

Gift of Mr. and Mrs. Ralph S. Johns, 1965.

701. Charles Kaziun, Brockton, Mass. Early 1960's. Small ovoid perfume bottle. In both base and stopper, colorless glass encloses a small upright yellow lily with red center and 4 narrow green leaves. Ground is gold-flecked light blue over opaque white. On curve are 6 thumbprint cuts. A tilted sub-miniature weight cut with punties forms the stopper. Gold "K" appears on underside of ground above colorless flat base. 1⅜" (4 cm.) diam.; 3" (7.6 cm.) overall height.

Gift of Mr. and Mrs. Ralph S. Johns, 1963.

712. Charles Kaziun, Brockton, Mass. Early 1960's. Double overlay weight. Nineteen spaced millefiori canes in red, green, and white are set on mound-shaped opaque light blue ground. The opaque red over opaque white overlay is cut with punty on top and 6 punties on curve. "K" cane with red hearts is visible on underside of ground. 2⁵⁄₁₆" (5.8 cm.) diam.

Gift of Mr. and Mrs. Ralph S. Johns, 1963.

700. Charles Kaziun, Brockton, Mass. Early 1960's. Small ovoid perfume bottle. Colorless glass encloses, in both base of bottle and stopper, a small upright blue lily with yellow center and 4 narrow green leaves, on a gold-flecked opaque pink ground. Curve of bottle is cut with 6 thumbprints. A tilted sub-miniature weight cut with punties forms the stopper. Gold "K" appears on underside of opaque ground above colorless flat base. 1⅜" (4.0 cm.) diam.; 3" (7.6 cm.) overall height.

Gift of Mr. and Mrs. Ralph S. Johns, 1963.

674. Charles Kaziun, Brockton, Mass. Early 1960's. Miniature weight has a center motif of opaque red rose surrounded by 3 pointed green leaves with 3 white pastry-mold canes spaced between the leaves—all on opaque turquoise blue ground. Gold "K" is on underside of ground above the clear base. Punty on top and 4 punties on curve. The weight is tilted and attached to flat, circular foot. 1¼" (3.2 cm.) diam.

Acquired 1963.

Plate 54

694

695

697

690

704

720

701

712

700

674

Plate 55

760. Dominick Labino, Grand Rapids, Ohio. 1967. Free-form sphere of transparent green glass encloses air pockets in an abstract design. "Labino 1967" is inscribed on underside of base. 3⅝" (9.2 cm.) diam.

Gift of "Friends of the Bergstrom Art Center," 1967.

709. Harvey K. Littleton, Verona, Wis. Early 1960's. Free-form design in transparent dark blue glass. Blown weight of nonlead glass in mushroom shape has large bubble enclosed in core and small one near top of crown. Dark canes extend from top of weight to flat base. 3³⁄₁₆" (8.1 cm.) diam.; 4½" (11.4 cm.) height.

Acquired 1963.

716. St. Clair Glass Co., Elwood, Ind. Early 1960's. Spherical weight. Colorless glass encloses design, at periphery, of eight crimped sections of caramel glass (made in the Indiana Tumbler & Goblet Co., Greentown, Ind., about 1900). A bubble appears between each section and a large, elongated bubble at center. Pontil mark on base. 3⁷⁄₁₆" (8.7 cm.) diam.

Gift of Neenah-Menasha (Wis.) Early American Glass Club, 1964.

702. Steuben, Corning, N.Y. 1963. Colorless crystal, designated as "Star Crystal," is cut in brilliant star-reflecting facets. 3½" (8.9 cm.) height.

Acquired 1963.

722. Francis Dyer Whittemore, Jr., Lansdale, Pa. 1965. Glass sphere is mounted in upright position on stemmed, circular, flat foot. Colorless glass encloses a dark red rose shading to white, which is surrounded by 4 green leaves. Opaque yellow signature cane with black "W" is visible at joining of leaves. 2⅛" (5.4 cm.) diam.

Gift of Mr. and Mrs. Ralph S. Johns, 1965.

721. Francis Dyer Whittemore, Jr., Lansdale, Pa. 1965 Colorless glass encloses white rose surrounded by 4 green leaves. Opaque yellow signature cane with black "W" appears on underside at joining of leaves. Glass sphere is mounted in tilted position on stemmed, circular, flat foot 2" (5.1 cm.) diam.

Gift of Mr. and Mrs. Ralph S. Johns, 1965.

723. Francis Dyer Whittemore, Jr., Lansdale, Pa. 1965 Colorless glass encloses yellow rose surrounded by 3 green leaves. Opaque gray signature cane with black "W" can be seen on underside of rose. Glass sphere is mounted in upright position on stemmed, circular, flat foot. 2¹⁄₁₆" (5.3 cm.) diam.

Gift of Mr. and Mrs. Ralph S. Johns, 1965.

759. Harold J. Hacker, Buena Park, Calif. 1965. Colorless glass encloses purple snake with raised head coiled on layer of transparent green spatter with goldstone flecks. "Harold J. Hacker 1965" is inscribed on base. 2¼" (5.7 cm.) diam

Gift of Mr. Harold J. Hacker, 1965.

757. Harold J. Hacker, Buena Park, Calif. 1966. Colorless glass encloses floating motif of single red poinsettia flower with 16 smooth, pointed petals around opaque yellow disk-center with faint red dots. Dewdrop bubbles appear on flower and leaves. Five green leaves and stem are visible at periphery. "Harold J. Hacker 1966" is inscribed on base 2⁵⁄₁₆" (5.8 cm.) diam.

Gift of Mr. Harold J. Hacker, 1967.

758. Harold J. Hacker, Buena Park, Calif. 1965. Colorless glass encloses black glass lizard with green spots standing on translucent layer of fine spatter in gold and pale yellow glass. "Harold J. Hacker 1965" is inscribed on base 2³⁄₁₆" (5.5 cm.) diam.

Gift of Mr. Harold J. Hacker, 1967.

Plate 55

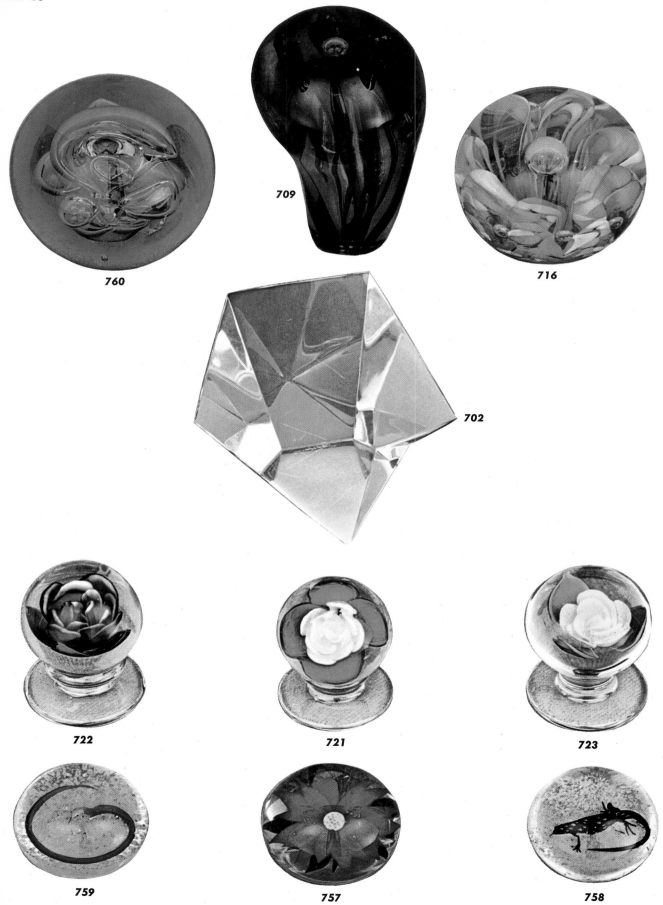

760

709

716

702

722

721

723

759

757

758

Plate 56

744. Gertrude Gentile, Gentile Glass Co., Star City, W. Va. 1967. Large, heavy, ovoid weight. Colorless glass encloses three opaque white (blue in center) lilylike flowers with elongated bubble centers and smaller bubbles near base, which is slightly concave. 3⅜₁₆″ (8.1 cm.) diam.

Gift of Mrs. Gertrude Gentile, 1967.

750. Joseph Zimmerman and Gene Baxley, Zimmerman Art Glass Co., Corydon, Ind. 1967. Large, spherical weight. Colorless glass encloses a large bubble with a ceramic squirrel in its center. At periphery are 5 opaque white, upright leaves decorated with green and yellow spatter, each with bubble at center. The letter "Z" is impressed on the concave base. 4″ (10.2 cm.) diam.

Gift of Mr. Joseph Zimmerman, 1967.

745. Frank Hamilton, Gentile Glass Co., Star City, W. Va. 1967. Ovoid weight. Colorless glass encloses, near top of crown, large flower with 8 pebbly petals, green alternating with yellow. Center of flower is a bubble, which extends toward base. Below flower are 5 smaller lily forms: blue, white, black, yellow, and green. Spaced bubbles appear near the flat base, which is slightly concave at center. 3⅝″ (9.2 cm.) diam.

Gift of Mr. and Mrs. John Gentile, 1967.

747. Joseph Zimmerman and Gene Baxley, Zimmerman Art Glass Co., Corydon, Ind. 1967. Spherical weight. Colorless glass encloses flower spray motif designed by Mrs. Lucie Webb: blue, pink, and yellow flowers and green leaves floating above a cushion of translucent cobalt blue. The letter "Z" is impressed on the colorless flattened base. 3¼″ (8.3 cm.) diam.

Gift of Mr. Joseph Zimmerman, 1967.

749. Joseph Zimmerman and Gene Baxley, Zimmerman Art Glass Co., Corydon, Ind. 1967. Large, spherical weight. Colorless glass encloses 3 cylindrical, flat-topped bubbles, each enclosing a tiny ceramic rosebud. At periphery of base is transparent green glass simulating leaves; spaced bubbles appear on and between the leaves. Letter "Z" is impressed on the colorless flat base. 3⅝″ (9.2 cm.) diam.

Gift of Mr. Joseph Zimmerman, 1967.

746. Jonathan R. Stone, Indiana Glass Co., Dunkirk, Ind. 1967. Knob weight. Colorless glass encloses multiple-colored umbrella-like form with bubble center. Five elongated bubbles (each has one pointed end) float beneath the motif near the flat base. 3¼″ (8.3 cm.) diam.

Gift of Mr. Jonathan Stone, 1967.

748. Joseph Zimmerman and Gene Baxley, Zimmerman Art Glass Co., Corydon, Ind. 1967. Spherical weight. Colorless glass encloses pink spatter over opaque white, lily-type flower with center bubble, near top of crown. At periphery, near base, are 5 upright pink and white petals, each with a bubble at center. The letter "Z" is impressed on the flattened base. 3⅜″ (8.6 cm.) diam.

Gift of Mr. Joseph Zimmerman, 1967.

751. Adolph Mocho, Sr., Vineland, N.J. 1960's. Colorless glass encloses, floating near top of crown, orange spatter butterfly with blue and yellow spots. Beneath the butterfly is a layer of opaque white spatter. The signature "A. Mocho" appears on colorless, flat, partly frosted base. 3⅛″ (7.9 cm.) diam.

Gift of Mrs. Jean Ricksecker, 1967.

Plate 56

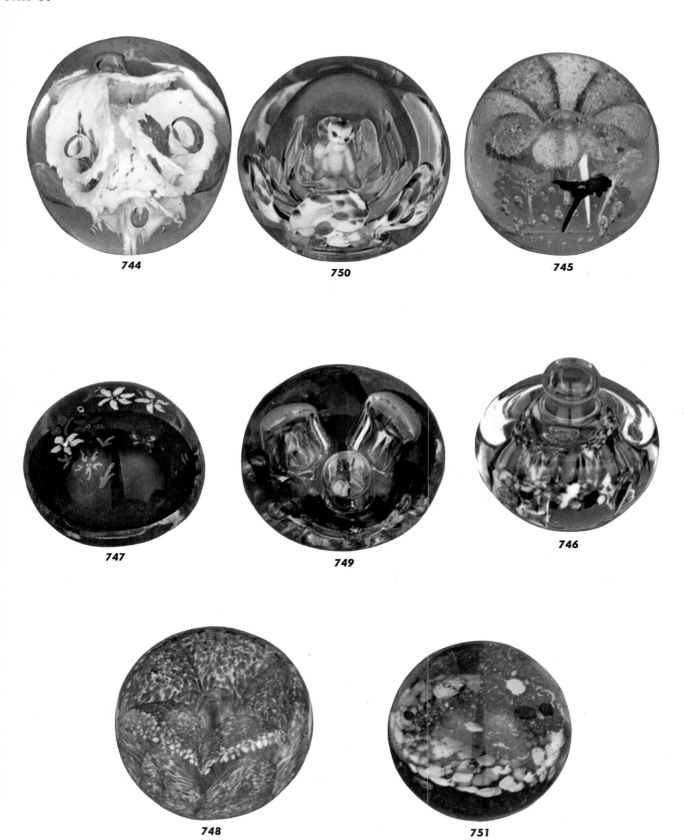

744

750

745

747

749

746

748

751

4

MISCELLANEOUS WEIGHTS

The reader will have realized, before reaching this final section, that the lines drawn between the divisions in this book are not always sharp. In several instances weights have appeared in inappropriate sections. The difficulties encountered in grouping the weights for color photography have been largely responsible for these variations, but it is hoped that reference to the individual attributions and to the index will mitigate any confusion there may be.

In this section, it has been particularly difficult to form groupings upon which general comments can be made, but there are one or two that deserve special attention—the Pinchbeck weights, for example (Plate 57). These Victorian curiosities take their name from the gold alloy often used in their decoration, an alloy invented by an Englishman named Christopher Pinchbeck long before any paperweights were made. The only glass used in a Pinchbeck weight is the lens-type crown placed over the motif; thus, to some collectors of glass paperweights the value of Pinchbeck weights is lessened. They are intriguing, however, for the great ingenuity necessary to their composition. The design, often a copy of a famous portrait or painting that is given decoration with a metal leaf, is three-dimensional, and this three-dimensionality is further intensified by the thick glass convex crown. Apparently, many of these weights were made during the paperweight vogue in the mid 1800's, and few duplications in design are known to exist. The bases of Pinchbeck weights are usually formed of pewter, often covered with velvet or leather, or of marble. The origin of these weights is a mystery, but the subjects depicted suggest both France and England as the locale. From the examples of peasant and rural scenes in Pinchbeck weights in the Bergstrom collection, one could surmise that the Swiss, too, might have had a hand in their making. This suggestion might also apply to the compass weight (489, Plate 58) of similar construction: a marble base, a metal wreath of flowers surrounding the functioning compass, and a thick glass crown placed over all.

Also of special interest to some collectors may be the three American weights in Plate 58 (531, 532, and 533). Their similar construction would seem to indicate the same source. They resemble the "Ducks in a Pond" weight (571, Plate 8), but are lacking the sophistication of that French-attributed example. In these three, the figures of the deer and swan are blown pieces; the basket motif in 533 may be of Sandwich origin, a possibility leading to our speculation that they were made in the New England area at some time between 1853 and the 1880's.

Since collectors frequently encounter Chinese-made weights, a few statements about them may be of interest. In the period following the First World War, fine French and American weights were sent to China, probably by American importers, to be copied. During the period from the late 1920's to 1948, many of these copies came back to the United States and to Europe. They are not difficult to recognize once one knows some of their distinguishing characteristics, such as the yellow-green cast of the encasing glass, the bubbles and swirls caused by impurities within the glass, the lightness in weight, and the frequent use of a mustard-yellow cane with red center in the millefiori types. Copies of Millville roses, antique French weights (Plate 62), flower weights (including poinsettia and morning glory), odd shapes such as cubes and boat shapes, and flat shallow-crowned weights are frequently seen. Although the beauty of these Chinese weights is usually lost through imperfections in the glass, we must admit that fine workmanship is evident in many of them.

It is not uncommon to find large-sized playing marbles, sometimes up to $7\frac{5}{8}$ inches in circumference, included in paperweight collections (Plate 59). Although the glass in them may be full of impurities and the surface nicked and scratched from use, marbles do have a decided attractiveness. Glass marbles are believed to have been made originally by Venetian glassworkers in the mid-nineteenth century; they were produced in Germany up to World War I. Since 1920, the production of marbles has been extensive in the United States, but American-made marbles usually do not exceed $2\frac{1}{2}$ inches in diameter.

The swirl type is the most popular marble among collectors. Spirals of opaque-colored threads and frequently a core of white filigree twist are embedded in the glass sphere (613, Plate 59).

A variation of the swirl marble is sometimes known as a "speckled marble"; in Germany, a "threaded marble" (614, Plate 59). The speckles are crumbs or chips of colored glass embedded within glass and frequently swirled.

Sulphide marbles vie with swirls in popularity, the enclosed sulphide usually representing an animal, bird, or child, often crude in its configuration and not accurately centered in the sphere (28, 33, and 33 A, Plate 59).

It is interesting to consider the reasons why certain of the so-called "related objects" shown in this book were made. One example is hollow glass balls. These came in various sizes and colors, and usually had a small opening or hole. From the time of the early glassblowers, they were known as "witch balls," and according to legend were hung inside the country people's cottages to ward off the evil eye. In England, blue glass balls were hung from cottage rafters "to turn the lightning," or in windows for their therapeutic value. A type of glass ball often accredited to Nailsea (English) glassmen frequently was made with its inner service daubed with a variety of colors (324, Plate 36).

Witch balls—usually rather crude—have also been found in many parts of the United States, particularly the East and Middle West. They were apparently made from the very beginning of American glassmaking up to the introduction of mass-production methods, about 1870. A few factories continued to manufacture them up to 1890. Globes in crude light green or colorless glass, usually without holes, were enclosed in cord nets and used as floats by New Jersey and New England seine fishermen. Glass balls were also made to match the early blown pitchers and sugar bowls—on which they served as covers.

Souvenir paperweights (1A, 473, 601, Plate 60; 42, Plate 50) deserve special mention. At the turn of the century, scarcely a parlor did not display among its bibelots a souvenir weight of some sort. Most common were those containing family portraits, a view of Niagara Falls or of one of the 1893 World Exposition buildings, or some other treasured memento. The picture was reproduced on paper and glued to the underside of a clear glass plaque.

The predominance of items in this section is, as you will observe, what the title indicates—miscellaneous; many of them are not identified and do not fall into the category of fine paperweights. However, to a multitude of collectors they have extrinsic value and interest, and for that reason are included in this book. They are displayed, for the most part, in the Bergstrom Paperweight Research Center study room. With few exceptions, they were collected by Mrs. Bergstrom herself, and illustrate her wide interest in any glass item related to paperweight manufacture.

The numbers used to identify the illustrations and their captions are the Bergstrom acquisition numbers. The information that follows the □ device in a caption is Mrs. Bergstrom's attribution of that item and other data about it from her records. Her spellings are retained.

Plate 57

545. Origin unknown. *Ca.* mid-19th century. Pinchbeck weight with velvet over pewter base. The motif, probably carved in wood, is covered with gold alloy and portrays, in relief, a group of peasants before a cottage. Thick, convex lens-type crown covers motif. 2¾" (7.0 cm.) diam.

□   Pinchbeck; no acquisition record.

(Illus. 83, Bergstrom book, 1948 and subsequent editions.)

567. Origin unknown. *Ca.* mid-19th century. Pinchbeck weight with circular marble base. Motif, in relief, is covered with gold leaf alloy and portrays a domestic scene with a mother and 3 children. Thick, convex lens-type crown covers motif. 2¹⁵⁄₁₆" (7.4 cm.) diam.

□   Pinchbeck; no acquisition record.

536. Origin unknown. *Ca.* mid-19th century. Pinchbeck weight with pewter base. The motif, in relief, portraying bust of Queen Victoria (slightly to dexter, and wearing crown) is probably carved wood and colored; it is placed on scarlet ceramic ground. "Victoria" appears in Pinchbeck gold letters to left of portrait. Thick, convex lens-type crown covers motif. 3¼" (8.3 cm.) diam.

□   Pinchbeck; no acquisition record.

(Illus. 82, Bergstrom book, 1948 and subsequent editions.)

523. Origin unknown. *Ca.* mid-19th century. Pinchbeck weight with pewter base. Gold alloy, painted motif portrays figures, in relief, of horse, man holding goblet, and child before background of trees, house, and so on. Thick, convex lens-type crown covers motif. 3¼" (8.3 cm.) diam.

□   Pinchbeck; no acquisition record.

538. Origin unknown. *Ca.* mid-19th century. Pinchbeck weight with pewter base. Gold alloy, painted motif, in relief, portrays a winding river, boat, bridge, and buildings on both banks of a river, with mountains in distance. Thick convex lens-type crown covers motif. 2¾" (7.0 cm.) diam.

□   Pinchbeck; no acquisition record.

546. Attributed to Austria. Flat rectangular-shaped glass covers sulphide plaque portraying 2 horses, lion, foliage, hillside, and so on. Entrapped air with silver appearance outlines the figures of the animals, the foliage, and the rocks. Paper covering on underside. "Patented G.S. & Co." is imprinted on lower edge of sulphide; "J. & L. Lobmeyer, Wien" appears on paper sticker. Edges of glass are beveled. 5⅝" × 3⅜" × ¾" (14.3 cm. × 8.6 × 1.9 cm.).

□   Unidentified; no acquisition record.

Plate 57

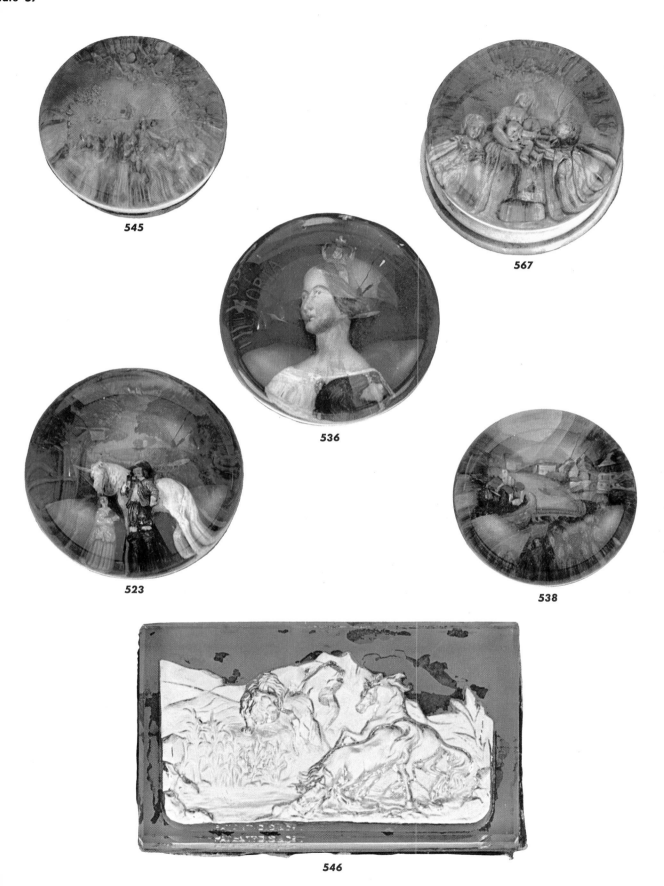

545

567

536

523

538

546

Plate 58

621 and **622.** Origin unknown; possibly Sandwich, Mass. *Ca.* 1825–88. Pair of ruby and white, double overlay fluid-burning lamps, with double wicks and attached snuffers. Cylindrical fonts have panels of circular and square cuts, with vertical groove cuts dividing the 4 panels. Mountings are brass; square marble bases. 3¾″ (9.6 cm.) side of base; 11″ (27.9 cm.) overall height.

☐ Unrecorded.

373. American; could be New England Glass Co., East Cambridge, Mass., or Boston & Sandwich Glass Co., Sandwich, Mass. *Ca.* 1852–75. Pair of hollow glass doorknobs. Colorless glass with gold interior is overlaid with opaque white. Cuttings in the overlay are star-shaped, circular, and oval. 2″ (5.1 cm.) diam.

☐ Unidentified; acquired Nov., 1940.

489. Origin unknown. (Construction is similar to that of Pinchbeck weights.) Solid crown of colorless glass is set over a functioning compass and mounted on circular marble base. Encircling the compass is a wreath of metallic green leaves and 2 bunches of tiny pink glass grapes. The crown is faceted with punty on top and 6 horizontal cuttings on curve. 3⅛″ (7.9 cm.) diam.

☐ Unidentified; acquired March, 1942.

75. Bohemian-Silesian. *Ca.* 1848. Cobalt blue single overlay. The motif is made up of 13 spaced canes on cushion of muslin ground. Circular facet appears on top and 3 rows of circular facets on curve. Colorless base is slightly concave. 2⁵⁄₁₆″ (5.9 cm.) diam.

☐ Unidentified; acquired Sept., 1937.

532. American; could be New England Glass Co., East Cambridge, Mass., or Boston & Sandwich Glass Co., Sandwich, Mass. *Ca.* 1853–80. Hollow crown is applied to a colorless base. Under the crown, an opalescent, translucent white deer with antlers stands on a rocky, pebbly ground. Crown is faceted with punty on top and 6 punties on upper curve. 2⅞″ (7.3 cm.) diam. (Similar in construction to 531 and 533.)

☐ Unidentified; acquired Nov., 1943.

533. American; could be New England Glass Co., East Cambridge, Mass., or Boston & Sandwich Glass Co., Sandwich, Mass. *Ca.* 1853–80. Hollow crown is applied to base on which is mounted a milk glass openwork basket containing blue and red roses; transparent green handle. Faceted crown has punty on top; 6 punties on upper curve. Colorless base is flashed with green on interior, and its edge is cut in diamond-shaped cuts. 3⁵⁄₁₆″ (8.4 cm.) diam. (Similar in construction to 531 and 532.)

☐ Unidentified; acquired Nov., 1943.

531. American, could be New England Glass Co., East Cambridge, Mass., or Boston & Sandwich Glass Co., Sandwich, Mass. *Ca.* 1853–80. Hollow crown is applied to colorless glass base, which is lined with translucent green glass flecked with mica; on the base sits an opaque white swan with pink eyes, beak, and wings. Swan has polished appearance. Crown is faceted with punty on top and 6 punties on upper curve. 3⅛″ (7.9 cm.) diam. (Similar in construction to 532 and 533.)

☐ Unidentified; acquired Nov., 1943.
(Plate #2, Jokelson, *One Hundred of the Most Important Paperweights,* identifies it as Baccarat.)

Plate 58

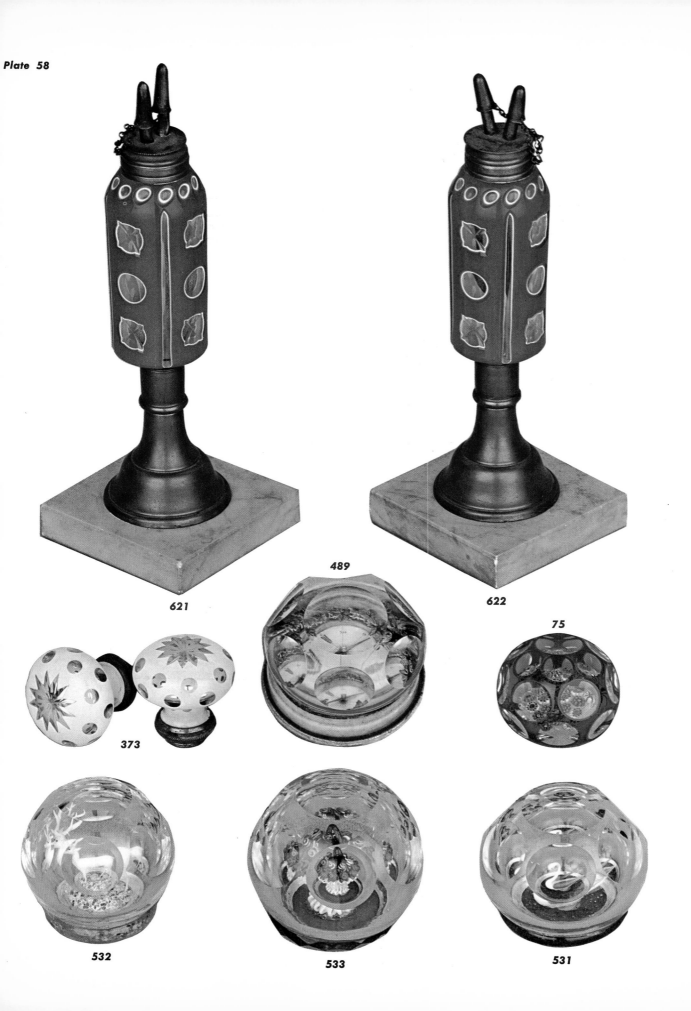

621

489

622

75

373

532

533

531

Plate 59

409. Origin unknown. Pair of wig stands of colorless glass. Tapered upper portion encloses varicolored mottled glass over opaque white, drawn up into peaks. A layer of colorless glass separates upper portion from lower, which is ball-shaped and encloses 4 elongated bubbles extending through 2 layers of varicolored spatter glass. Applied colorless glass standard is stemmed and has thick, circular, flat foot. 6½" (16.5 cm.) overall height.

☐ Unidentified; acquired May, 1941.

26. Origin unknown. Tall, slightly tapered wig stand. Colorless glass encloses mottled varicolored glass and goldstone drawn upward from base to within an inch of top to form peaks. Applied standard has knopped stem and circular flat foot. 10⁹⁄₁₆" (26.8 cm.) height.

☐ French; acquired April, 1937.

729. American. Pair of spherical scent bottles. Interiors are decorated with opaque blue spatter. Ball-shaped stoppers enclose pink and blue spatter with 4 bubbles, simulating a lily flower. Exterior of bottles, including necks, is spattered with pink enamel. 3³⁄₁₆" (8.1 cm.) diam.; 5" (12.6 cm.) overall height.

☐ Unrecorded.

463. Origin unknown. Heavy ovoid weight with flattened base. Colorless glass encloses upright flower motif (umbrella form) made of crudely formed pink, cobalt blue, turquoise, and opaque white canes. Canes are slurred or pulled to form 5 petals and drawn downward, to form stem, into interior of opaque white bowl. Five spaced canes of similar colors are impressed into rim of bowl, which rests on base of weight. Pontil mark on underside. 3¹⁄₁₆" (7.8 cm.) diam.

☐ Unidentified; acquired June, 1937.

28. Attributed to German or American manufacture. 1840–1926. Marble. Colorless glass encloses sulphide figure of lamb. 2" (5.1 cm.) diam.; 6¼" (15.8 cm.) circum.

☐ Unidentified; acquired June, 1937.

33. Attributed to German or American manufacture. 1840–1926. Marble. Colorless glass encloses sulphide figure of a young girl, kneeling with mallet in hand. 2¹³⁄₁₆" (7.2 cm.) diam.; 7" (17.8 cm.) circum.

☐ Unidentified; acquired June, 1937.

33A. Attributed to German or American manufacture. 1840–1926. Marble. Colorless glass with yellow tinge encloses sulphide figure of child in sitting position, blowing a horn. 1¹³⁄₁₆" (4.7 cm.) diam.; 5⅝" (14.3 cm.) circum.

☐ Unrecorded.

52. Attributed to Whitefriars Glass, Ltd., Wealdstone, Middlesex (England). *Ca.* 1935. Weight of translucent amethyst glass has spaced pinprick bubbles near surface. Flattened base. 2¹⁵⁄₁₆" (7.4 cm.) diam.

☐ Unidentified; acquired Aug., 1937.

614. Attributed to German or American manufacture. 1840–1926. Marble. Colorless glass encases design of sections of red and blue spatter, slightly swirled, over opaque white. In Germany, this type is referred to as a "thread marble." 2¹⁄₁₆" (5.3 cm.) diam.; 6½" (16.5 cm.) circum.

☐ Unrecorded.

70. Attributed to Venice. *Ca.* 1930. Very clear colorless glass encloses "Roman" spiral—red, white, and blue strands and red, yellow, and green strands are spiraled near the surface. In center, from base to top of crown, is spiral of coarse opaque white strands. Flat base. 2¹⁵⁄₁₆" (5.8 cm.) diam.

☐ Unidentified; acquired Sept., 1937.

613. Attributed to German or American manufacture. 1840–1926. Marble. Colorless glass encloses spiral strands of red, green, and blue around a core of slightly spiraled white filigree strands. 2" (5.1 cm.) diam.; 6¼" (15.9 cm.) circum.

☐ Unrecorded.

Plate 59

409

729

463

26

28

33

33A

52

614

70

613

Plate 60

736.   Origin unknown. Heavy ovoid scent bottle with flat base. Ball-shaped stopper is faceted in diamond cuts and has a tapered finger, which is frosted and extends to base. 2⅜" (6.1 cm.) diam.; 4¾" (12.1 cm.) overall height.

☐   Unrecorded.

39.   American. Icosahedron (20-sided) weight is transparent amber glass. 2⁷⁄₁₆" (6.2 cm.) diam.

☐   Unidentified; acquired June, 1937.

17.   Origin unknown; possibly Dutch. Spherical wig stand is mounted on standard with baluster stem and flat, circular foot. Colorless ball encloses 2 layers of mottled multiple-colored pebble ground through which 4 elongated bubbles and a center larger bubble pass and extend to base. Pontil mark appears on top of crown. 3¼" (8.3 cm.) diam. of ball; 5⅝" (14.3 cm.) overall height.

☐   Unidentified; acquired May, 1936.

410.   American; probably Midwest; possibly Sandwich, Mass. 19th century. Translucent brown glass turtle is free formed. 5¾" (14.6 cm.) length.

☐   Unidentified; acquired May, 1941.

48.   Origin unknown. Free-formed hen. Colorless glass encloses layer of varicolored mottled glass. Pontil mark appears on underside. 4½" (11.4 cm.) length. (Similar to 49.)

☐   Unidentified; notation "old glass"; acquired Aug., 1937.

49.   Origin unknown. Free-formed hen. Colorless glass encloses layer of varicolored spatter glass. Pontil mark appears on underside. 3¼" (8.3 cm.) length. (Similar to 48.)

☐   Unidentified; notation "old glass"; acquired Aug., 1937.

562.   Origin unknown. Free-formed pig. Colorless glass has interior decoration of ruby and opaque white spatter glass. 4" (10.2 cm.) overall length. (Similar items have bee attributed to Val St. Lambert, Belgium.)

☐   Unrecorded.

1A.   Origin unknown; probably American. Reproductio on paper of the painting "The Cherub Choir," in brow tones, is fastened to concave underside of flat, circular gla weight. 3" (7.6 cm.) diam.; 1" (2.5 cm.) deep.

☐   Unrecorded.

110.   American; possibly Pittsburgh area. *Ca.* 1870. Colo less glass encloses black and white sulphide figure of a do standing in green grass, on opaque white ground spattere with green and blue glass. 2⁵⁄₁₆" (5.8 cm.) diam.

☐   Unidentified; acquired May, 1938.

601.   American. Heavy, pressed rectangle of colorless gla with convex top and legs at corners covers "mother pearl" plaque on which is painted a gilt medallion wi "Notes" in center. Surrounding the medallion is gilt le and scroll design over salmon pink and black backgroun Underside of plaque is coated with wax to hold it in plac 4" × 2¾" × 1⅜" (10.2 cm. × 7.0 cm. × 4.0 cm.).

☐   Unrecorded.

473.   American. *Ca.* 1893. Souvenir weight. Reproductio on paper of "World's Columbian Exposition 1893 Machine Hall" is fastened to the underside of a flat rectangle colorless glass (rounded corners). 4⅛" × 2⅝" × ⅞" (10 cm. × 6.6 cm. × 2.2 cm.).

☐   Unidentified; acquired Dec., 1941.

633.   Origin unknown. Glass sword with translucent coba blue blade. Colorless glass haft has yellow, red, and gre ribbon spiral enclosed. Applied colorless glass guard h cobalt blue applied edging. 27" (68.5 cm.) length.

☐   Unrecorded.

Plate 60

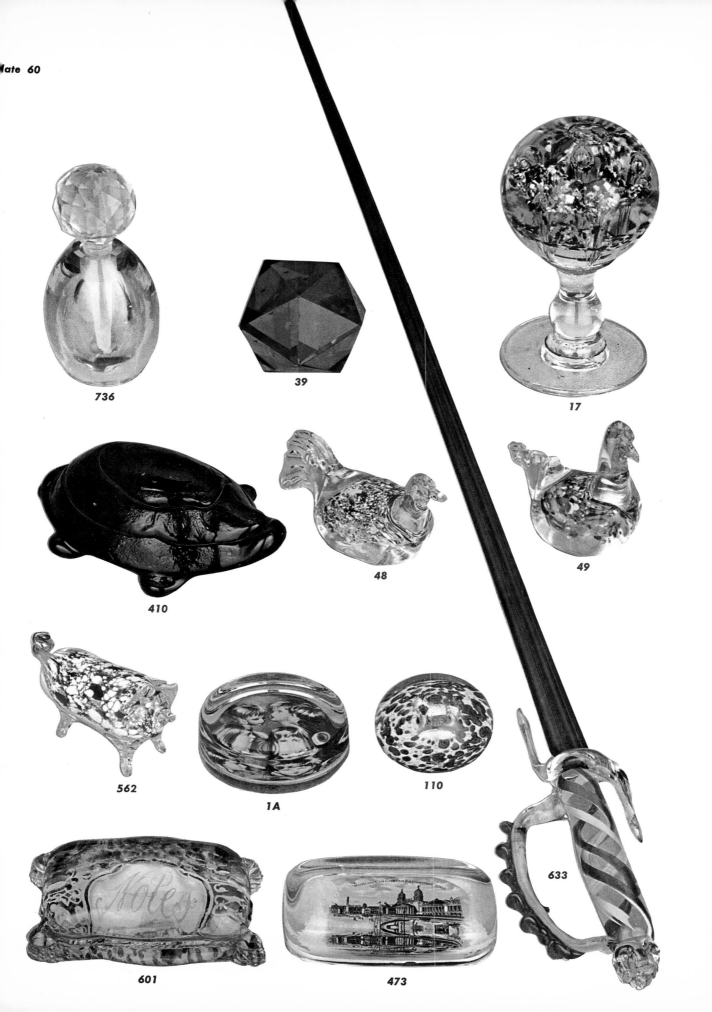

736

39

17

410

48

49

562

1A

110

633

601

473

Plate 61

27. American. Covered glass bowl. Cover is as large as the bowl into which it fits. Colorless thick glass encloses, in both parts, pink, yellow, and red spatter glass design with 4 elongated bubbles. Ball-shaped finial. 4" (10.2 cm.) diam.; 7" (17.8 cm.) overall height.

☐ Unidentified; acquired June, 1937.

740. Millville, N.J. Heavy, spherical table ornament. Pale green glass encloses design, near top of crown, of thinly spattered glass in white, yellow, red, and green in mushroom form. Four elongated bubbles project from stem of mushroom. 4³⁄₁₆" (10.6 cm.) diam. (Made to rest on standard.)

☐ Millville; no record of acquisition.

(#18, p. 41, 1940 Bergstrom book; p. 42, subsequent editions.)

29. Prob. Isle of Wight. Bell-shaped weight of colorless glass filled with colored sand arranged to portray, on obverse, a castle scene and, on reverse, trees, foliage, and a gate. Green velvet is glued to underside. 3⁷⁄₁₆" (8.7 cm.) diam. at base; 9¼" (23.5 cm.) height.

☐ Unidentified; acquired June, 1937.

327. Origin unknown. Ovoid weight or ornament with double-footed base. Colorless glass encloses, from base to top of crown, multiple-colored nodules of glass. Pontil mark appears on underside of foot. 2⅝" (6.6 cm.) diam.; 4¼" (10.8 cm.) overall height.

☐ Unidentified; acquired May, 1940.

21. Attributed to Gillinder & Sons, Philadelphia, Pa. *Ca.* 1876. Souvenir Centennial celebration weight. A frosted pressed glass hand holds pressed glass circular weight into which has been inserted a brown turtle with black moving legs, head, and tail, resting on green ground. Fluting appears on sides of weight and circlet of beading on inside of top of crown. (A patent for this type of turtle weight was issued to H. E. Geron of Springfield, Ohio, in 1948.) 2½" (6.3 cm.) diam. of weight; 4¼" (10.8 cm.) overall height.

☐ Unidentified; acquired June, 1937.

268. American. Dome-shaped colorless glass ink bottle has narrow neck with flange at mouth. Near the flat base is a layer of multiple-colored spatter glass. Ball-shaped stopper is

colorless. Underside has pontil mark, and "1830 epoque" on a paper sticker. 3⅜" (8.6 cm.) diam. at base.

☐ Unidentified; acquired Sept., 1939.

25. Origin unknown. Ovoid-shaped colorless weight ha spaced pinprick bubbles near surface. Paper sticker readin "Spain" is on flat, smooth base. 2¼" (5.7 cm.) diam.

☐ Unidentified; acquired March, 1937.

111. American. Large colorless glass weight has gra tinge. Midway in weight is layer of opaque gray glass o which is etched, in black, a bust portrait of an America Indian with long hair, earrings, head feathers, and a neck lace of boar's teeth. At periphery is circle of green, red, an blue spatter glass. 3¹¹⁄₁₆" (9.4 cm.) diam.

☐ Unidentified; acquired Jan., 1938.

305. Origin unknown. Dome-shaped weight. Colorles glass encloses opaque white mushroom with red top bordere in white, growing out of translucent green, cloudy groun with many tiny bubbles. Colorless flattened base has sligh pontil mark. 2⁹⁄₁₆" (6.5 cm.) diam.

☐ Unidentified; acquired March, 1940.

522. Attributed to Gillinder & Sons, Philadelphia, Pa. *Ca* 1876. Colorless glass encloses figure of black horse wearin red blanket, resting on a white paper disk that is inserted i underside of weight. Horse's head and tail move. Weigh has flat top and diamond-shaped cuts on curve. 1⅞" (4.8 cm.) diam. (Turtle weight 21 with moving parts, attribute to Gillinder & Sons, is a souvenir weight made for 187 Centennial. This horse seems to be of similar construction.

☐ Unidentified; acquired April, 1943.

40. American. Cube of colorless glass has beveled edges 1¾" (4.5 cm.) each side.

☐ Unidentified; acquired 1936.

41. American. Cube of transparent blue glass. 1⅝" (4. cm.) each side.

☐ Unidentified; acquired 1936.

598. Egg-shaped footed weight of sparkling, pressed colorless glass. Underside of foot has incised star design an circlet of beading. 2¹¹⁄₁₆" (6.8 cm.) length of egg.

☐ Unrecorded.

Plate 61

27

740

29

327

21

268

25

111

305

522

40

41

598

Plate 62

359. Chinese. 1925–40. Copy of a Saint Louis (French) weight. Greenish-yellow glass encloses upright center bouquet of 5 small varicolored opaque flowers with bubble centers; surrounding green leaves are pulled down, touching a white latticinio basket. A twist of red and white strands with white filigree threads forms a handle for the basket, with a cane on each side at joining of handle to basket. Flat, smooth underside. 2¹³⁄₁₆″ (7.2 cm.) diam.

☐ Baccarat; acquired Aug., 1940.

573. Chinese. 1925–40. Copy of a Millville rose. Yellow-tinged glass encloses pink Millville-type rose with 14 pink petals shading to lighter pink at tips, and 5 green leaves extending to base. Small, circular foot with collar is flat and smooth on underside. 3⅛″ (7.9 cm.) diam.

☐ Unrecorded.

37. Chinese. 1925–35. Shallow weight. Colorless glass encloses patterned millefiori yellow canes with red centers, and blue and white canes at periphery. Light in weight. 2½″ (6.3 cm.) diam.

☐ Unidentified; acquired March, 1935.

738. Japanese. 1960's. Ovoid weight. Colorless glass encloses 4 lavender and opaque white morning glory flowers with bubble centers; stems rise from varicolored flowerpot. Smooth, flat underside. 2⅜″ (6.1 cm.) diam.

Gift of Dr. W. H. Potts, 1966.

254. Origin unknown. Colorless glass encloses 5 flowers, each with 5 petals and cane center. The rounded petals are translucent amethyst glass with dabs of opaque white in centers. Thin stems and pale green leaves extend downward into a translucent red dish or basket. Flat, smooth underside. 2¾″ (7.0 cm.) diam. (The canes in this weight are of superb quality; they resemble the canes in weight 71, Plate 2; 283, Plate 43; and 445, Plate 44.)

☐ Baccarat; she also noted that this type of weight might be English; acquired Sept., 1939.

739. Japanese. 1960's. Melon-shaped weight of colorless glass with translucent royal blue sphere inside. Outside is ribbed. Flat smooth base. 3″ (7.6 cm.) diam.

Gift of Dr. W. H. Potts, 1966.

56. Chinese. 1925–35. Shallow miniature weight of patterned millefiori. The dull red and the green-and-white canes are predominantly star-shaped. Smooth, flat base. 1⅞″ (4.8 cm.) diam.

☐ Unidentified; acquired Aug., 1937.

64. Chinese. 1925–35. Macédoine weight. Varicolored canes and filigree and opaque segments are arranged at random, filling the weight to top of crown. Light in weight. Colorless base. 2⁵⁄₁₆″ (5.8 cm.) diam.

☐ Modern Japanese; acquired Sept., 1937.

243. Ancient glass beads alternate with pink quartz beads with a small gold bead between the larger beads. The glass beads have visible millefiori canes and are attributed to the Hellenistic-to-Roman period, from the third to the first century B.C.

☐ Egyptian; acquired June, 1939.
(Illus. 1, Bergstrom book.)

359

573

37

738

254

739

64

56

243

Plate 63

763. Origin unknown; possibly Sandwich, Mass. *Ca.* 1870–88. Glass plate has the rim bent down on 4 sides to form a square. Plate is decorated on both top side and underside with pinwheel swirl of opaque blue and opaque white strands radiating from center. Topside strands swirl in opposite direction from underside strands, creating a latticinio-type design. 7½" × 7½" (19.1 cm. × 19.1 cm.).

☐ Unrecorded.

761. Origin unknown. Heavy, shallow bowl. Colorless glass encloses flattened spiral twists of opaque strands of glass (light blue on one side, white on the other) contiguous in parallel lines. At rim is applied, encased opaque white spiral. 9" (22.9 cm.) diam.

☐ Unrecorded.

764. Origin unknown. Shallow bowl. Colorless glass encases flattened tubular white filigree spirals coiled in the shape of "snails," with translucent red centers, placed in 2 concentric circles around a "snail" at center. Encased white filigree coil is applied to rim. Trace of pontil mark on underside. 8" (20.4 cm.) diam.

☐ Unrecorded.

762. Origin unknown; possibly Sandwich, Mass. *Ca.* 1870–88. Colorless glass dish or plate with striped decoration. Radiating from center in pinwheel swirl are hollow rods of opaque white, yellow, and pink, with goldstone stripes interspersed. Rim is edged with applied thread of red glass. Four points of pontil mark are visible on underside. 6¹⁵⁄₁₆" (17.7 cm.) diam.

☐ Unrecorded.

765. Origin unknown; possibly Boston & Sandwich Glass Co., Sandwich, Mass. *Ca.* 1870–88. Finger bowl and saucer are free blown of colorless glass striped with goldstone. The thin glass is light in weight; both pieces have ruffled rims. Underside of bowl is concave; 4 points of pontil mark are visible on underside of saucer. 4¹³⁄₁₆" (10.6 cm.) diam. at rim of bowl; 6½" (16.5 cm.) diam. of saucer.

☐ Unrecorded.

87. Attributed to Paul Ysart (Scotland). *Ca.* 1930. Mille fiori weight with variety of canes, most of which are hollow serrated tubes with interiors of various forms. Pinpoint bubbles appear among canes. Translucent dark green ground. Smooth, flat underside. 3" (7.6 cm.) diam.

☐ Unidentified; acquired Oct., 1937.

35. Origin unknown. Colorless glass encloses 2 layers of pebble ground, lined with opaque white on underside. Top layer is predominantly red, the lower predominantly green. Central bubble is near crown; 4 bubbles extend downward through the layers. Flattened colorless base has concave center. 3¼" (8.3 cm.) diam.

☐ Bristol; acquired June, 1937.

766. Attributed to Mt. Washington Glass Works, New Bedford, Mass. *Ca.* 1870–94. Six glass flowers (counterclockwise):

a. Red dahlia-type flower with many thick, rounded upright petals and yellow stamen center. Two transparent pale green ribbed leaves and stem are applied.

b. Pansy with 3 yellow lower petals and 2 purple upper petals has applied black glass veins; red dot appears in center. Transparent pale green ribbed leaf and stem are applied.

c. Tulip has 6 jagged-edged petals of opaque white with red stripes. Pointed stamen of colorless glass is covered with chips of opaque yellow. Ribbed, transparent green leaf and stem are applied.

d. Morning glory type of flower in translucent amber glass.

e. Daisy type. Twelve opaque white petals are encased in amber glass; green center is outlined in black. Transparent pale green ribbed leaf and stem are applied.

f. Blue and white dahlia type of flower has opaque white petals in center and blue petals at outer edge. Petals are thick, rounded, and encased in clear glass, which gives them a shiny appearance. Yellow stamen center. Two transparent pale green ribbed leaves and stem are applied.

☐ Unrecorded.

Plate 63

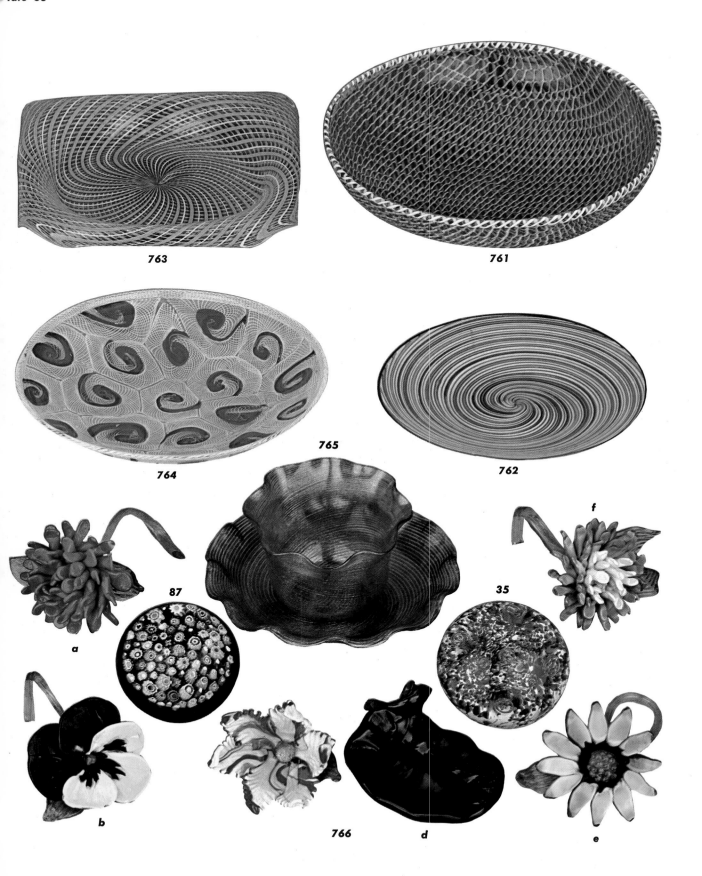

763

761

765

764

762

87

35

a

f

b

766

d

e

BIBLIOGRAPHY

All items in this bibliography are to be found in the Paperweight Research Center at the Bergstrom Art Center and Museum, Neenah, Wisconsin.

Books and Pamphlets

AVILA, GEORGE C. *The Pairpoint Glass Story.* New Bedford, Mass.: privately published, Reynolds-DeWalt Printing, Inc., 1968.

BARRET, RICHARD CARTER. *Blown and Pressed American Glass.* Manchester, Vt.: Forward's Color Productions, 1966.

————. *Identification of American Art Glass.* Manchester, Vt.: Forward's Color Productions, 1964.

BEDFORD, JOHN. *Paperweights.* New York: Walker and Company, 1968.

BERGSTROM, EVANGELINE H. *Old Glass Paperweights.* Chicago: The Lakeside Press, 1940; New York: Crown Publishers, Inc., 1947.

BOZEK, MICHAEL. *Price Guide Handbook of Glass Paperweights.* North Hollywood, Calif.: Treasure Chest Publications, 1961.

BROTHERS, J. STANLEY, JR. *Thumbnail Sketches.* Kalamazoo, Mich.: J. Stanley Brothers, Jr., Publications, 1940.

BURBANK, GEORGE E. *A Bit of Sandwich History.* 1939.

Catalogue of Old English Glass. 2nd edition. March, 1937. Arthur Churchill, Ltd., 34 High St., Marylebone, London.

Cristal de France. Text by Marie-Claire Auvray. Paris: Messrs. Lallemand, Publishers, 1967.

CROMPTON, SIDNEY (ed.). *English Glass.* Ward Lock & Co., Ltd., 1967.

ELVILLE, E. M. *The Collector's Dictionary of Glass.* London: Country Life, Ltd., 1961.

————. *Paperweights and Other Glass Curiosities.* London: Country Life, Ltd., 1954.

FROTHINGHAM, ALICE WILSON. *Spanish Glass.* New York: Thomas Yoseloff, 1964.

Glass from The Corning Museum of Glass. Corning, N.Y.: The Corning Glass Center, 1965.

HAYNES, E. BARRINGTON. *Glass Through the Ages.* Baltimore, Md.: Penguin Books, 1966. (Reprint of 1959 revised edition.)

HOLLISTER, PAUL, JR. *The Encyclopedia of Glass Paperweights.* New York: Clarkson N. Potter, Inc., 1969.

HONEY, W. B. *English Glass.* London: Collins, 1946.

IMBERT, R., and AMIC, Y. *Les Presse-Papiers Français.* Paris: Art et Industrie, 1948.

JOKELSON, PAUL. *Antique French Paperweights.* Privately published, 1955.

————. *One Hundred of the Most Important Paperweights.* Privately published, 1966.

————. *Sulphides.* New York: Thomas A. Nelson, 1968.

KILNER, C. A. *Fifty Years.* Oak Park, Ill.: privately published. (Reproduction of a book on the Kilner Brothers of England, 1894.)

KNITTLE, RHEA MANSFIELD. *Early American Glass.* New York: D. Appleton-Century Co., 1939.

Boston Sunday Herald Magazine. "Artist in Glass," Nayman, Harriet. May 14, 1967, pp. 22, 24–25, 27, illus. (On Charles Kaziun.)

Christian Science Monitor. "Art in Paperweights," Kahn, Dorothea. June 23, 1945, pp. 10–11, illus.

Collectors Guide. "More Glass Paperweights," Legge, J. M. D. June, 1965, pp. 62–65, illus.

————. "Old Glass Paperweights," Legge, J. M. D. May, 1965, pp. 41–43, illus.

Connaissance des Arts. "Les Boules Presse-Papiers," August 15, 1955, pp. 31–35, illus.

Hobbies. "Another Episode in Glass Paper Weight History," Ettinger, F. Sumner. November, 1935, pp. 71–72.

————. "Collecting Paperweights," Lyon, Charles Woolsey. February, 1938, pp. 70–77, illus.

————. "Comments on Paperweights," Yaeger, Dorothea. October, 1941, pp. 62–67, illus.

————. "English Green Glass Paperweights," Kilner, C. A. October, 1941, pp. 71–72.

————. "The First Hundred Are the Easiest," Moore, T. B. October, 1941, pp. 68–69.

————. "Glass Paperweights," January, 1939, pp. 75–76, illus.

————. "Glass Paperweights," Boore, J. P. March, 1958, p. 73; April, 1958, p. 90, illus.; May, 1958, p. 72; March, 1959, p. 72, illus.

————. "Glass Paperweights," Slade, George H. September, 1939, p. 58, illus.

————. "Glass Paperweights Attributed by Association," Boore, J. P. February, 1958, p. 84.

————. "Glass Paperweights, Watch Your Language," Boore, J. P. Part I, September, 1958, pp. 82–83, illus.; Part II, October, 1958, pp. 72, 88, 92, illus.;

Part III, November, 1958, pp. 72–73, illus.; Part IV, December, 1958, pp. 72–73, illus.; Part V, January, 1959, pp. 72–73, illus.; Part VI, February, 1959, pp. 72–73, illus.

————. "Glass Paperweights, What Is a Fake?" Boore, J. P. August, 1958, p. 80.

————. "How We Found the Oscar Wilde Collection of Paperweights," Rowe, Barbara Bastien. October, 1941, p. 122.

————. "Incognito Collectors and Collections," Thacher, Thurston. October, 1941, p. 61, illus.

————. "Medium Priced Paperweights," Lee, Ruth Webb. October, 1941, pp. 59–60, illus.

————. "The Mysterious Witch Ball," Ramsay, John. October, 1939, pp. 59–60.

————. "Old Glass Paperweights," Boore, J. P. July, 1958, p. 76; January, 1961, p. 72; March, 1961, pp. 76–77, 80, illus.; March, 1964, pp. 82–85, 91, illus.

————. "Old Glass Paperweights, Baccarat Part III," Boore, J. P. June, 1966, pp. 98F–98G, illus.

————. "Old Glass Paperweights, A Brief History of the Art," Boore, J. P. June, 1961, pp. 90–91.

————. "Old Glass Paperweights, Clichy Part I," Boore, J. P. August, 1961, pp. 90–92, illus.; Part II, January, 1962, pp. 82–84, illus.; Part III, February, 1962, pp. 88–89, 92–93, illus.; Part IV, June, 1962, pp. 82–84, illus.; Part V (conclusion), August, 1962, pp. 68–69, 88, illus.

————. "Old Glass Paperweights—Some Little Known English Makers," Boore, J. P. February, 1961, pp. 80–81, illus.

————. "Paperweight Buttons," Brown, Dorothy Foster. October, 1961, p. 52, illus.

————. "Paperweight Buttons," Couse, L. Erwina. October, 1941, p. 20.

————. "Paperweight Collectors' Round-up," October, 1941, pp. 55–58, illus.

———. "Random Observations on Paperweights," Boore, J. P. January, 1958, p. 81.

———. "Steeple Weights," Bergstrom, Evangeline H. October, 1941, p. 73.

———. "Thoughts on French Paperweights," Revelli, Yvonne Sohn. October, 1941, pp. 70–71, illus.

House Beautiful. "Paperweights," Lyon, Charles Woolsey. August, 1936, pp. 18, 57–58, illus.

Illustrated London News. "A Page for Collectors," Davis, Frank. November 1, 1952, p. 732, illus.

Indianapolis Star Magazine. "Treasures in Glass," November 29, 1953, illus.

Réalités. "French Paperweights," March, 1957, pp. 5–9, illus.

Spinning Wheel. "The Pairpoint Story," Revi, Albert Christian. March, 1966, pp. 10–12, illus.

———. "Swirl and Sulphide Playing Marbles," Miller, Roger C. November, 1966, pp. 20–21, illus.

———. "William T. Gillinder's Contributions to Glassmaking," Fitzpatrick, Paul J., Ph.D. May, 1966, p. 22, illus.

Woman's Day. "Woman's Day Dictionary of American Glass," Gaines, Edith. August, 1961, pp. 19–34, illus.

———. "Woman's Day Dictionary of Paperweights," Jenkins, Dorothy H. July, 1965, pp. 25–32, illus.

Yankee. "Signed with a K," Hickey, Margaret Condon. November, 1966, pp. 96–97, 212, illus. (On Charles Kaziun.)

Club and Organization Literature

The Bulletin of the Paperweight Collectors' Association is referred to as *PWCA Bulletin.* (Edited and published by Paul Jokelson, 47 Windsor Road, Scarsdale, N.Y.)

The Glass Club Bulletin is the Bulletin of the National Early American Glass Club. (Mr. Lea S. Luquier, President, 171 Reservoir Road, Chestnut Hill, Mass.)

Journal of Glass Studies is published annually by The Corning Museum of Glass, Corning, N.Y. (Paul N. Perrot, Editor.)

National Button Bulletin is the Bulletin of the National Button Society. Published bimonthly. (Miss Erwina Chamberlain, President, Box 38, Milford, N.Y. 13807.)

Bergstrom Paperweight Symposium (1967 Booklet). "The Ancient Millefiori Technique," Perrot, Paul N., pp. 8–16.

————. "Antique French Paperweights," Jokelson, Paul (discussion leader), pp. 74–82.

————. "Bacchus and Other English Weights," Hollister, Paul, Jr., pp. 17–29.

————. "Contemporary American Paperweights," Melvin, Jean Sutherland, pp. 60–67.

————. "Early American Paperweights," Wilson, Kenneth M., pp. 105–19.

————. "The Importance of Grinding and Polishing of Glass Paperweights," Ogren, Fred, pp. 33–35.

————. "Ohio-Made Paperweights," Knower, Franklin H., pp. 36–46.

————. "Paperweight Making," Kaziun, Charles (discussion leader), pp. 83–95.

————. "Sales at Sotheby's," Clarke, T. H., pp. 68–73.

Bulletin of the Art Institute of Chicago. "A Collection of Glass Paperweights," September, 1938, pp. 72–74, illus.

Columbia County Historical Society (Bulletin). (Kinderhook, N.Y.) "A Brief History of Glass Paperweights," Lyon, Charles W., Jr. Fourth Annual Exhibition, 1940, pp. 3–5.

———. "Catalogue of Paperweights," 1940. (From the collection of Mrs. J. H. Sinclair.)

———. "Paperweight Exhibit," 1947.

Glass Club Bulletin. "The Art of Louis Comfort Tiffany," Joseph, J. Jonathon, A.I.D. March, 1964, No. 69, pp. 9–12, illus.

———. "Aventurine Glass," Pattinson, Lillian G. March, 1961, No. 57, p. 7.

———. "Dorflinger Glass," Wheaton, Mrs. George. March, 1963, No. 65, pp. 8–9.

———. "Glossary of Glassmaking Terms," September, 1966, No. 79, pp. 11–12.

———. "John Degenhart," Melvin, Jean Sutherland. June, 1964, No. 70, pp. 8–9, illus.

———. "The Mt. Washington Glass Company and Its Relationships in the Late Nineteenth Century," Wilson, Kenneth M. March, 1966, No. 77, pp. 3–7, 10–12, illus.

———. "The New England Glass Company Exhibition," Rogers, Millard F., Jr. December, 1963, No. 68, pp. 11–12, illus.

———. "New York Glass," Schwartz, Marvin D. June, 1964, No. 70, pp. 10–11, illus.

———. "Nicholas Lutz," Lutz, Victor. June, 1962, No. 62, pp. 8–9, illus.

———. "Paperweights Inside and Out," Lawson, Mrs. Robert. December, 1960, No. 56, pp. 4–5, illus.

———. "The St. Clair Glass Company," Phillips, Mrs. Herschel. Christmas, 1965, No. 76, pp. 8, 12.

———. "Sandwich Glass," Kershaw, Doris. December, 1963, No. 68, pp. 1–5, illus.

———. "South Jersey Glass and Glassmakers," Branin, M. Lelyn. September, 1965, No. 75, pp. 2–10, illus.

———. "The Two Dorflingers Who Cared," Barger, Helen. December, 1966, No. 80, pp. 3–5, 12, illus.

———. "The Union Glass Company of Somerville, Massachusetts," Pattinson, Lillian G. December, 1961, No. 60, pp. 4–7, illus.

Glass Notes. "Notes on Terminology for French Paperweights," Clarke, T. H. December, 1952, No. 12, pp. 40–44, illus.

Journal of Glass Studies. "A Glass Recipe Book of the New England Glass Company," Rogers, Millard F., Jr. 1965, VII, pp. 107–13, illus.

———. "Joseph Lobmeyer and His Glassworks in Slavonia," Despot, Miroslava. 1962, IV, pp. 103–107, illus.

———. "Millefiori Glass in Classical Antiquity," Oliver, Andrew, Jr. 1968, X, pp. 48–70, illus.

———. "The Miracle of Enclosed Ornamentation," Brothers, J. Stanley, Jr. 1962, IV, pp. 117–26, illus.

———. "Sulphides and Medals," Polak, Ada. 1966, VIII, pp. 116–19, illus.

———. "Wheel-Engraving and -Cutting; Some Early Equipment," Charleston, R. J. 1964, VI, pp. 83–100, illus.; 1965, VII, pp. 41–54, illus.

———. "Zanesville Glass," Smith, Miles A. 1960, II, pp. 113–23, illus.

National Button Bulletin. "The Paperweight Buttons of Weinman, Rutter, Israel, Kaziun, and Erickson," Kasemeyer, Jean. November, 1963, pp. 251–61, illus.

PWCA Bulletin. "Addenda to Paperweight Bibliography," Leffingwell, B. H. June, 1963.

———. "American Glass Paperweights and Their Makers," Melvin, Jean Sutherland. 1966–1967, p. 40, illus.

———. "Another 'Mystery' Paperweight," Graham, Lloyd J. June, 1959, illus.

———. "Art of the French Glass Paperweight," Elville, E. M. June, 1959, illus.

———. "The Art of Paperweight Making," Israel, Jaques. June, 1963, pp. 21–23, illus.

————. "The Art of Paperweights," Hacker, Harold J. 1968, pp. 11–14, illus.

————. "As Seen from the Glory Hole," Kaziun, Charles. June, 1962, illus.

————. "Baccarat Silhouettes," Boore, J. P. June, 1964, pp. 16–18, illus.

————. "A Beautiful 'Mystery' Paperweight," Leffingwell, B. H. June, 1959, illus.

————. "Bergstrom Reviewed," Boore, J. P. June, 1963, pp. 26–29, illus.

————. "Bibliography Pertaining to Glass Paperweights," Leffingwell, B. H. June, 1958.

————. "The C. J. Carroll Collection of Paperweights," Clarke, T. H. June, 1959, illus.

————. "Charles Kaziun," Swift, Caroline Hyde. June, 1956, illus.

————. "Chinese Paperweights," Elder, Robert A., Jr. June, 1958, illus.

————. "The Colonel Guggenheim Paperweight Collection," Elder, Robert A., Jr. June, 1960, illus.

————. "Cristalleries et Verreries de Vianne (Cristal d'Albret)," 1966–1967, pp. 19–20, illus.

————. "The Crystal Cameos of France," Martin, Mary. June, 1958, illus.

————. "A Date with Silhouettes," Nagel, Fred A. June, 1957, illus.

————. "Dated Paperweights," Sisson, Barbara Bowles. June, 1963, illus.

————. "Description of Paperweight Restoration," Ogren, Fred. 1966–67, pp. 22–23, illus.

————. "Mr. Djevahirdjian's Collection," Jokelson, Paul. 1968, pp. 28–31, illus.

————. "Early American Portrait Medallions on Glass Paperweights," Chamberlain, Georgia S. April, 1955, pp. 18–22, illus.

————. "Embedded Glass and Crystal (Embedded Cameos—Crystal Medals)," Emperauger, J. P. Part I, June, 1958; Part II, June, 1959, illus.

————. "Enchanting Paperweights Signed PY," Nagel, Fred A. 1968, pp. 3–8, illus.

————. "English Patented Paperweights," Revi, Albert Christian. June, 1964, pp. 42–46, illus.

————. "The Estelle Doheney Paperweight Collection," Lawrence, Ronald M., M.D. June, 1965, pp. 46–50, illus.

————. "Facts Concerning the John Fitzgerald Kennedy Paperweight by Baccarat," Vulliet, André. June, 1965, illus.

————. "A Few Words about Baccarat," Vulliet, André. 1966–1967, pp. 34–35, illus.

————. "Flint Institute of Arts Collection of Paperweights," 1966–1967, pp. 38–39, illus.

————. "The Florence E. Bushee Collection of Paperweights," Elder, Robert A., Jr. 1968, pp. 15–21, illus.

————. "The Fourth Factory," Revi, Albert Christian. June, 1965, pp. 3–10, illus.

————. "From the Gaffer's Chair," Kaziun, Charles. June, 1964, pp. 6–9, illus.; June, 1965, pp. 42–44, illus.

————. "A Garland of Weights," Manheim, Frank J. 1968, pp. 39–40, illus.

————. "Gilliland Paperweights," Leffingwell, B. H. June, 1959, illus.

————. "The Glass Industry of Cleveland, New York," Davison, Mary E. June, 1959, illus.

————. "A Glassman's Collection," Challinor, Frank. June, 1959, illus.

————. "Glossary of Terms Used by Glass Paperweight Collectors," Boore, J. P. June, 1961.

————. "The Guggenheim Collection," Clarke, T. H. June, 1961, illus.

————. "Henry Miller's Design for Paperweight Door Knobs and a Flower Vase,"

Revi, Albert Christian. June, 1960, illus.

―――. "Hidden Facets of a Paperweight," Hansen, Ronald E. June, 1965, illus.

―――. "How Baccarat Revived the Art of Making Sulphide Paperweights," Nagel, Fred A. June, 1956, illus.

―――. "The Identification of French Paperweights," Elville, E. M. June, 1956, illus.

―――. "Isadore Ribas," Ribas, Joseph E. 1968, p. 9, illus.

―――. "The Lafayette Cameo Paperweight," MacIntire, Mrs. Alan. April, 1955, p. 27.

―――. "Lampwork—Its Significance to Paperweights," Hansen, Ronald E. June, 1964, pp. 19–22, illus.

―――. "The Lillie and Aaron Straus Paperweight Collection," Elder, Robert A., Jr. June, 1961, illus.

―――. "The Lindon Collection," Clarke, T. H. June, 1957, illus.

―――. "The Little Pigs That Went to Market," Lee, Ruth Webb. April, 1955, pp. 3–6, illus.

―――. "Miniature Portraits in Glass Rods," Revi, Albert Christian. June, 1958, illus.

―――. "Modern American Paperweights," Sisson, Barbara Bowles. June, 1961, illus.

―――. "Modern Glass Paperweights," Revi, Albert Christian. June, 1961, illus.

―――. "Modern Paperweight Reproductions," Sisson, Barbara Bowles. June, 1962, illus.

―――. "Modern Venetian Paperweights," Elder, Robert A., Jr. June, 1959, illus.

―――. "The Modest Collector and the Snake in the Glass," Hollister, Paul, Jr. June, 1965, pp. 29–31, illus.

————. "The New Baccarat Millefiori Paperweight," Elder, Robert A., Jr. June, 1961, illus.

————. "The New England Glass Works" (1856), 1966–1967, pp. 26–27, illus.

————. "The Odyssey of a Paperweight," dePoncins, M. October, 1954, pp. 15–17.

————. "Paperweights at Old Sturbridge Village," Wilson, Kenneth M. June, 1957, illus.

————. "Paperweights by Nicholas Lutz," Lee, Ruth Webb. October, 1954, pp. 7–11, illus.

————. "Paul Ysart," June, 1956, illus.

————. "Pinchbeck Paperweights," Tomlinson, Jay B. April, 1955, pp. 6–8, illus.

————. "The Problem of the Origin of the Stourbridge Glass Trade," Haden, H. Jack. June, 1964, pp. 47–50, illus.

————. "Propos d'un Collectionneur Napoléonisant" (1929), Greppe, Pascal. Translation of selections by Paul Jokelson. 1960, illus.

————. "PW Means Paperweight Button," Adams, Jane Ford and Albert, Lillian Smith. June, 1956, illus.

————. "The Rebirth of the Millefiori at Baccarat, 1957–1964," Chaumeil, Guillaume. June, 1965, pp. 39–41, illus.

————. "Report of Final Portion of the Guggenheim Sale," Dennis, C. R. C. June, 1962, illus.

————. "A Report from Sotheby's Auction Rooms," Clifford-Smith, Edwina. 1968, pp. 32–37, illus.

————. "A Report from Sotheby's Auction Rooms," Dennis, Richard C. June, 1963, pp. 30–33, illus.; June, 1964, pp. 38–41, illus.

————. "A Report from Sotheby's Auction Rooms," Tillman, Alan G. June, 1965, pp. 14–16, illus.

————. "The Robert Q. Lewis Collection of Sulphides," Lyons, Louis. June, 1960, illus.

————. "The Schuell Collection of Miniature Weights," Tillman, Alan G. 1968, pp. 43–47, illus.

————. "Shearings from the Gaffer's Chair," Kaziun, Charles. 1966–1967, pp. 32–33, illus.

————. "Some Facts About Old Baccarat Weights," Vulliet, André. 1966–1967, pp. 36–37, illus.

————. "Some One in Venice," MacHarg, James A. June, 1956, illus.

————. "Steuben Paperweights," Jokelson, Paul. June, 1965, p. 45, illus.

————. "Sulphide Buttons," Ertell, George. June, 1962, illus.

————. "Sulphide Paperweight of Général de Division François Ingold," Jokelson, Paul. 1966–1967, p. 17, illus.

————. "Sulphide Paperweight of Saint Louis, King of France," 1966–1967, p. 16, illus.; 1968, p. 23, illus.

————. "Sulphide Paperweights from 1850–1952," Sisson, Barbara Bowles. June, 1964, pp. 33–37, illus.

————. "Swirl and Sulphide Marbles," Slusser, Esther. June, 1961, illus.

————. "Symposium Smash Hit!" Nagel, Fred A. 1966–1967, pp. 41–44, illus.

————. "Upgrade to Topgrade," Nagel, Fred A. 1966–1967, pp. 28–31, illus.

————. "Vicke Lindstrand," June, 1962, illus.

————. "Was There a Glass Conspiracy?" Boore, J. P. June, 1963, pp. 18–19, illus.

————. "The 'Weights' of History," Smith, Barbara A. Part I, June, 1964, pp. 10–15, illus.; Part II (1800–1900), June, 1965, pp. 32–38, illus.; Part III (1900–1967), 1966–1967, pp. 9–15, illus.

————. "Zachary Taylor Sulphide Paperweight," Marsh, Mrs. William R. April, 1955, p. 23, illus.

Toledo Museum of Art (Catalogue). "New England Glass Company 1818–1888," 1963.

Miscellaneous

Catalogues of paperweight sales:
　　Christie's, London
　　Francis Clemson Cross sale, Parts I and III, White Plains, N.Y., June and
　　　　October, 1960, illus.
　　Parke-Benet Galleries, Inc., New York (from 1953)
　　Plaza Art Galleries, New York
　　Sotheby's & Co., London (from 1950)

"Foreign Influences in American Paperweights," Hollister, Paul, Jr. Xerox of lecture given at Old Sturbridge Village, October 28, 1966.

"Important Problems of Paperweight Research," Elder, Robert A., Jr. Manuscript of lecture given at Paperweight Collectors' Association convention, October, 1961.

INDEX

In certain of the index entries, only a few page references are given as examples, since it would be relatively useless to list several score page-references for terms that are mentioned on the majority of the pages in the book. Italic page numbers indicate illustrations.